Some Grief Some Joy

Some Grief
Some Joy

Story Copyright © 2018 by: Leo Vadalà
Copy Editor: Tiziano Thomas Dossena
Cover Artwork By: Luke Mindell
Cover Design By: Dominic A. Campanile

ISBN: 978-1-948651-03-5
Library of Congress Control Number: 2018914454

Published by: Idea Press (an imprint of Idea Graphics, LLC) — Florida (USA)
www.ideapress-usa.com • email: ideapress33@gmail.com • editoreusa@gmail.com
Printed in the USA - 1st Edition, December 2018

LEO VADALÀ

Some Grjef
Some Joy

DEDICATION

All I am, all I have accomplished in life – all, absolutely all! – I owe to my brother Domenic, or Mimmo, as we called him. And to him I dedicate this novel.

His crucial role in my life would be ample justification for this dedication, but that is not the reason why I am honoring him. My dedication is not meant as a compensation for goods received or services rendered, as a *"quid pro quo"* of some kind. No, that's not the case at all – I am honored to dedicate this novel to him simply because my brother was a very good man, a morally just man.

Mimmo and his wife Angelina – or Ange, as everybody called her – welcomed me in their home when I came to the United States from Italy in 1951. I was then a young and callow boy of sixteen and – except for three years in the Army – they provided for me entirely until I went on my own eleven years later. And their care was not limited to just food and shelter – from the first day of my arrival I became a part of their family; they treated me just like one of their own children, and showered me with the same love and unlimited affection that I had received from the family I left in Italy.

Mimmo was my brother, but to me – and to countless other people – he was much more than that. He was also a father, a friend, a teacher, an adviser and everything you would want to see in a fellow human being. He was also an incredibly well learned man, a philosopher, a poet, a friend to everybody and a deeply religious man, profoundly sincere in his beliefs, with an unflagging devotion to his Church and its teachings.

This last characteristic surely represents the most remarkable difference between him and me. I lost long ago whatever little Christian faith I had while remaining – I hope – a decent human being.

It's not unusual to see sharp dissents or serious arguments occur among siblings, even in the best families. I lived with my brother for eleven years and was close to him for an additional forty-five years, yet I cannot recall ever having any serious disagreements or arguments with him.

Credit for this goes entirely to him, of course. Surely, while in the process of molding a man out of a young and immature boy, I must have given him plenty reasons or opportunities to be angry at me, to holler at me or to simply discipline me. Still, I cannot recall one single time when he actually did. His "molding" style was quite simple – lead by example. And give love, love, love. And then more love.

Our only significant difference, as I have already pointed out, was founded upon our religious beliefs or – to be precise – his religious beliefs, as I have none. We did debate endlessly on this subject, but always in a joshing, humorous, bantering sort of way. Neither one of us ever won those arguments – he freely admitted to the past failures of his Church, but always looked at them as human failures, not doctrinal failures.

When Mimmo died, his three boys – Pietro, Nick, and Leo – respectfully asked their uncle Lillo to say a few words at his funeral. I had to decline because nature has endowed me with a very emotional personality. I cry at the drop of a hat – just show me or tell me the most pathetic sob story and you'll see tears gushing out of my eyes.

At his funeral, I was crushed with sorrow and in tears most of the time. I knew that if I had to get up to say even something as simple as "Thank you, Mimmo" I would have made a damn fool of myself. And so I declined.

Just one thing I would have wanted to tell him, though – one thing, that is, in addition to "Thank you, Mimmo... a hundred... a thousand times thank you!"

I would have wanted to tell him that while our religious discussions always ended in a draw, I would now have to admit that I wished – indeed, I even hoped – that he were right in his belief of an eternal life after death.

For if he were right, I could have said "Arrivederci" instead of "Addio."

ACKNOWLEDGEMENTS

My heartfelt thanks to all who encouraged me to continue writing this novel even when I was ready to chuck it in the dustbin where I thought it belonged.

Special thanks to my good friend – and "Words With Friends" nemesis - Rosie Greer, who somehow managed to read it through in its entirety and, to my everlasting shame, pointed out to me – a certified, card carrying member of the grammar Nazi party – not only some factual inaccuracies but also some misspelled words.

Oy vey!

TABLE OF CONTENTS

CHAPTER 1 1
CHAPTER 2 13
CHAPTER 3 25
CHAPTER 4 41
CHAPTER 5 57
CHAPTER 6 67
CHAPTER 7 93
CHAPTER 8 107
CHAPTER 9 115
CHAPTER 10 127
CHAPTER 11 137
CHAPTER 12 155
CHAPTER 13 171
CHAPTER 14 199
CHAPTER 15 223
CHAPTER 16 231
CHAPTER 17 247
CHAPTER 18 275
CHAPTER 19 285
CHAPTER 20 299
CHAPTER 21 323
CHAPTER 22 335
CHAPTER 23 363
CHAPTER 24 387
CHAPTER 25 407
CHAPTER 26 419
EPILOGUE 429
APPENDIX 441

PART I

A BOY

Take one fresh and tender kiss
Add one stolen night of bliss,
One girl… one boy…
Some grief… some joy…
Memories are made of this…

Memories are made of this –
Words & Music by Terry Gilkeyson,
Richard Dehr, and Frank Miller

CHAPTER 1

Nothing doing, the damned lawn mower just wouldn't start. I'd pulled the crank about thirty times already and nothing, just a flat clunk, clunk, clunk before the sudden, grinding halt. *Screw it all*, I told myself; I'll go buy a new one at Home Depot.

It's always like that, every single year. Trying to get that sucker started after a long and cold winter has always been a bitch; especially with a twelve-year-old mower. A twelve- year- old mower that has never been serviced, I should add.

Out of sheer desperation, I gave it one last pull. The engine seemed to sputter a bit, – oh, please, please, please God! – it coughed for about five seconds then died again. But it had shown signs of life! I fed a bit more gas and pulled the crank again keeping my fingers crossed – this time it coughed for about ten seconds before quitting again. But I smelled blood, it was just a question of time, I knew it.

One more pull and **TA– DA!** Victory at last! The engine sputtered for a few seconds, then caught on and began running like a brand new lawn mower. **YES! YES! YES!**

In my mind Pavarotti was singing **"Vincerò, Vinceroò, Vinceeeeeeerooooooò.**

Fact No. 1: The lawn did look shoddy, a real mess, the way it always does in early spring, and spring had come earlier than usual this year. The fertilizer spread late last October had done its job – too damn well, in fact! – and tufts of dormant grass and wide-awake weeds were sprouting up all over.

I'd been meaning to give the lawn its first mowing for the past couple of weeks – it needed it badly. All lawns in the neighborhood had already been mowed at least once, some of them twice, and Maria had repeatedly and pointedly mentioned she had already glimpsed a few ill-concealed looks of disapproval from our neighbors for the shabby appearance of our lawn. But...

Fact No. 2 – cutting grass has always been the ultimate pain in the ass for me, and I kept finding excuses to postpone doing it.

Until last year I had it made. Pete lived less than a mile away, and every year from early April till mid– November he used to come over about once a week and cut the grass himself. And if he was busy he would drop off little Leo to do the job.

Pete is my son, he's 35 now, and Leo is my grandson, he's 11. Pete cut my grass for free, of course, but when he dropped off Leo I always slipped the little guy ten or fifteen bucks. Pete wasn't too happy about that, but I insisted – kids need to learn that work has its own rewards, I explained, and he relented.

Pete started taking care of my lawn about three years ago, after that one time when I foolishly overworked on a hot August afternoon – cutting grass, precisely. I got so badly dehydrated that I had collapsed.

Maria panicked and immediately called Pete. He came right over, called 911 and had me rushed to the hospital in an ambulance.

It turned out to be no big deal after all. I was in the emergency room for just a few hours, long enough for them to drip some kind of solution in my arm, but they all got bent out of shape because of it.

When they sent me home I insisted I was OK, but Pete wouldn't hear it. From then on he took over all lawn– related operations: mowing, fertilizing, weed control, the whole nine yards. And like I said, I had it made.

A couple of months ago, however, Pete got a promotion and his company transferred him to its Dover Office in downstate Delaware. To be closer to his job, he sold his home and bought himself a 4– bedroom colonial in a new development less than a mile away from where he works. He now lives a good 60 miles from my house, and for him to come upstate now would be a trip. And little Leo, of course, doesn't drive yet. Anyway, he doesn't do it anymore.

Still, Pete – always worrying about me – before moving downstate had made arrangements to hire at his expense a lawn maintenance firm to take care of my lawn. And that's when I put my foot down. Thanks, but no thanks, I told him – I am not a cripple yet and, much as I don't like cutting grass, I can still handle it.

Needless to say, I had to assure him and everybody else I would be careful, I would drink plenty of fluids, take breaks every half-hour or so, that kind of stuff. He finally relented, but not before making me swear and promise I would call him immediately if for any reason I couldn't do the job.

Saturday was a gorgeous day, clear and not too warm... and I had run out of excuses. Maria had even threatened to call Pete, so there I was, cutting grass for the first time in three years, and not minding it all that much.

I was already feeling a bit tired, though, mainly because over the past few years I've let myself go and I am not in very good shape. Plus, cranking up the lawnmower had taken a lot out of me and, anyway, I was feeling fatigued. I had only mowed about half the lawn and I could already feel rivulets of sweat rolling down my neck.

Mindful of that nasty episode of three years before, I thought I had better take a break and rest a while, get a drink of water or some-thing. I knew I would never hear the end of it from everyone if I got careless and would need medical attention again.

Rounding the corner of the lot, there she was – like clockwork! – Maria, waiting for me out on the lawn right next to the garage. She had a glass of something in her hand: ice– cold lemonade, guaranteed.

My wife does that all the time – she seems to know exactly when I'm beginning to get tired. Whenever I do any kind of outdoor work – shoveling snow, trimming bushes, or whatever – she comes prepared, and at just the right time. I love her for that also.

I maneuvered the mower in her direction and stopped right next to her. After turning off the engine, I wiped my neck and forehead with a small towel I always carry with me whenever I do any outside work.

"You look tired, honey. Rest a while and have some lemonade," she said handing me the glass. Then, suddenly recollecting something, she added: "Oh, by the way, I almost forgot... Tony left a message on the phone. He sounded kind of funny... He says to call him back as soon as possible... It's very important, he says..."

"Very important? Yeah! Sure!" – I sneered as I reached for the glass. "He just wants to know what time we start playing cards to-night... Wanna bet?"

I then thanked her for the drink and blew her a kiss in appreci-ation. She smiled, blew me back a kiss and started to go back inside. She then stopped, turned around and told me: "I'm going to take a shower now. Don't forget, I'll be babysitting for Rosa tonight. Monday is their tenth anniversary but they're going out for dinner tonight to celebrate."

She started to leave, then, almost as an afterthought, added: "If you want more lemonade there's a pitcher full on the kitchen counter, but please don't make a mess when you go in, I just mopped the floor. You be careful now, please. Rest for a while, you can finish cutting grass later."

Rosa is our oldest daughter, she's 33 now, and she's got two kids; we also have the twins, Phil and Lucy, they are 29, they are all married and have kids.

Any interruption in grass cutting is always welcome, important news or not. I lingered outside a while and just relaxed, breathing in the fragrant smell of freshly cut grass and enjoying a long sip of cool lemonade. After brushing off blades of grass from my pants, I then removed my shoes and walked inside the house.

Tony answered after only one ring. Tony Ravello is a friend from way back. He used to live in New York – he and his brother Jack – but they both moved to Delaware some thirty years ago when they realized things in the Bronx were getting to be a bit too hectic to raise a family. We talk two or three times a week just to keep in touch, plus we play cards together about once a week, a friendly poker game.

Tony answered with his usual "Hello!", a "Hello!" that sounds like "Yellow!"

"Hi, Tony... You called?... What's up?" – I asked him.

"Oh! Hi, Lillo..." – he murmured. Family and close friends, they all call me Lillo.

I knew something was wrong the minute he said 'Hi' because Tony never says 'Hi' and he never murmurs when he answers the phone. His standard reply is a very cheery: "Hey! Hollywood! What's happening?"

He calls everybody Hollywood, I don't know why.

"Is something wrong, Tony?" – I asked, tensing up.

"Has anybody called you yet?" – He asked, still with a strangely subdued tone of voice.

I relaxed. Just what I thought – surely he was referring to the card game we have most Saturday nights. All the guys always check with me to find out if the game is still on, who will be there, where we play and what time the game starts.

I don't know why they call me because there is absolutely no need for it. Every time we play poker we always decide where the next game will be. After the last hand, we take a roll call and ask around to find out who can play the next Saturday – if not enough guys can make it for whatever reason, then we just cancel it and goodnight. But if we have at least five turkeys available, we decide at whose house it will be.

We rotate all the time, my house, your house, his house and so on. Still, for some damned reason, every Saturday morning I get about five or six calls to find out if the game is still on, where we play, what time we start, and who'll be there. I keep official tracks of those stats.

"No, I haven't heard anything yet. You are the first customer who called." – I told him – "But didn't we agree to play at Nicky's last week? As far as I know, I'm pretty sure that's where we are supposed to play, usual time."

Then, just in case there might be any last minute changes, I quickly added: "Look, I'm cutting grass right now. Tell you what, why don't you call Nicky and find out if the game is still on? If for any reason he can't host, let me know. We can call the guys – what can I tell you– we'll make some other arrangement. We can play at my house if necessary."

Maria wouldn't have been too crazy about that because every time we play we always make a glorious mess: crumbs and ashes all over, a house full of smoke, glass rings on the table and scuff marks on the floor. But I was eager to play, I'm always eager to play.

I love our Saturday night poker games, I love the interaction among the players, the bullshitting, the jokes, the tension, the cursing; I love the competition, the gregariousness. I even enjoy hearing the same "I just don't have any luck" alibi's time after time after time from the same players, Danny and Tony in particular. And I love winning, of course. And I do win, more often than not.

Danny is a good guy. He is in his 70s and is now retired after busting his ass for about 35 years on the assembly line at Chrysler.

At times it's a bit hard to understand him. He has been in this country well over forty years but his English is still pretty shaky and heavily accented. And his Italian isn't much better, frequently intermingled as it is with words spoken in the dialect of Puglia, the southern Italian region he came from. But he is a hell of a nice fellow, a real piece of chocolate.

He is the kind of guy who chokes up whenever he narrates some real sob story or even some fictional tearjerker he has seen on TV. He is a bit like me in that respect and – just like me – he also loves opera, Puccini in particular.

He lives only about a mile away from me. Once I invited him to come over so we could watch "La Boheme" on Channel 12 together. During the entire transmission, he didn't utter one single word. He just sat transfixed on the sofa, literally living the opera. And at the very end – when Mimì dies and Rodolfo screams a desperate "Mimì... Mimì!" – damn if he didn't start crying; I mean, he literally burst into sobs. I won't lie, I felt like crying myself – damned Puccini brings a lump to my throat also – but I managed to hold it in.

A rare feat for an Italian, I've never heard him raise his voice in anger and – an even rarer feat – I've never heard him use a cuss word.

He has tons and tons of other good qualities, but card playing is definitely not one of them. Playing poker with him is like taking candy from a kid – you just can't lose. He just looks at his cards and hardly pays any attention to what the other players display and how they can potentially beat his hand. And, of course, he doesn't bother to figure out such arcane trifles as what the odds are of getting the cards he needs.

But you'll never hear him admit he is a lousy player. After yet another losing session he invariably repeats the same old refrain, like a broken record – cards just don't like him, he ruefully says. And he has had a string of bad luck since we started playing cards some 25 years ago.

And it would be even worse if I didn't help him out some. When we play cards I always try to sit next to him. If I drop out and he plays, I give him some advice on how to play his hand, mostly advising him to drop out if he has lousy cards.

Many times I've asked myself why he keeps on playing the game despite the clobbering he gets time after time after time. God knows. I guess it's because once in a rare while even he wins. Also, he is fairly well off and can afford to lose 30 bucks or so just about every time we play.

Tony, on the other hand, is a decent player. He knows how to read cards and figure percentages. But he has one fatal flaw – he doesn't like to be bluffed out of a hand. In and of itself, that isn't too bad a flaw – hell, I don't like it, nobody likes it! But in his case it is a fatal flaw because he also believes that someone is always trying to bluff him out; just about every single hand.

At the card table we call him Stonewall Jackson, a nickname he has earned for himself because nine times out of ten he just won't drop out. He knows the odds are stacked against him and yet he won't fold his hand, not even if you point a loaded machine gun at him. It's a *macho* thing with him; he just has to stay in to the bitter end.

"No, you are not going to bluff me out!" – He'll defiantly sneer to his opponents. And that flaw, of course, makes him a frequent loser.

His brother Jack, on the other hand, knows the game well and is an excellent player. He even gives the appearance of being a professional gambler, looking and dressing like one, always showing up perfectly groomed and nattily attired. He hardly ever participates in our raucous bull sessions, and his face has always got that intense, determined, concentrated look that tells you he has come to play.

Unlike his brother, if he has a weak hand or if he figures the odds are against him he'll drop out. And even when he does drop out he still watches the hand to its conclusion just to get a feel of how the others are playing. I know for a fact he also follows avidly the *"Texas Hold 'em"* shows on ESPN.

Nicky Ravello – Tony and Jack's cousin – is also an excellent player, maybe even the best in our group. The three of us – me, Jack and Nicky – are pretty much on the same level in technical knowledge of the game, but Nicky also excels at surreptitiously gauging his opponents' reaction as they get their draw cards and correctly guessing what kind of hand they hold. Sneaky Nicky, we call him.

Joe Rossi and his brother-in-law Vince Stella, partners in a fruit-vending stall at the New Castle Farmers Market, are just mediocre players, barely a step above Danny, and they lose more often than not. Like Danny, they are also fairly well off and can afford to lose a few bucks when we play.

Jack and Nicky are the only competition I really have and, just like me, they are consistent winners. None of the consistent losers, however, will ever admit, or much less recognize, they just don't know how to play the game well. Their invariable litany is: "I just don't have any luck" or "You are always too damn lucky."

And, naturally, you'll never hear me, Jack or Nicky openly say we are good players or brag about our expertise. As we sympathize with them, our refrain is always the same: "Yes! No question about it, tonight lady luck was in my corner... But you know how it is, a bit of luck always helps."

We readily admit we were incredibly lucky, and we then encourage them by saying that – who knows? – maybe the wheel of fortune will point in their directions the next time we play. As it always does, three or four times a year, maybe.

"No, I didn't mean that." – Tony said, still sounding oddly subdued, almost sniveling – "Nobody called you yet?"

"No, why?" – I asked, tensing up again – "What's going on?"

"You haven't heard about Vince and Joe?"

"No, what happened?"

"They were in a car accident, a terrible car accident…" – He stammered, and his voice was quavering now, like he was just about ready to start sobbing.

"**WHAT⁉⁉…**" – I hollered, and I must have screamed out loud because two seconds later Maria came rushing down the stairs, almost stumbling down the last few steps in her haste to come down.

She had just finished showering and still had a towel tied turban-like around her wet hair. She was wearing this pink plush robe I had given her for Christmas six or seven years ago. It's kind of ratty looking now, but she keeps wearing it.

She must have had nothing underneath because she was holding both folds in front to keep it closed. That's the way Maria is – we have been married over 35 years, but she still has that same sense of modesty she had when she was a young girl.

"What happened?" – She demanded, clearly agitated.

Stunned as I was, I motioned to her I was OK, but she kept coming closer with a worried expression and a questioning look on her face. Again I signaled to reassure her I was OK, but she kept gesturing at me, thrusting forward and shaking up and down her free hand with fingers bunched up, trying to find out what was going on. I kept reassuring her, but she silently kept pressuring me to let her in on what I had heard. The look on her face said it all – anxious to hear what was going on, but also scared to find out.

Tony was really crying now, his voice barely audible in between sobs.

"Yeah! They were in a bad car accident on their way to some orchard downstate." – He managed to say – "Vince is dead… and some other guy also. Joe is in intensive care at Beebe's Hospital. They don't think he is going to make it. He's in very bad shape, very bad."

And that knocked me for a loop, literally. I've had my share of grief in my life and, to this day, hearing of sudden tragic news like that physically impairs me to the point that I'm temporarily out of commission.

I can't even explain exactly what happens to me. I get this trance-like sensation, a sensation that lasts briefly, fortunately – just a minute or two – but during that time I get this numb, paralyzing feeling, sort of like when one plunges in a pool of ice– cold water.

Seeing me leaning against the wall with a blank expression on my face and beginning to hyperventilate, Maria rushed to sustain me and to help me out.

"Easy now, honey, take it easy... it's OK." – She kept reassuring me gently. She then took the phone from my hand and talked briefly to Tony. When she heard the bad news she drew a sharp breath, covered her mouth and made a quick sign of the Cross. She briefly told him I was very upset and would call him later, then she hung up.

Still holding me, she kept caressing the top of my head, led me to the kitchen table and made me sit down.

As usual, my malaise didn't last long. A couple of minutes later I was still shook up but feeling much better.

Man! That was a hell of a shock! Vince and Joe were good friends, very dear friends of ours, like family really. I had first met them when I had come over from Italy – they were traveling on the same boat I was. They came from Ofena, in Abruzzo, in central Italy, and were on their way to Philadelphia where their families had already established residence. They were about 19 or 20, but to me – a little 16– year– old runt of a kid – they looked like grown men. Knowing I was traveling on the boat by myself, they had befriended me and had become my self–appointed chaperones.

After we debarked in New York we had lost track of each oth-er. Then, some 20 or 25 years ago we had reconnected when, by pure chance, I had found out they had moved to Delaware. Maria had asked me to stop at the New Castle Farmers Market to inquire about fresh rabbit meat from the Amish butcher; while there, I happened to pass by a fruit stand, where I saw these two guys who somehow looked familiar.

A bit intrigued, I stopped and bought some veggies I didn't even need. As I casually chatted with them, I found out they were Italians. A couple of inquiries and – Bingo! – they were the same Vincenzo and Giuseppe who had come over from Italy with me. Vince was now married to Joe's sister and they both owned and operated this fruit stand at the Farmers Market and doing quite well.

They did remember befriending a scrawny little kid on the boat, but they would never have recognized me. We embraced each other like long lost friends and I became one of their regular customers.

We began socializing and got to know each other real well. Later on, they joined our card– playing group. Like all the other card players, they had also become my customers, opening personal accounts for themselves plus a business account at WSFS (Wilmington Savings Fund Society), the bank where I am employed.

CHAPTER 2

I'm the manager of the Union Street branch, in the Little Italy section of Wilmington. I have been at that same location since day one, and that's nearly 40 years ago. WSFS hired me because they needed an Italian speaking person to deal with the hundreds of Italian immigrants living in that neighborhood, and I fit the bill.

When I first started working at WSFS, easily ten percent of our customers were Italian– born guys with scant knowledge of the English language, and another twenty percent were first or second generation Italians. Many of my customers have since died and many others have moved to the suburbs but, to this day, a substantial percentage of my customer base is of Italian origin.

Practically nobody comes over from Italy to stay nowadays, but until fifty or sixty years ago Italian immigrants still crossed the ocean in droves. They did so for the only reason immigrants from all over the globe came – and still come – to America: they believed they would find here the opportunity to work and make a better living than at home.

I am an Italian immigrant myself, but I am not your typical "just off the boat" character looking for that precious opportunity.

Unlike most of my compatriots, I had it fairly easy when I first set foot in this country, and I'll never bore you with tales about the insur-mountable obstacles I had to overcome or the backbreaking hardships I had to endure to succeed in this land. And that's because I hardly had any, thanks to my brother Domenic – or Mimmo as we called him. With his sponsorship, I came to America 48 years ago when I was a 16-year-old kid, and he took care of me for quite a while.

When I came over, I wasn't looking for that 'precious opportunity' because I was too young and really too clueless to think in terms of labor, of a career choice, of what I figured I would be doing to make a living, that sort of stuff.

I know this will sound hopelessly simple if not outright retarded, but it's a fact: in my blessed ignorance, I believed – I mean, really truly believed! – that coming to America meant automatic wealth, period. I was so naïve, so green, such a wide-eyed dreamer that I believed – really truly believed! – that it was just a question of showing up and I would become rich, fabulously rich.

Not to justify my idiocy, but I must add that this belief of mine was not an isolated case of terminal naiveté. In post-World War II Italy, most of my young friends – and even many adults – shared that same belief. To most Italians, America meant wealth, period!

Nearly everyone looked to America as the only country in the world that practically guaranteed a better standard of living than the one they had. And I am also certain that most everyone would have welcomed the opportunity to immigrate to America.

I am sure, however, that most of them – the adults, anyway – had sense enough to know they would have to work for a living. In those days jobs in Italy were scarce, and the few jobs available paid barely enough to eke out a living.

Most Italians would have gladly crossed the ocean, confident they would find here a job, any job that would allow them to be better off than in Italy. Not me, pal!

Like I said, I wanted to come because I believed – really truly believed! – that America meant easy street, fat city, gravy train! Automatically!

Dear God! Even now, after all these years, I can't help smiling and shaking my head in disbelief when I recall the giddy fantasies, the improbable dreams and the comically puerile flights of fancy floating inside my thick skull.

When I finally got that precious visa that would allow me to come over, and I knew it was just a matter of weeks before I would sail to America, all my waking hours and even the nights – especially the nights! – were spent visualizing what my life there was going to be like.

And everything was coming up roses! Not one single negative feature marred whatever scenario I dreamed up. Without exception, every road I took led to some enchanting location, and every enchanting location had pleasurable things to do – none of them even vaguely resembling work, mind you!

And it didn't end there, naturally – my vagaries were a merry-go-round of chimerical castles-in-the-air, a succession of whimsical daydreams where every pleasurable thing I did was sure to be followed by other, even more pleasurable events. And all of these happenings invariably took place in hazy yet clearly sumptuous scenarios; and every scenario had me at center stage, serene, confident, **BELONGING** there! And with just a hint of a smile on my lips, the blasé smile of one who sees the pre-ordained fulfillment of an event.

You see, I was going to **America! The United States of America!** Get that? I mean, I was actually going to live there, the land of plenty, the land of opportunity, the land where the word poverty wasn't even in the dictionary, the land where buildings were so tall they came up with the word skyscraper to describe them, the land where everyone drove those big-ass cars you saw in the movies, the land of Hollywood, Gary Cooper, Rita Hayworth, John Wayne, Clark Gable, the Statue of Liberty, neon lights, cowboys, glitz and glamour. America!

ME!... ME!... ME!... IN AMERICA, BY GOD!

I was going to America and – as I was saying – I knew, I just knew I would become incredibly wealthy. It was inevitable! It was a given! I had King Midas' touch!

I was sure I would be living in a fabulous home, like the ones Fred Astaire socialized and tap danced in. And just like him, I would always be wearing a tuxedo, of course; and I would be driving a huge car. No, no, no, what am I saying? A chauffeur in livery would be driving my luxurious Cadillac, just one of the fleet of cars I would own; and my pockets would be bulging with hundred dollar bills; and I would have dozens of people obeying my orders; and adoring servants would anxiously be tending to my every need; and I would generously be distributing huge tips to bellhops, waiters, cabdrivers. Hell! I even saw myself doing some fancy prestidigitation, as I would make a folded bill appear magically, with a snapping motion, between my index and middle fingers, my generous reward given with a wink and a knowing smile to whoever had done some small service for me – nothing smaller than a twenty. Of course.

I'm telling you: compared to me, King Midas was a pauper!

And then the payoff – I also knew that someday I would make a triumphant return to Italy where I would be the envy of all my friends and relatives. Of course.

How I would achieve all that wealth wasn't quite clear. Why clutter such a lovely adolescent fantasy with a bunch of insignificant details? I just knew it would happen, and that was good enough for me.

To be sure, there was some vague justification, some dim semblance of what could loosely be called a line of reasoning behind this rose-colored vision of my future life in America.

I was acquainted, for instance, with a few *paisans* who had emigrated to the United States back in the 20s and 30s and had then retired in Italy, and they all lived in nice homes, they all drove nice cars, they all seemed to be quite wealthy. And I knew of others who still lived in America and occasionally came to Italy on vacation, and they all seemed to have plenty of money to throw around.

Definitely, all of them seemed to be well off, much better off than the local folks. Furthermore, I had also made an amazing discovery: most of them – **hell, all of them!** – didn't have any special education; like a college degree, that is. Nothing! Not even a high school diploma! Hell! Not even an elementary school diploma! I was literally shocked when I found out that many of them could hardly read or write, and those few who could had barely achieved a second or third grade education!

Yet all of them – no exceptions! – always dressed in rather garish but clearly expensive clothes, they all owned or rented cars, they didn't seem to have a care in the world, and they always treated in bars, restaurants and what have you. All of them – no exceptions! –always had a confident air, a jovial manner, a take-charge attitude, a cocky assurance even. And all of them – no exceptions! – behaved like people who had arrived, people who knew what it was all about, people who had the world by the balls, people who looked at the future without any worry – a behavior that contrasted sharply with the diffident, insecure demeanor of the locals.

One of them was Nick Ravello, my brother's father-in-law, Tony and Jack Ravello's uncle and Nicky Ravello's grandfather. I first met him in 1950, the year before I came to America. He had returned on vacation to his hometown, Torre Faro, a picturesque fishing hamlet near Messina, on the northeastern corner of Sicily. He had returned for a four months' vacation, mind you!

It was his first trip back after a thirty-year absence. Nick had come over by boat, a luxury liner, and first thing he did as soon as he hit town was spend a ton of money to rehab his old family home, adding a second story, indoor plumbing and so on.

To get around, he hadn't rented a car. He had brought his own ride from America, a brand new Pontiac, with automatic transmission and air conditioning – this in a time when nobody in Italy even knew there was such a thing as an automatic transmission or air conditioning for automobiles.

Keep in mind this was 1950, when American cars were still big-ass gas-guzzlers with enough room inside to easily accommodate six people. Keep in mind also that in those days there weren't all that many cars in Italy, and the few you saw belonged to the very wealthy – nobody else could afford one.

The Italian auto industry was just cranking up after World War II, and the few cars it turned out were small contraptions you could easily fit in the Pontiac's trunk. The only motorized transportation most folks could afford were motor scooters like "*Vespa*" and "*Lambretta*" that had been introduced a few years before and were getting to be quite popular.

17

Nick was one pleasant and peculiar piece of work. A jovial man of about sixty, he had a solid reputation of having been and still being an unrepentant skirt chaser, a virtuoso ladies' man, a fiercely dedicated and very successful philanderer. And I know for a fact that his reputation was well earned.

He had gone to the United States about thirty years before, and the word was that he had not just emigrated but had actually escaped, had been run out of town – so to speak – by a posse of angry fathers and cuckolded husbands who were after his hide.

I had heard different versions of how he had made his way to America, but the one I heard most frequently – and liked best – was that as he was blissfully engaging in one of his amorous trysts, a friend – banging on a windowpane – had rushed to alert him that an angry mob was out looking for him to tan his hide. He had barely had time to put on his pants, jump out of a window and run for his life. Afterwards, he had managed to hide in the hold of a ship, the ship had sailed and he found himself in America.

Cute story, if true, definitely the kind of story one would associate with someone like Nick. Keep in mind: this took place in the early 1920s. In those days, in Sicily just looking at a woman the wrong way would practically guarantee a six-inch slash on your face. And Nick didn't just look; with him it was always *"veni, vidi, vici"* – I came, I saw, I conquered. With all the emphasis on "I came."

His conquests and his escapades had turned him into some kind of folk hero, an erotic Robin Hood, and the locals still talked with undisguised awe and ill-concealed envy of his amorous exploits of 30 years before.

In fact, when my parents found out my brother was going to marry his daughter, they weren't all that thrilled at first because they still remembered – three decades later – Nick's exploits and his less than sterling reputation. They were kind of worried some of his traits might be passed on to his daughter or to my brother's children.

Now, however, his jovial and friendly manners made him accessible and very popular with just about everybody, and even my parents seemed to like him.

Despite the big age difference between the two of us, he was always pretty chummy with me. Surely, that was mostly because I was his son-in-law's brother, but I believe it was also because we both shared a mad passion for singing and were pretty good at it. Indeed, he was more than pretty good – he had a fabulous tenor voice, and it was well known that many of his youthful conquests were the results of the passionate and sensuous midnight serenades he used to sing under the windows of the *belle du jour*, accompanying himself with a guitar.

Nick was an average 5" 7" tall. He was a bit chunky now, had a ruddy complexion and receding gray hair. Still, he had strikingly handsome and manly features but, mainly, a commanding presence. A roguish, mischievous twinkle danced constantly in his blue eyes, especially when talking to the ladies. He had this provocative and enviable way of conversing with them in a familiar, humorous way, together with a droll knack for making fairly intimate comments or allusions to them without being outright scandalous.

One could easily see how in his youth he must have been a truly dashing, romantic figure. It wasn't hard to imagine how, with his rugged good looks and his great singing voice, women would throw themselves at him. And that, by the way, was his rationalization for his incessant philandering – he always claimed it wasn't him going after the ladies, it was they who hounded him, and how could he refuse them?

Despite his less than sterling reputation, he really was a hell of a nice guy, generous to a fault, with a self-effacing sense of humor, always giving rides in his big car to whomever needed one and always buying ice cream cones and sodas for us kids.

Since his return, in addition to spending a ton of money to rehab his house, he had also bought a *fulua* – a huge fishing boat used mainly to catch swordfish – and had hired a four-man crew to operate it. This last piece of business had been done against my brother's advice, and Nick later admitted he should have listened to him.

My brother had warned him that this new enterprise would show a profit only during those few months Nick was in Sicily. After he left – my brother predicted – the daily catch would show a marked decrease, meaning of course that the daily catch would still be the same but would be reported as sharply reduced to the absentee owner. And that's exactly what happened.

But the biggest splash Nick made was when it was revealed that he had donated another ton of money to buy a pipe organ for the town church.

To his credit, when he made the donation he had requested anonymity, but anonymity in a small Sicilian hamlet is simply contrary to the laws of nature. Within days – **HOURS!** – of the donation, everyone in town knew who had given the money, when it was donated, why it was donated, how much had been donated, in what denomination, and maybe even the brand name of the pipe organ. It was such a grand and generous gesture that most town folks – who liked him personally but still made sure their daughters or sisters wouldn't go for a ride in his car – began to think that maybe the Lord had performed some miracle.

On the Sunday when the new organ was first played, the parish priest celebrated a highly anticipated *Messa Solenne* (High Mass). It was the kind of ceremonial nobody would miss, and I was there along with just about everybody else in town.

The church was packed to capacity, literally standing room only. Rickety loudspeakers had to be placed outdoors on the steps of the church to allow the overflow crowd crammed in the small square outside the church to listen to the religious function. Even the bishop from Messina turned up for the celebration.

Halfway through the Mass, first the parish priest, then the town mayor and finally the bishop publicly acknowledged Nick Ravello as a friend of the church and a benefactor. With the kind of overblown histrionics peasant folks love to hear, they gave a dramatic and stirring report of the enormous sacrifices Nick had made and the multiple hardships he had experienced and overcome in America.

"... but despite encountering a plethora of adversities, despite facing innumerable obstacles, the kind of adversities and the kind of obstacles that would

have crushed any ordinary man, he steadfastly and resolutely persevered... because Signor Ravello is not an ordinary man...

His hand firmly on the helm, he guided his ship through the stormy seas, and through his hard work and his tenacious capacity he managed to keep a steady course without being distracted by mundane frivolities, until he finally achieved his well-deserved success...

But success never went to his head. Mr. Ravello always was and has always remained a modest man. And now, ever mindful of his humble origins, he wants to show his gratitude to God for all the grace He has bestowed on him...

*And what better way to express this gratitude than by donating to the church – **YOUR** church! – the means to sing God's praise?"*

Amen!

And, to be sure, they urged everybody to look up to *Signor* Ravello as the shining example to follow to achieve fulfillment in life. Finally, to the applause and the acclaim of the entire congregation, they dispensed on him and his family the abundant blessings of the church. Needless to say, no mention was made of the dozens of seductions he had been credited with before leaving town in a hurry thirty years before, and the few he was rumored to have snuck in since his return.

As the new organ blared triumphantly behind the altar, the parish priest, the bishop and for all I know the cardinal and the pope himself, joyfully dispensed plenary absolution for those sins of the flesh, with some change left over for future ones.

Typical of all the '*Americani*' who came to Italy to stay or were there on vacation, Nick had very little formal education.

Once I got to read a letter he had written to my brother Mimmo who had remained in America to mind the family business while Nick was vacationing in Italy. I got to read it – just a few lines, really – because I happened to be at his house when he had finished writing it. Needing to mail it immediately, Nick had asked me if I could please take it to the post office, put a stamp on it and drop it in a mailbox. Before sealing it, however, he had kindly asked me if I wanted to add a greeting to my brother.

I just scribbled 'Saluti e baci' (Greetings and kisses) and signed my name. As I did, however, I sneaked a look at a couple of paragraphs of what Nick had written. I'm telling you, it was awful! The grammar, the spelling, even the handwriting was at a second or third grade level.

But just by listening to them talking you could tell these 'Americani' had little or no education. All of them spoke mostly in the Sicilian dialect and what little Italian they spoke was filled with elementary syntax and pronunciation mistakes.

Their conversations were frequently filled with American words mangled into approximate Italian or Sicilian – giobba for job, troccu for truck, storu for store, dezzoll for that's all, salamabbech for son of a bitch, and so on. And they never even bothered to translate those words in Italian, fully expecting people to understand what they were talking about.

I figured – what the hell! – if they had all managed to become so wealthy with little or no education, I should be able to become not just wealthy but filthy rich.

At that time I was attending the fourth year of 'ginnasio', the equivalent of the 10th grade in America. In other words, I had already had much more formal education than any of them had had in their entire lives.

And that, basically, was the rather shaky foundation on which I was building all my American dreams.

To be honest, I really wasn't all that brilliant in school. If truth be told, I was one patented dickhead, always goofing off and barely passing in most subjects. In fact, I should have been in the fifth year of 'ginnasio', but the year before I had flunked and I had to repeat the fourth year.

I knew, however, or I was pretty sure anyway, that I wasn't a total dumb ass. My poor academic performance could be traced to one reason – I never really applied myself.

First, I was distracted by my passion for soccer – I was always out playing soccer in the streets with my friends instead of hitting the books or doing my homework. I can't even begin to tell you how many times my mom boxed my ears, not so much because playing soccer interfered with my school work, but because playing soccer interfered with the health of the only pair of shoes I owned.

And second, I had only recently discovered some very fascinating differences between boys and girls, and I'd begun spending way too much time looking at girls, or trying to get them to look at me. And with fair success I should add.

Whoa! Hold on now! Don't get the idea I was a budding Casanova, or even a budding Nick Ravello... Hell, I wish! In those days, the most a boy of my age could aspire to accomplish with a girl was to "accidentally" bump into one at play in the schoolyard. And if it was your lucky day, you just might get to touch her butt or her budding breasts, or hit the jackpot and cop a feel, as Holden Caufield would say.

I'm not even sure I knew what I would or should have done, had I managed to actually get my hands on a real live girl, but the hunt was on, so to speak, and I had started doing the incredibly foolish things young boys did – and still do – to get noticed by young girls.

Anyhow, between soccer and girl-watching my grades suffered badly, and that's why I had flunked the previous year. I did plan to continue my education in the United States, however, and I had pledged to myself I was going to become a model student.

And that was the basis for my get-rich-quick beliefs. A reasonable assumption – I thought – an assumption shared by all my classmates, by the way. As a matter of fact, when they found out I was going to quit school in Italy to go to America, all of them – to a man – exclaimed "*Che culo!*", which means "What ass!", a crude expression Italians use when they think someone has had incredible luck.

That's because all of them also assumed that going to America meant I was going to become at the very least another Nick Ravello, which was already a hell of a lot more than what any of them realistically hoped to become.

It didn't quite pan out that way, but I can't complain.

CHAPTER 3

I am the odd one in my family, for various reasons.

To start with, I am the tallest one in the Vadalà clan. It's not like I'm a beanpole, mind you! I only stand 5' 10", but I "tower" over my brother by a full 3 inches and by even more over the rest of the family.

Another oddity is my musical ability. I have already mentioned I can carry a tune decently; what I left unsaid is that the rest of my family is tone deaf. Well, I'll say it now – my brother, my sisters, my mom and dad, they are all tone deaf.

I am also the only non-believer in my family. My brother and my sisters, they are all extremely religious and very sincere in their beliefs, I'm quite sure of that. Me, I'll be going straight to hell because the only commandment I consider worth observing is the fifth one – I believe – the one that says "Thou shall not kill."

It's the only one I have strictly observed. So far at least. And with some reluctance, I might add.

I consider the Ten Commandments optional. And by that I mean that in theory they can be useful. In practice, it's a different story – they are a farce. Not even the saintliest of all saints could faithfully observe them – or even should, I would say. Name any one of the Commandments and I can give you a good, valid, legitimate reason for breaking it. Yes! Even the "Thou shall not kill" one! Especially that one!

I have personally broken the other nine, usually with a justifiable reason for doing so. More often than not I have even enjoyed breaking them, and I can only think of a very few occasions when I have felt a need to repent or felt any shame for breaking them.

Another distinguishing oddity is my dislike of anything marine. I am not a huge fan of the beach, the sea or any type of sea vessel.

This particular aversion truly makes me the black sheep of my family, so to speak, as it goes against the way my entire family had been steeped in for generations.

My father, my grandparents and great grandparents were practically born and raised on the sea and loved it; my brother, my uncles, my cousins and all my relatives go crazy for boats and the sea, and at some time in their lives most of them even made a living on or from the sea either as fishermen or as seamen.

Everyone in my family, including my mother, my sisters, aunts and uncles, nephews and cousins, all worship the ocean – the crazy nitwits! Their idea of happiness is to lie down on a beach or to be lulled by the waves on some type of vessel listening to seagulls shrieking above them. Not this kid.

As for swimming, my brother was a champion swimmer in school, my dad sliced through the water like a shark, my sisters were like Esther Williams, even my mother, who was a chunky lady, was quite a good swimmer. Me, those few times I venture in the water I barely manage to stay afloat. Like a turd, I suppose.

My brother has had a succession of boats one bigger than the other – the last one a 36-foot long ocean liner with sleeping quarters and all – and you have no idea how many times he has asked me to go fishing with him. I can't and won't go because I get seasick – bad, *mucho* bad. And only folks who know what it means to be seasick know what I am talking about.

I did go fishing with Mimmo once, back in the day. He promised me I would be OK; he assured me the weather forecast called for no wind, no rain, no nothing. And in fact the sea was flat as a table – I must admit – no wind was blowing, it was a gorgeous day overall, with hardly any wave motion at all. I had even taken some Dramamine just to be on the safe side.

Still, I managed to get seasick, not too much actually, just a bit nauseous, but enough not to risk eating any of the sandwiches and stuff we had brought, or even drink a beer. And to cap a crappy day, I got sunburned and we didn't catch a damn thing. Bottom line, I didn't have a good time at all, and I figured – Christ! – if I got a little sick with the boat practically still and me stuffed with Dramamine, what would happen if the boat did a seriously serious rock and roll? With me on board?

I get seasick just thinking about it.

From then on, every time my brother asked me to go fishing with him, the answer was always 'no way, José, just bring me some fish'. And then I would add 'if you catch any, that is.'

That was always a private joke between us. That's because, in addition to his almost mystical attachment to the sea, my brother had an insane passion for fishing. He considered fishing not just a pastime but an art form, and didn't spare any expense to practice it. He had spent a fortune on fishing gear, acquiring the latest technological gadgets, even an underwater radar or whatever, I forget what it's called, some gear that lets you see if a school of fish is passing below, he explained. Not to mention the cost of the boat itself, of course.

Still, most times he went fishing his catch hardly covered the bottom of a mid-size plastic cooler. I used to kid him a lot about it, and even he acknowledged that it would have been a hell of a lot cheaper, and would have resulted in him getting a much larger variety of fish, if he had bought an entire fish market.

I definitely am not a big fan of the sea or even the beach, but it wasn't always like that. I was never much of a swimmer, but when I was a young man I used to look forward going to the seashore, especially when we vacationed down in Sicily where they have a gorgeous beach.

What soured it all for me – forever and ever. Amen! – was the sea voyage from Genoa to New York when I first came to the United States.

Brutal! Cruel! Inhuman! Let me tell you, that was the trip from hell! Compared to that, the trip on the "Titanic" was a serene boat ride in a lily pond. I swear, for two weeks I barfed up even the milk my mother gave me. I mean, I couldn't keep anything down, throwing up even the air I was breathing. Two solid weeks!

It traumatized me for life, that's how bad it was. And while as a kid I enjoyed going to the beach or even on boat rides, since that trip I wouldn't go near a boat if my life depended on it.

Because I know my life depends on it.

I left Italy on Nov. 14, 1951 aboard the *"S. S. Vulcania,"* a passenger ship that – along with its sister ship *"S. S. Saturnia"* – provided regular transatlantic service between Genoa and New York.

I was a 16--year-old kid on the threshold of puberty, leaving my home, my country, my family and all my friends. And not caring one little bit about it.

To this day I can still see myself at the ship's railing on that gray, rainy morning as tugboats slowly moved the *"S. S. Vulcania"* away from the pier. I can still hear the lugubrious howl of her foghorns. And I can still see myself joyfully waving goodbye to my weeping mother and sisters who were sadly waving back from the dock.

My dad was there also, valiantly trying to be cheerful for me, briskly waving at me and smiling. But at one point – it's still fresh in my mind! – at one point I saw him suddenly turn around and wipe his eyes, overcome with emotion. And I still remember leaning on that railing until Genoa – my beloved hometown – became first an indistinct mass of land and then finally disappeared on the distant horizon.

Was I sad? Did I cry? Did I feel or act like someone who was leaving his hometown, his family and his friends? No, No, and No! Absolutely No!

I was going to the United States of America, man! And I was going to become rich, filthy rich. That's what was on my mind!

New York – November 28, 1951!

I remember that day like it was yesterday – a crystal clear day, the sky as blue as it can possibly get, the sun shining brilliantly and a cold wind blowing like mad.

Damn, it was cold! Cold as a dead witch's tits! I had never ever felt that bitter cold in my life – I mean, after all I was coming from sunny Italy.

My entire wardrobe consisted of about three or four pairs of short pants, an equal number of shirts, one jacket, some underwear, socks and a couple of hankies. And that's about it.

In Italy in those days all young teenagers used to wear short pants and that's what my mom had packed for me. In fact, I don't remember ever owning long pants, and she didn't know enough to get me some. It wasn't her fault, of course – where we lived the weather was rarely below 50 degrees, even in winter, and long pants just weren't necessary.

Thank God I did have a jacket and a pullover that either my mom or one of my sisters had knit for me, or I know I would have died of pneumonia even before docking.

When the ship entered New York harbor, all passengers had rushed outside excitedly to look at the Big Apple, although I don't think it was already called that in those day.

I'd managed to elbow my way right to the railing and there I leaned, entranced, wide eyed, watching along with the other passengers the beautiful Manhattan skyline parade in front of us in that glorious sunshine.

The Statue of Liberty went gliding by along with Ellis Island. I had never heard of Ellis Island, the legendary stop off place where millions of immigrants from all over the world had to be registered before entering the United States, but I was familiar with the Statue of Liberty, having seen it in many photographs as well as at the movies.

Seeing it in pictures and stuff, however, doesn't really give much of an idea of what it's really like, just like one can't get much out of seeing the Coliseum or St. Peter's Basilica or the Eiffel Tower in a postcard.

Seeing Lady Liberty up close for the first time is something else. All I can say is that it took my breath away; it literally gave me goose bumps.

Imposing! Magnificent! Overwhelming! Those are just a few of the adjectives that can truly convey its grandeur, its nobility! Additionally, it filled me with a big-time adrenalin rush knowing it was just the prelude, the harbinger of the many fabulous things waiting for me in America.

People kept pointing out this and that skyscraper but they all looked the same to me. The only one I recognized and had heard about was the Empire State Building, the tallest one at that time.

I still recall my amazement – everyone's amazement! – when we learned in school that, with its 103 stories, it was the tallest building in the world. **One hundred and three stories**, can you imagine? Supposedly, during a fierce windstorm it even swayed a bit, that's what somebody had told us, and – crazy kids that we were! – we actually pictured it swinging wildly from side to side like a reed, with people inside holding on for dear life. I also remembered reading that a few years before a military plane had crashed into it on a foggy day.

In those days the Manhattan skyline was the most easily recognized skyline in the world – probably still is, even without the Twin Towers. The shortest building seemed to be at least fifty stories high, quite a contrast with my hometown where we bragged about having two of the tallest buildings in Italy. And the taller of those two 'skyscrapers' – both built during the Fascist regime – was about thirty stories high.

I was impressed, impressed and ecstatic, that's all I can tell you. My teeth were chattering like a machine gun, and in that bitter cold every breath sliced into my lungs like a knife, each exhalation turning instantly to vapor. But I hung in there.

You couldn't pry me away from that railing with an ice pick, and that's what you'd probably have needed because, like I said, I was freezing my ass off.

But I was elated, I was in a state bordering ecstasy, rapture, I was just plain and simple happy. Man, oh man, was I happy!... Happy to be in America, happy to be starting a new and magical chapter in my life, happy to be alive, happy that I'd soon be seeing my brother who had better be there to meet me at the dock, but mostly happy, deliriously happy to be leaving that goddamned ship where I had puked my guts out for the past fourteen days.

November 28, 1951! My life, my real life began on that day, the day I arrived in the United States. The preceding 16 years were an anonymous period of time spent just waiting for that date, years so non-descript that I hardly remember any part of them. In fact, the only meaningful memories I still retain of the first 16 years of my life are those somehow connected with my coming to America.

My brother had preceded me here by three years. He worked in the Italian merchant marine as the second officer on the *"Bacicin",* a small cargo ship transporting scrap metal between America and Italy. When his ship docked in Norfolk, he took one look around and said 'Jesus Christ! What the hell am I doing on that rust bucket?', and decided on the spot to jump ship and stay in this country.

Actually, why he definitely decided to jump ship is a fascinating true story, certainly an anecdote worthy of being told.

Mimmo had always admired America and, like millions of others, he was grateful to this country for what it had done for Italy immediately after the war through the Marshall Plan. Like most Italians, he also believed one could easily make a better living here than anywhere else, and had considered coming to this country either as an immigrant or the fastest way – by jumping ship.

What kept him from doing it was the fact that he had just started working in the merchant marine, and he loved his new job. To him the sea was like amniotic fluid – he simply couldn't live without it. Additionally, his new job was the starting point for a promising maritime career, a career that potentially could have led to his becoming the skipper of a cargo ship or even an ocean liner.

He swears that the catalyst, what really made him decide to jump ship and stay in this country was an ordinary book of matches.

As he is fond of relating it, when his ship docked in Norfolk he got a pass to go ashore. And, naturally, he had gone to town for the usual reason most sailors go to town when their ship is in port – to get laid.

He never did say – and I never asked – if he got lucky or not, but he says that while he was in town barhopping and looking for action, he had also stopped in some store to buy cigarettes to bring back to Italy.

American cigarettes were not only notoriously better than the Italian ones, but were hard to find in Italy, available only as contraband on the black market. Furthermore, in those days one pack of American cigarettes was the grease, the magical ingredient that oiled every wheel and opened every door in the labyrinth of Italian bureaucracy.

Mimmo bought quite a few cartons of cigarettes and, as he was paying for them, the cashier had tossed several books of matches on the counter. Back then, every time you bought a pack of cigarettes, the cashier would also automatically hand you a pack of matches for free, something my brother didn't know.

When the cashier gave him the matches my brother asked in halting English how much he owed for them. Shrugging, the guy had told him: "Nothing, they are on the house".

My brother was dumbfounded. In those days, Sicily – where he was born – was one of the leading producers of sulfur in the world, and sulfur is used to make matches. Still, everywhere in Sicily and in Italy a pack of matches cost money – I don't know how much, but they charged you for it. Here, instead, when you bought smokes – much better and much cheaper than the Italian ones – they'd just toss four or five books of matches at you, for free!… Imagine that!

And that's when my brother said 'Jesus Christ! What the hell am I doing on that rust bucket?'

Long story short, after jumping ship he caught up with this *paisan*, Nick Ravello, who lived in Maryland. Nick had this daughter, Ange. Ange and Mimmo started making eyes at each other and in no time they were married.

Nick was a self-employed businessman and my brother started working for him. Lots of people – most of them so-called Italian friends – sneered when they heard my brother had married Ange, snidely hinting that the only reason he had done that was to marry the boss' daughter.

And he had, of course! – but let me set the record straight.

Nick was an entrepreneur with a keen eye for what could be a real moneymaking business, but he had little or no knowledge of how to run a business. He didn't know a budget from a gadget, and had no sense of how to cut expenses, how to advertise, how to price, how to sell. Nothing.

He did have enough sense to know his limitations, and he had hired people to take care of the mechanics of running a business. Those people cost money, of course, and cut heavily on his net income. Furthermore, Nick loved the ladies and the ponies, two losing propositions.

Bottom line: Nick had a gold mine but was barely scraping by.

On the other hand, my brother was a graduate of a Nautical Institute in Italy, and besides learning all about stars, navigation and whatever else is needed to run a ship, he had also learned a thing or two about business administration, accounting, etc.

When he started working for his father-in-law, he established some rules, prepared a budget, eliminated a few jobs and drastically cut expenses. And that's when things started humming.

So it was no longer a question of my brother marrying the boss' daughter, but more a question of a boss getting lucky in becoming my brother's father-in-law.

My brother and Nick occasionally did have some serious differences, always business related. Basically, whenever he had a windfall Nick liked to spend money, and screw the budget – along with whatever else he could screw. My brother, on the other hand, believed in a sound business policy and stood up to Nick's requests for more spending money.

Despite their occasional spats, I never heard Nick disparage my brother. In fact, people always told me he was fond of saying: "The Lord sent Domenic to me!"

November 28, 1951! A magical day for me! Yes! I still consider it a day for celebration, like my birthday, or my wedding anniversary!

The "*S.S. Vulcania*" docked, and this wide-eyed, dazed and more than a bit intimidated little kid scrambled down the gangplank carrying a shabby suitcase and looking around for a familiar face among the huge crowd of people waiting on the dock.

Thank God, my brother was there waiting for me along with his wife Ange.

It was the first time I had seen her – I just knew her from pictures. My brother had met her shortly after arriving in America, they had gotten married after a brief engagement and they already had a kid, a baby boy named Pietro, like my father.

In Sicily, by the way, tradition dictates that you name your first-born son after your father and your first-born daughter after your mother. If you don't, you are considered a shit. And the tradition doesn't end there – you should also name your second-born son after your wife's father and your second-born daughter after your wife's mother.

As it happens, my paternal grandfather's first name was Domenico, and this same name was given to my parents' first-born son, my brother. My maternal grandfather's first name was Letterio, and I got stuck with that official moniker.

Letterio is a very unusual first name even in Italy. It's popular only in the immediate area around Messina, the town in Sicily where my parents came from. It's common there because in Messina they venerate the "*Madonna della Lettera*" (Madonna of the Letter). And no, it's not the Madonna who sings… it's the other one, Jesus' mom.

A local legend says this Madonna wrote a letter to the inhabitants of Messina praising them for their devotion, blessing them, and promising all kinds of favors. Promises never kept, of course.

Because of their devotion to this Madonna of the Letter, they coined the name Letterio for boys and Letteria for girls. While Letterio is my official first name, nobody in Italy ever called me that, except perhaps to make fun of me.

My immediate family and all my friends call me Lillo. "Leo" came later, when I started working at the bank. My branch manager valiantly tried to call me Letterio, but he kept mangling the pronunciation. To simplify matters, at some point he started calling me Leo. I liked it, adopted it, and that has been my name in American circles since then.

Ange was a very pretty young lady, with dark wavy hair, kind eyes, a pleasant smile and very warm and friendly manners. She put me at ease immediately, treating me like her kid brother. I liked her right away, and in no time at all she made me feel like we had known each other all our lives.

The big fat Buick my brother was driving was even roomier than Nick Ravello's Pontiac. It was a 1949 Buick Roadmaster, the top of the line model of the Buick family, the one with the four portholes on the front fenders.

My brother casually mentioned the car was nothing special. It was, in fact, two years old already, and added that in America cars changed models every year.

And that was the first of many astounding news about America. Imagine that! All car companies had new models coming out every single year!... In Italy those few piss-ant cars you saw were around since creation.

New models came out every ten or fifteen years, and when they did, it was such big news that it even displaced politics and soccer from the front pages of newspapers.

The latest car model to come out in Italy had been introduced a couple of years before I left. It was a new version of the Fiat 500, I believe, and it was the first new model the Fiat factory had launched on the market since well before the war.

I swear this is no lie but it was just a bit larger than a coffee can and just about as solid or comfortable. But it was about six inches longer than a previous model of the 500 – "*Topolino*" it was called – a cute little bugger but, honest to God, too small even for pygmy dwarves.

When this latest model of the Fiat 500 came out, most people – including yours truly – looked at it as a triumph of Italian engineering. Man! We used to rave about its longer shape and what to us looked like sleek, aerodynamic lines. We even proudly compared it to the American cars we used to see at the movies.

Yeah! Sure! The only thing it had in common with American cars was that it had an engine and four wheels, and that's just about it.

I had been inside an Italian car only once in my life and that had come about on a fluke. There was this girl in my class I had been panting after – Franca was her name. Her dad was a taxi driver, he drove a Lancia taxi, a car marginally bigger than a Fiat, but still about half the size of my brother's Buick.

After school we always used to walk home, a good two-mile walk. We didn't have school buses then. School buses?... Are you kidding?

But this one time – I don't remember what happened, Franca's dad was passing by, I guess – he had stopped at the school to pick up his daughter with his taxi. Since I lived only a couple of blocks away from her, Franca asked him if he would give me a ride along with some other girl who lived in the neighborhood also.

At first he declined because he had luggage to deliver somewhere. And on the back seat of the taxi there was, in fact, one large suitcase that didn't fit in the trunk – but then he good-naturedly agreed. He managed to squeeze the suitcase on the front seat next to him, and us three kids piled in the back seat crammed together, and I do mean really crammed together. In fact, crushed together.

And let me tell you, apart from the thrill of actually riding in a car for the first time in my life, I didn't mind the tight quarters one bit. In fact, I made damn sure the crush got even crushier.

I kept rubbing my leg against Franca's leg and, at every curve – and Genoa's streets are all twists and curves – I went way overboard practically falling on top of her. And she didn't seem to mind that one bit because when the curve went the other way she would go way overboard to practically fall on top of me. And I didn't mind **that** one bit.

That was the first and only time I ever rode in an Italian car. A couple of years later I got to ride in an American car, Nick Ravello's Pontiac.

Nick was a hell of a nice guy – I've already mentioned that – always making himself available to anyone who needed any kind of help. He never seemed to mind taking us kids for rides, and frequently he would even take the time to show us how the car worked, the brakes, the steering wheel, the lever shift, the turn signals, and so on. Plus the radio of course – to us kids the radio was possibly that car's biggest attraction.

Hardly anybody in town had a radio at home, and being able to listen to songs and stuff in a car – and in a luxurious American car, to boot! – was for us kids *"la dolce vita"* way before Fellini even thought of that term.

A lot of folks took advantage of Nick's good nature and frequently asked him to give them a ride somewhere, but none of us kids would have had the nerve to ask him for a ride. We just looked at that car dreamily, as if it was a UFO from outer space. But when he had to go to the city or wherever, for whatever reason, if I was around he would always ask me to come along, and if other kids were with me, he would invite them also.

Naturally, all my buddies – knowing I was tight with him because of my brother – always managed to hang around with me just in case Nick had to go somewhere. I mean, a ride in a Pontiac – plus an almost sure ice cream cone or a soda – wasn't something you could get easily in those days in Sicily or anywhere else in Italy.

I'd had several short rides in the Pontiac, but the ride of my life came when Nick took us (me, my mom, my two sisters, plus his wife of course) from Sicily to Genoa, my hometown. That was a good 700 miles trip with three adults and three teenagers occupying that car, and we fit just fine.

That came about because his four-month vacation was just about over, and he had to return to America on a ship that sailed from Genoa.

Our first stop was in Rome – my first ever visit there – and we stayed there a full day. Nick took us around to see St. Peter's and other sights, we ate in a nice restaurant – another first for me – and stayed at some hotel. We left Rome the next day and arrived in Genoa about eight or nine hours later. And what a glorious arrival that was!

To get to our Genoa apartment we had to drive by *"I Giardinetti"* (The Little Gardens), an itsy-bitsy park located about two blocks from

37

where we lived. It's a circular area of about an acre with a few trees, some iron benches, a water fountain and a newspaper kiosk.

It was our favorite hang-out place – weather permitting. All male kids and young adults always gathered there in clusters strictly apportioned by age group.

My age group would usually congregate in the area around the newspaper kiosk. That's where the sports papers were displayed, their headlines always fodder for heated discussions. But mostly, that's where we could also ogle the tits of the sultry Hollywood stars on the covers of magazines, all the while spinning wildly colorful yarns about the wildly improbable erotic exploits we would have performed had we been able to put our hands on all that voluptuous flesh.

Now, keep in mind that in those days in Italy – and everywhere else in Europe – American cars were still considered the top notch... no, no, no, that's not quite right!... More, much, much more than that! They were considered the ultimate, the untouchable, the incomparable, the *ne plus ultra,* the most luxurious mode of transportation in the world, make that the universe.

Even in a fairly large city like Genoa, we saw maybe three or four American cars a year, usually belonging to some wealthy American tourist vacationing on the Italian Riviera. And every time one of those behemoths appeared from somewhere it attracted a crowd, people just went gaga, one look was all you needed and you just knew, you just automatically understood, it was a given that there went luxury, wealth, class, opulence, elegance, you name it.

OK, picture this! A brand new Pontiac appears in a neighborhood where you hardly ever saw a car, much less an American car.

As usual, all my buddies were hanging out next to the newspaper kiosk in this little park, when suddenly this dazzling vision appears, this gorgeous chariot glides by, with its sleek lines, huge fenders, two-tone paint job, whitewall tires and enough gleaming chrome to make bumpers and grills for fifty Fiats.

It was like time had stopped.

Someone in the crowd saw the Pontiac approach and quickly

pointed it out to all the others who immediately stopped ogling at magazine covers to gaze open-mouthed at this magical mirage slowly progressing forward.

And when that splendid chariot glides by, who is that little fellow cheerfully waving at them from the back seat of that big, fat-ass, luxurious Pontiac?...

IT'S ME, GUYS! ME! ME! ME!

And that's when hysteria broke out.

The apartment house where we lived was about three hundred yards away from that little park and the Pontiac just kept going, but now it had a crowd of about twenty kids running like crazy after it.

When we parked – and there was parking space galore all over Italy back then. Hell, try that now if you can! – when we parked, the car was immediately surrounded by all my friends who wanted to know the who, the what, the when, the where and the why.

Me?... Oh sweet, sweet Lord Jesus God! You should have seen me! I got out of the car very cool like, nonchalant, like I'd been around cars like that all my life, all *déjà vu* stuff to me, totally enjoying my fifteen minutes of fame that actually turned into three or four days, that's how long Nick and his wife stayed with us before sailing back to America.

During those few days, Nick of course gave rides to all my friends, bought ice cream cones and sodas for all and generally increased my popularity with the group by a factor of ten at least.

I still remember how some of my friends, the ones with a mechanical turn of mind, were totally fascinated by the wonder of the air conditioning system and, mainly, by the automatic transmission.

"You mean there is no clutch, no gears to shift?" – They would ask incredulously. "And how does it work?"

Nick didn't know that either and didn't even try to hide his ignorance. He just let them open the hood and stare wide-eyed at the huge eight-cylinder motor and whatever else was under there.

CHAPTER 4

America! America! God bless America! I mean that, I really mean it. And no, I'm not waxing patriotic. And I'm not being sarcastic either.

Imagine, if you can, what it's like for a sixteen-year-old Italian kid, a starry-eyed, immature, and – yes! – bewildered Italian kid arriving in New York in 1951.

It's five, ten, fifty, a hundred new emotions and experiences rushing at you all at once. And you try to absorb them, inhale them, digest them, assimilate them, accept them, discard them, compare them to previous experiences, file them for future use. It's heaven, it's an exhilarant chaos, it's a nonstop turmoil, it's a constant barrage of mouth opening wonders, and it's an intoxicating roller coaster ride of incredible discoveries. It's gawking at a myriad new gadgets, it's learning that each new gadget will soon be replaced by newer and more efficient ones which in turn will soon be replaced by even newer and even more efficient ones. It's experiencing that "what will they think of next" feeling, it's taking this expectation of constant improvement for granted, it's understanding, really understanding what Americans mean when they boldly state 'You ain't seen nothing yet'.

It's America! THE UNITED STATES OF AMERICA!

And I was there!... Me! Me! **ME! ME!**... Finally!... Yes! Yes! **YES! YES!... GOD BLESS AMERICA!**

Mimmo tossed my rickety suitcase in the Buick's trunk and we headed home, which was Rising Sun, a small village in Maryland. Before leaving New York, however, he stopped somewhere in Manhattan to have lunch in this humongous cafeteria.

I had been in a traditional restaurant only once in my life – that one time in Rome the previous year – and the cafeteria experience was an absolute first for me.

Trays, self-service, an assembly line of food to choose from, some that looked fairly appetizing, others that looked like shit, hundreds of customers, more customers just at lunch hour than most restaurants in Italy would serve in a month, no waiters, you just pointed a finger to whatever you wanted and an attendant would dish it out for you, at the end of the food line a cashier to check out your order, you sat wherever there was an empty table and, on every table, napkins, ketchup, mustard, sugar, salt and pepper.

How neat, how efficient, how... how so... how so **American!**

I had my first hot dog – I liked it! My first taste of ketchup – a bit tangy, but I liked that also! My first French fries – loved them, especially with ketchup! And my first iced tea that I had selected because I thought it was a Coke.

I was familiar with Coca Cola because it was already being sold in Italy in those fancy little bottles that everybody saved as if they were precious jewels. I had only tasted it once or twice before – probably Nick had treated me because my family just didn't have the dough to spend on frivolous things like that.

Like everything else that came from America, Coca Cola was the stuff to drink if you wanted to be cool or impress somebody, while – on the tobacco side – Lucky Strike, Chesterfield or Camel were the cigarettes of choice for the plebeian folks, and Pall Mall for the very rich. And all the American smokes – I've already mentioned it – available exclusively on the black market.

I thought the iced tea was Coca Cola, but as soon as I tasted it I made a face and damn near spat it out because it was bitter – I hadn't put any sugar in it. I didn't know any better, of course.

Mimmo smiled and explained that it was iced tea. I had never even heard of the concept of iced tea. I am pretty sure I had never even had hot tea in my life before. Like all Italians I was strictly a coffee drinker, but I did know that tea was a beverage brewed like coffee, to be sipped hot. Once I put sugar in it I liked it, and I just processed the entire experience as one of the innovative ways Americans have of doing things.

Traffic in New York got my attention next – traffic lights at every intersection, alternate "One Way" streets, thousands of cars, myriad people coming and going everywhere and wide streets and avenues, all very long and very straight.

To really appreciate what I felt, you have to put things in the proper context. Italy was not a hick country, by all means – it was and always has been a civilized country. Hell, we taught civilization to just about the entire world! But it wasn't an industrial power either – that came later, much later. Furthermore, it had come out on the losing end of a hell of a long war only a few years before.

In all of Genoa, my hometown – a city roughly the size of Baltimore – there were maybe two dozen traffic lights, if that many. And apart from a couple of streets downtown, the longest stretch of straight road you will find there is a couple of hundred yards long. Everything else is all twists and turns.

Compare Genoa's labyrinth of narrow and twisting streets to New York's miles-long streets, all very wide and straight as arrows, crossed at regular intervals by other streets equally long and straight, with about two dozens traffic lights at every intersection, "Walk" and "Don't Walk" signs, yellow cabs everywhere and zillions of people massed on wide sidewalks. Keep that in mind, and you will better appreciate what I felt.

Mimmo made it a point to drive through Times Square at 42nd Street, even then bursting with neon signs in broad daylight.

Four or five movie houses lined both sides of the street – right next door to each other! – their illuminated marquee's listing the featured movies, all of them double-features. Double-features! Can you imagine?!? Two movies for the price of one!

Mimmo pointed out the huge Camel cigarette sign showing a guy blowing out perfect smoke rings every ten seconds or so. As he drove slowly through Times Square, I just stared out of the car window at that well-organized chaos, gaping silently, my mouth as wide open as the guy in the Camel ad.

To paraphrase what's his name – Winston Churchill, I believe – to me that initial New York experience was bewilderment, wrapped in astonishment, inside amazement. Talk about future shock! Whoever wrote that tome must have had someone like me in mind.

And that was just the beginning!

When we took the Lincoln Tunnel to get out of town, Mimmo casually remarked we were traveling under water.

"Ma va! Davvero?" – was my stunned reaction, the Italian version of "You got to be kidding me!"

But it was true, of course.

Next came the New Jersey Turnpike – they were then putting the finishing touches to it, but it was mostly open.

Here, again, context is a must. We had long roads in Italy. Hell! Romans built roads 2,000 years ago that we still use today, and that's exactly my point! Most roads in Italy were built for chariot traffic.

Over the years they had been improved to adapt them to "modern" traffic, which then consisted mainly of bicycles, motorcycles and not that many cars. But most roads were also quite narrow by American standards, even the major highways. A majority of them were paved – a few with cobblestones – but several were still unpaved, and all of them were twisting and curving like mad. The gorgeous *"autostrade"* that criss-cross Italy today came later, much later.

And here I was, riding in a fat Buick Roadmaster on this stupendous New Jersey Turnpike, two lanes going and two lanes coming. Incidentally, just for the record, today I consider the New Jersey Turnpike the most boring stretch of interstate travel in the entire cosmos. But back then it was a marvel, something I knew I would have to write about to my parents, my sisters and all my friends in Italy.

And right after the turnpike, another marvel – the Delaware Memorial Bridge, a 2-mile long suspended span inaugurated just a few months before. And soon after that we arrived in Rising Sun.

Mimmo and Ange lived just outside that small town in a huge stone house, over 150 years old, with lots and lots of open fields around it. The house and all the land around it – well over 100 acres – belonged to his father-in–law Nick who lived nearby, but my brother lived there rent-free with his wife and kid.

Nick had two businesses, a manure dealership (so help me!) and a mushroom growing business, and the two enterprises were closely related. The manure dealership was the main business – Nick had contracts with nearby racetracks to haul away horse manure. He used some of the manure as fertilizer for his own mushroom houses and sold most of it to nearby mushroom growers in Pennsylvania. My brother was the general manager of both businesses.

I met my nephew Pietro, a cute little bugger, only two years old and smart as a whip, talking a mixture of Italian and English and asking me all kinds of questions: who are you, where did you come from, do you want to play with my truck.

And you better believe I wanted to play with his truck! He had this toy fire truck about as big as a Fiat – I had never seen anything so huge in my life. He could sit in it and wheel it around with pedals!

Again – be patient, please! – context is a must. In my entire life I had had exactly two toys: a small toy car and a soccer ball.

Please bear with me and let me tell you the story of both. Toy car first.

In Genoa, not far from the school I attended there was this store, a "*tabaccheria*", a tobacco store that also sold newspapers, candy, pencils, school supplies and sundry stuff. Like most stores in Italy, it was about as big as an elevator, but it did have a small display window where they had displayed this large bowl filled with wrapped candies. Next to the candy bowl, perched on a small shelf, was a small toy car.

Next to the container, a handwritten sign said: "*Compra una caramella. Se la fortuna ti aiuta, vincerai l'automobile*" (Buy one candy. If luck helps you out, you can win the car). Each piece of candy cost one lira, about half a cent, and one of those candies supposedly contained the winning ticket.

On my word of honor, that toy car – loosely shaped like an American car – was about two, definitely not more than three inches long. It was made of tin, had no undercarriage, had tiny rotating wheels, and was painted a vulgar yellow – it was the kind of toy even McDonald would be embarrassed to offer as a giveaway!

Give that crap as a present to your kid today? Don't even think about it. He would throw it in your face. And then **HE** would disown **YOU!**

I was then about thirteen or fourteen. When school was out, all us kids would practically run home to get our "*merenda*", a little snack to tide us over till dinner. And when we passed in front of that store on our way home, we would invariably stop and gaze at that toy car in the window as if it was the real Batmobile. Dreaming of owning it, of course.

We never had an allowance in those days, or at least I never did. I hardly remember how we used to scrape up some dough. We occasionally did chores for some old lady, carrying bags or helping out, while some of the more enterprising kids became 'regulars' at local stores, delivering stuff, cleaning or just being all around helpers. Every now and then, we did get some loose change at home, usually in conjunction with a holiday, a birthday or a name day.

Whenever we managed to score some *lire*, we would head to the movies first – that was our primary source of entertainment. But if by some miracle we did have 1 or 2 *lire* left over, we would make a beeline for that store to try our luck.

The number of candies in the container kept getting smaller and smaller. I bet the store keeper knew which piece of candy contained the winning ticket and for a while he hadn't even placed it in the container. At some point we estimated there were fewer than 50 pieces of candy in the bowl, so we figured the chances of someone fishing out the winning piece of candy were pretty good.

And this one day I went in clutching 1 *lira* in my fist. I loafed around for a couple of minutes looking at this and that, waiting for one customer to be waited on. When he left, I then approached the salesgirl

– a sweet young thing I was making eyes at – and told her I wanted to try my luck and buy one piece of candy. Her name was Olga – I still remember it – and she was the storeowner's daughter. She was just about my age and I liked her a lot. And she knew it.

She brought the candy bowl to the counter so I could fish out one piece.

"Please, Olga, you get one for me..." – I pleaded with a half rueful and half amused smile – "... And please, please, please... make me win."

She smiled at me and I thought she gave me a conspiratorial wink. She then placed her hand in the bowl, took out one piece of candy and gave it to me.

I unwrapped it slowly, the way a poker player slowly squeezes his draw cards and.... **OH, SWEET, SWEET JESUS, JOSEPH, AND IMMACULATE MARY!... OH, ALL SAINTS IN HEAVEN!... OH, MERCIFUL MOTHER OF GOD!... I HAD WON THAT TOY CAR!**

A comparable thrill today would be hitting the top prize in the Power Ball lottery, nothing less. I rushed outside clutching that toy car and screaming excitedly to all and nobody: *"HO VINTO! HO VINTO! L'HO VINTO IO!"* (I won! I won! I won it!), while all my buddies gathered around me chorusing: *"CHE CULO!"* (What ass!)

And that was my first toy. I still wonder whatever happened to that piece of shit.

The second and last toy I ever had came about two or three years later, and this one was definitely a more substantial one – it was a soccer ball, a real soccer ball.

Soccer was our passion, our life, I've already mentioned it – but it really was much more than that, it preoccupied our entire existence. We breathed it, we lived it, we followed the local teams, we knew the stats of each individual player, we constantly argued about who were the better players and, of course, we always second-guessed the coaches' selections, especially when our team lost. Our plans for the future did not contemplate occupations like becoming a doctor, an attorney, an engineer or what have you. No, no, no... Nothing as menial or as bland as that. Our ultimate goal was to be in the starting lineup of the Genoa soccer team or the newly formed Sampdoria team, both of them playing in the Italian Serie A, or Major League Division.

And of course we played the game whenever and wherever we could. The whenever was after school and on weekends, and wherever was literally wherever, and in Genoa that meant in the streets.

Genoa simply did not have any playing areas, and still doesn't. The city is right on the sea, but it's built mostly on mountains that jut right out of the sea. There are very few flat areas, mostly downtown, and every square inch of level ground has a building on it, so we played in the streets.

Our favorite playing area was *Via Napoli,* a street just around the corner from where I lived. It was about thirty feet wide, was paved and had very sporadic vehicular traffic, just a few scooters and a car now and then. It also had a trolley track, but trolleys went by only every half hour or so.

The sidelines of our 'stadium' were on one side the retaining wall of a schoolyard, and on the other the jagged edges of the rock drilled when that street was built. The goalposts (loosely speaking, of course) – about one hundred feet away from each other – consisted of chalk marks on the asphalt, or two sticks, or stones or articles of clothing or whatever just laid there in the middle of the street. To us, it was Yankee Stadium!

Soccer needs a ball, of course, preferably a soccer ball but – as the saying goes – beggars can't be choosers. To us beggars, anything roughly round-shaped was fine.

We had this guy in our gang who even went so far as to removing wool from his parents' mattress, unbeknown to them naturally. He would then wrap a handkerchief or whatever around it, tie it very tightly with some string and make a very serviceable ball about the size of a tennis ball, and we would use that for weeks until it broke apart.

We rarely got to play with a real rubber ball. We just didn't have the dough to buy one. Those few times we did play with a real rubber ball, it would always be a very small one, of course – about the size of a tennis ball – usually owned jointly by several kids who had shared the cost of buying it.

When the match ended, the joint owners took turns taking the ball home and safeguarding it until the next match. We took turns because keeping the ball was a privilege since you could also play with it at home. It was also an awesome responsibility because if – God forbid! – anything happened to it while it was in your possession, if you would lose it or whatever, you would have been responsible for replacing it.

There was always a risk element in playing soccer in the street because it was not allowed. If the cops came – and the sons-of-bitches did come frequently in civilian clothes – they would confiscate the ball. If the ball was made of rags we didn't give a damn, of course – we could easily replace it with another one made with rags. But if it was a real rubber ball, it represented a substantial loss for us.

Anyway, my brother had just gotten married in America, and every time he wrote home – about twice a month – he always included a five or a ten-dollar bill for my parents, a pretty good sum in those days.

And then once – it may have been Christmas or around my birthday – Mimmo sent the usual five or ten spot to my parents, but he also included another fin with instructions for my mother to buy me a soccer ball.

When I read that letter – oh man! – I damn near swooned. Oh, sweet Jesus in heaven! Oh, sweet, sweet Immaculate Mary!... Me! **ME!**... Owning a real leather soccer ball! Oh, I wouldn't tell my friends, of course, until I actually had it. Oh, I would just spring it on them as a surprise. Oh, you just wait until I walked up to them with this magical sphere under my arm! What a surprise for them! What would they say? The envious stares! Is it yours? How did you get it? May I touch it? May I hold it? May I bounce it?

Mom and I went downtown to a sporting goods store and looked at different soccer balls, or at least I looked because my mom most definitely was not a soccer mom and didn't know soccer from bicycle racing.

One of the balls they had did cost the equivalent of about five bucks, and we settled on that one. There was an itsy-bitsy problem though – in fact, a humongous one. I also needed a pump and a needle to inflate the ball plus some leather grease to prevent the stitches from drying up, and that was something like a couple of bucks more. And that's when my mom balked.

She wasn't too happy about buying the soccer ball in the first place – it was an extravagant expense. She would have preferred using that money to buy me a shirt, a pair of pants or shoes, something I really needed. Anyway, she wasn't going to shell out any extra money.

I pleaded and begged, I promised I would become a good student; I would never break a curfew again, cross my heart and hope to die! I swore I would do all kind of chores – please, mom, please! – and I don't know what else I pledged to do to make her come around.

And finally mom relented. But no way on earth was she going to pay what the guy wanted. Are you kidding?

And she then went to work. Practically grabbing the sales guy by the lapels, she began jewing down the price. The poor guy tried to resist, gave some inane reasons why the price was what it was, but that poor soul just didn't have a chance.

I don't know what it's like in Italy now, but back then price haggling on practically every piece of goods was a national sport. Bigger even than soccer.

To Italians, the price tag on any item didn't mean squat. It was just a figure, a point of reference, a number that every item in the store had to have to indicate its approximate value. Everyone, even the storekeepers – especially the storekeepers – knew that the number was usually inflated and hardly anybody actually paid that.

Italian storekeepers had a good nose and a sharp eye. If some feeble-minded customer from the boondocks walked in their store, they would con him by saying in a chummily confidential tone of voice. "These shoes? They are hand-made, you know? Well, as you can see, they are 300 *lire,* and they are on sale now, the usual price is 375 *lire.* But don't worry, I'll take care of you. **FOR YOU** I'll make a special price of 260 *lire.*"

Then, pretending to look around cautiously, as if afraid someone would eavesdrop and demand a similar 'bargain', they would add almost whispering, "But please don't tell anybody…"

Even after the bogus discount, the hick still would have paid a far higher price than those shoes were actually worth, even after you factored in the storekeeper's legitimate profit.

My mom always paid whatever she believed the shoes were worth and she could get them for 200 *lire,* or even less, she was that good.

If price haggling had been an Olympic sport, mom would have gotten platinum, gold, silver, and bronze medals, and her records would never be broken. I swear, if she set her mind to it, she could get them to lower the price of anything, even a bus ticket.

Just so you know what I'm talking about, listen to this! It's the Gospel!

I went back to Italy on vacation in 1962 – it was my first visit there after eleven years in the United States. I was fully Americanized by then and I had either forgotten or considered outdated or irrelevant several Italian customs, including this bargaining bit.

My father came to pick me up at the airport in Milan together with my married sister and her husband. Mom had already gone down to Sicily to open up their summer cottage.

We stayed in Genoa for a few days before going down to Sicily, and I used them to catch up with old friends and relatives, as well as to do a bit of shopping on my own.

In 1962 Italian industry was at the beginning of a massive economic boom and was cranking up big time. Italian fashion was making headways even in America, with Italian shoes in particular getting a reputation as the ultimate in foot fashion.

Just for the record, I most definitely am not and have never been a fashion *maven.* In fact, I haven't purchased any wearing apparel for myself in ages – my wife does that for me now. Back then, however, whenever I needed any type of clothing or gear, I always used to shop for it in the cheapest stores, and the first places I always checked out were the "On Sale" racks.

That one time in 1962 I saw in a store window this pair of black pointed shoes that I liked. I asked the salesman in the store if he had them in my size – 11 ½.

They use different measures in Italy and I had no idea of what my "Italian" shoe size was. The guy then measured my foot and, yes, he did have them in stock. The listed price for those shoes was displayed in the store window right next to the shoes. I didn't remember exactly what it was so I asked him.

He mentioned it, fully expecting – I'm sure – that I would ask for some kind of a discount that, almost certainly, he was ready to offer. Again, I forget what the actual price was, but I just took out my wallet and paid exactly what he asked for them.

Now, I'll acknowledge up front that I am not good at haggling about prices, but I am not a feeble-minded hick from the sticks either. My best excuse was that I was fresh from eleven years in the United States where some dickering on price is kosher only on big-ticket items – a house, cars, furniture, boats, that kind of stuff. Everything else, you just pay whatever the ticket price says – no dickering! – and I assumed the same was true in Italy.

Anyhow, the guy in the shoe store immediately realized he had a live one on his hands, so he suggested I get shoe polish, a shoe brush, two pairs of socks, an extra set of shoestrings and even a shoehorn. And I said yes, yes, yes, yes, and yes. And I paid cash for everything of course.

So maybe I was a bit feeble-minded.

A few days later we went down to Sicily. Mom hadn't seen me in eleven years, and she cried for happiness when she saw me.

At some point during my stay I showed her the shoes I'd bought.

"Very nice!" – She said – "How much were they?"

I told her and she inquired: "And how much did you pay for them?"

"I just told you…" – I said, and repeated the price, I forget how much it was.

"You mean you actually paid the sticker price?" – She asked astonished.

"Of course," – I said – "that's what it said and that's what I paid, mom..."

She looked at me with a look that I can hardly describe – stupefied, incredulous, almost horrified.

"Lillo, please... Please, do it for the soul of your grandmother, don't tell me you also paid for the polish and all this other crap." – She said, pointing to all that crap. And she was near tears.

"Of course I paid for it, mom. What did you expect? You think he would give it to me for free?" – I asked innocently, adding – "Why are you so upset?"

Because – I swear – I had no idea why she was so agitated.

"Why?" – She screamed, enraged – "You are asking me why? *Gran testa 'i minchia!* (You big dickhead!)". Mom had a pretty salty tongue and didn't mince words. "Who the hell did you take from? Not from me, for sure!" She was fuming, literally.

I'd never seen her so mad. Grabbing my arm, she then proclaimed in a tone of voice that didn't allow any contradictions: "How long are you going to be here? Five more weeks? From now on, all the time you are here, if you buy something, anything, **ANYTHING, YOU HEAR?** Even a damn newspaper... make damn sure I'm there with you!"

Like I said, the guy in that sporting goods store didn't have the ghost of a chance. She got the soccer ball, **AND** the pump, **AND** the needle, **AND** the leather grease for the equivalent of about $ 5.50. The sales guy decided to throw in the towel before she'd demand a pair of soccer shoes, shin guards, and maybe some tickets to next Sunday's soccer match in the bargain.

When I got that soccer ball, for a few months I was the king, the emperor, the *"duce supremo"* of Genoa and surrounding territory. I was the kid who owned a real, true to life, honest to goodness, leather soccer ball, regulation size, the same kind they used at the stadium where the professional teams played... **ARE YOU LISTENING?**

Me! Me! **ME! ME!** Man, I swaggered around like my shit didn't stink, and everybody, even kids much older than me, kissed my ass just to touch that ball, to hold it, to squeeze it a bit, to head it once or twice.

I swear I used to take it to bed with me, and I would constantly grease the stitches to make sure they wouldn't dry up – that's what the sales guy had recommended.

As for actually playing with it, I didn't get to do too much of it.

That ball was born under an evil star. There is no doubt in my mind that somebody – surely one or more of my envious friends – had put the *"malocchio"*, the evil eye, on that soccer ball.

You don't believe in the evil eye? Listen to this, and then you can judge.

The first time we played with that ball was on our street, *Via Napoli* – I was scared shitless the cops would come around and confiscate my ball, but my friends somehow had managed to talk me into using it.

Less than two minutes into the game and one of those dickhead cops in civilian clothes came out of nowhere and indeed confiscated the ball. To get it back I had to pay a fine of about 50 *lire*, an enormous sum for us kids in those days. I don't remember where or how I managed to scrape up that kind of dough, but I did, and a few days later I ransomed my ball back.

Lesson learned, and that was it for me as far as playing on the streets! The second time I used the ball was in a real soccer field… loosely speaking, that is.

In our neck of the woods there was a Catholic orphanage run by the Salesians. It had an outdoor courtyard a bit larger than a tennis court, less than half the size of a real soccer field. It was a private area used exclusively by the orphaned kids in the institute, a place where they could run around in, play tag, but mostly an open space where they could also play soccer.

At both ends of the field, almost flush against the retaining walls, the Catholic fathers had even erected goal posts, smaller than regulation size and with no nets, of course, and they had also drawn a midfield line and two small penalty areas.

The field was fairly level but had no grass, just hard-packed clay with lots of little stones and dust galore. If you fell down during a game – and kids always did – your knees and legs would be like hamburger.

Due to the small size of the field, each team could field only about five or six players instead of the usual eleven, but that was OK with us – even when we played in *Via Napoli* we played with a reduced number of players. Anyway, the second time I used my soccer ball was in that field.

That came about because kids on our team belonged to the local branch of a church-sponsored organization called *"Azione Cattolica"*, Catholic Action, a youth-oriented club with its headquarters in a dingy clubhouse salvaged from a church storage room and equipped with a mini ping-pong table, about a dozen folding chairs, some religious magazines and little else. *Signor* Servetti, the director of the organization, had talked to the priests at the orphanage and had arranged to play a game between the orphans and a select team from the *"Azione Cattolica"*.

That particular match was touted as a "challenge" match and – oh dear Lord! – I still remember the air of excitement all us kids felt in anticipation of the big day.

The Catholic fathers had agreed to hold the match on their field, especially after *Signor* Servetti had let them know that one kid in his group – yours truly – had a real, honest-to- goodness, regulation-size soccer ball. It was understood that we would be playing the match with that ball.

The orphaned kids usually did play with a small rubber ball just a bit larger than a tennis ball, but playing with a real soccer ball would have been a treat even for them. As for myself, I didn't object to using my soccer ball at all. To start with, saying no to a Catholic priest was unthinkable, it was the equivalent of refusing to do a favor for God in person, but mainly I was more than happy to use my soccer ball as I was eager to kick it a few times myself.

The day of the big match finally came and off we went to play at this "stadium". Our group, comprised of about 10 "Catholic Action" players, marched enthusiastically on the orphanage determined to beat those hapless orphan kids by a score of 6-0, minimum.

The game was maybe ten minutes old and we were indeed already leading 1-0 when, during a scramble in our penalty area, one of those orphaned kids took a shot on our goal, a real cannon shot. Our goaltender acrobatically flew in the air and managed to deflect the ball, barely enough to prevent the tying goal.

Great save, fabulous save… except that the goddamned ball goes and hits the crossbar right where it joins the goal post, exactly at the pointed corner where the two 4 x 4's met. And naturally the goddamned nail holding the goddamned post and the goddamned crossbar together was still protruding and, **KABOOM!!!…** the leather broke apart, as well as the air chamber inside it.

And that was the premature death of my soccer ball!

And you still don't believe in the evil eye? You gotta believe!

It wasn't the kid's fault, of course, but in that instant I totally lost it. I became hysterical and it took forever to calm me down. It was like I'd lost my mom or my dad. Even worse, if you really want to know the truth.

Good thing that kid was already an orphan. Still I wished on him the death of all his family, past, present and future, plus his own of course, a slow painful death!

I cried all the way home, carrying the corpse of my soccer ball under my arm, and had to compose myself before going through my front door. I didn't have the guts to tell my mom and dad what happened. Mom would have thrown a fit.

Fortunately, everything turned out all right and there were no serious consequences for me at home. I always kept the soccer ball out of sight, anyway, and nobody even noticed its absence. Had they asked, I could always say the ball just needed inflating.

And those were the only two toys I had had in my life, so when I saw that big-ass fire truck you better believe I wanted to play with it.

I mean, I pretended like I was just playing with my little nephew, the way you do with little kids… you know, going vroom, vroom, vroom, but I could imagine myself having this huge monster truck in Italy, showing it off to everybody, and what would all my friends say.

CHAPTER 5

It was a day of firsts.

My first look at a television set – my brother had a TV console with a round screen, a round screen a little over a foot in diameter. Remember, this was 1951!

Jesus Christ! A TV set meant movies at home plus all the other programming!

It wasn't 24-hours a day programming yet, but it was more than enough for an entertainment-starved kid from Italy. Additionally, it showed all sorts of sports, boxing, wrestling, basketball, baseball – that I didn't know at all – but no soccer, damn it!

I had heard about television, but had never seen one before – TV programming didn't start in Italy until about 4 or 5 years later. Seeing it there, in my brother's house, was like seeing a real, live miracle happening in front of your eyes.

I didn't understand much coming out of that TV, unfortunately – I had studied some English in Italy, but my level of conversational knowledge was still very limited. But it was still a miracle.

The TV set – a Muntz model, if memory serves – always did have some minor bothersome problems. The most annoying was that you frequently had to adjust the vertical and horizontal lines but, imperfections and all, it was entertainment, home entertainment at its best.

Another first – Mimmo showed me the record player he had. We did have one in Italy also, but his was an automatic, three speeds record player, the kind where you could stack 7 or 8 records and play music for hours. For the first time I saw long-playing records, and the 45 RPM records, the ones with the big hole in the middle

Mamma mia!... America! America!... What will they think of next!

Even as I write, I realize how incurably nostalgic all this is. For all practical purposes, record players are now extinct.

In my basement I still have about two hundred Long Playing records, easily over five hundred small 45 RPM records, and I even have a few 78 RPM records, these last ones all heavily scratched. They are just sitting there gathering dust or mold along with a beat-up console radio-record player that doesn't work anymore.

About twice a year I go down in the basement with the express purpose of getting rid of useless junk, the obsolete flotsam and jetsam that accumulates in every basement simply because 'you never know when you may need it'.

In my heart I know those records belong in that category. They haven't been played in about 20 years and chances are they'll never be played again, so why keep them? Holding on to them doesn't make any sense, I am fully aware of that, and yet I know I will never throw them away.

It's pure, undiluted nostalgia, I know, but I regard them as precious and irreplaceable mementos of my youth, of my entire life in fact. They are my tenuous and yet solid link to pleasant recollections of happy days in school, raucous gatherings of carefree teenagers at jukebox joints, joyous parties of young adults at the beach, quiet evenings at home, not to mention tender memories of candlelight dinners at that cozy restaurant, after hours cocktails in nightclubs, close dancing with that special one of the moment, suggestive gazing by ravenous eyes, wild weekends occasionally ending in unforgettable nights of passion.

Yes, my record player doesn't work anymore, and I'm not planning on getting a new one anytime soon, but those records will stay.

We did have a record player in Italy. We had two in fact, but neither one could be compared to the one my brother had. We also had about a dozen records – all of them 78 RPM, of course – that we played over and over again.

Ever since I can remember, we had this very old record player – a gramophone we called it – that my father had bought somewhere well before I was born, when he worked in the merchant marine. It was about as big as a carry-on suitcase, and you had to wind it up with a pull-out handle to get it moving. It was our only source of home entertainment – we had no radio, and television of course hadn't been introduced in Italy yet.

Once – I remember – we somehow misplaced the handle, and for weeks we couldn't play those few records we had. We were desperate – it was the equivalent of losing a remote nowadays. Much worse, actually.

To hear some music, we even tried to turn the turntable with our finger – that's how desperate we were – but the music that came out alternated between too slow or too fast and, anyway, it sounded awful. When we finally did locate the handle, it was like finding a lost piece of precious jewelry.

The needle had to be changed every so often, after playing five or six records at the most. But needles cost money and were hard to find, so we changed the needle after playing about 20 or 30 records, or even more. As a result, those few records had grooves the size of ditches. I wouldn't mind having that gramophone now – it would probably be worth quite a bit of money as an antique.

And then, suddenly, it was the big time for us. Mimmo worked at the "Ansaldo" shipyards in Genoa and had gotten his degree at the Nautical Institute studying at night.

Wanting to pursue a career in the merchant marine, he had left the daytime job he had. When he quit, he got some kind of severance pay and he surprised the family by buying a tabletop radio with a record player. It was a historical event for our family, an event so memorable that I even remember the brand name – it was called "Fara Radio".

This happened sometime around 1946 or 1947 when even having a simple radio was an unheard of luxury for a lower-middle class family like ours. Owning a combination radio-record player made us feel, if not rich, certainly part of the affluent society.

I didn't lose much time before describing every juicy detail of that magical instrument to my friends. I even invited them home just to see it sitting there on a bureau, with its gleaming wood veneer surface. The thing was about as big as a medium-sized microwave oven, the radio on the bottom and the record player with a hinged cover on top.

For us kids, the radio was the most fascinating part. In addition to RAI – the Italian radio network – it also had a short-wave band where you could get foreign programs; in theory, at least.

I said fascinating, but fascination is too weak a word to describe our feelings, our sense of wonder, our anticipation of what arcane magic would be pouring out of that instrument whenever we tried to get something on the short-wave band.

The knob had to be turned oh so sloooowwwwly to tune into some unknown foreign station, and now and then you would capture the fragment of a foreign word or a song here and there, always accompanied by a long series of whistles in various ranges.

Curiously enough, instead of annoying us those whistles somehow added to our sense of expectation, to our stupefaction, to our feeling that something fabulous, something magical, something supernatural, was about to happen.

What we did manage to get were just snatches of conversation, a word here and there, even a bit of music now and then, and if by some miracle we did manage to tune in to a foreign program, never perfectly clear, always with some substantial interference, we would stare at each other wide-eyed and listen to it literally with our mouths open, even though we didn't understand one single word.

It was a miracle, some sort of sorcery – I mean, that little box actually joined us with God knows which remote part of the world.

Any extraordinary acquisition automatically provided us kids with a distinct edge over all our friends, and the purchase of that combination radio-record player was a perfect example. It was something to brag about, it made us feel superior, it clearly indicated we were upwardly mobile on the socio-economic ladder.

I still remember with mild amusement my boastful attempts to impress my friends with the technical details of that appliance, the number of tubes it had, the function of each knob, how the record player worked, the short wave band feature, etc.

With mild amusement, I said... Hell, even now, when I think about it, I can't help snorting with laughter because I was bluffing my ass off. The fact is, I didn't know then – and still don't know to this day – what tubes were, what their function was, or if it was better to have more or less of them.

Years ago, somebody told me that transistors had replaced tubes, but here we go again: I swear I have no idea what a transistor is or what it does. Fortunately, my friends knew just about as much, possibly even less than I did, so I could and did get away with passing myself off and giving myself airs as an expert in that field.

To provide further credibility to my newfound expertise, I had memorized a few technical details from the instruction booklet that had come with the radio, and I would recite them with practiced ease, with the air of someone who had been around those instruments all his life.

I knew I was making an impression on them – and scoring all sorts of points – by the way they looked at me, with envy and awe, mixed with some deference, like I had done apprentice work with Marconi himself.

Oh, by the way!... Mimmo once wrote us a letter from America and, scotch taped inside the letter was – **TRUMPET BLARE! ... TA– RA– TA– TA– TA!!!... A REAL DIAMOND STYLUS!** – a needle that needed to be changed after playing God knows how many records!

That diamond stylus –**DIAMOND!** Hot Damn! Can you imagine? **DIAMOND!** – increased even further the already mythical aura surrounding everything Americana. Hell!... Even that itsy-bitsy piece of scotch tape made a big impression on us!... Man! What a fabulous convenience that was!

The telephone – another first!... Mimmo had a telephone, of course, just like most other families did. In America, of course.

In the first sixteen years of my life in Italy I had used the telephone exactly once, and even that had been an epic, if not downright historical occasion. It was around 1949 or 1950, and my brother – **YET ANOTHER TRUMPET BLARE! – TA RA TA TA TA!!! – MIMMO CALLED US FROM AMERICA!!!!!**

In post-war Italy, less than one family in a hundred had a phone, and those few who had one used it mostly to make a very limited number of strictly local calls. Making or getting a simple long-distance call was already an extraordinary event. Getting a call from America was the equivalent today of getting a phone call from God, no less!

We didn't have a telephone – nobody at our economic level had one – but our family doctor did have one, and he had generously allowed us to receive the call in his office on a Sunday, when the office was closed to his regular patients.

Transcontinental calls were not like today where you just dial a number and in 10 seconds you can talk to someone in Timbuktu. Back then, a call could only be made through a labyrinth of connections involving the telephone operators of both countries who then forwarded the call to a regional telephone operator, then to a local operator, and finally to the number you wanted to reach. If all went well.

My brother had informed us by mail that he had arranged for the call to come through on a certain date and at a certain time.

Easily two hours before the call was scheduled to arrive, my entire family plus assorted relatives were already cramped in the doctor's office waiting for the phone to ring. And as the fateful hour approached, we were all literally staring at the phone with nail-biting anxiety, waiting for the damn thing to ring. And when it finally did ring, we all jumped, but nobody really knew what to do. I doubt if a phone had been touched more than five times by all present.

My dad finally picked up the receiver and hollered a peremptory *"Pronto!"* (Hello!).

Some operator instructed him to stay on the line till she could put the call through. And as she spoke, my dad kept looking at the instrument wondering – I'm sure – where that voice was coming from.

After several tries the operator managed to make the connection. When my dad heard Mimmo say *"Pronto... Ciao papà, come stai?* (Hello... Hi dad, how are you?)" on the other end of the line, he promptly burst out crying and couldn't say a word. He just handed the receiver to my mom, a bad move because she was already crying. In between sobs she just managed to say *"Come stai?* (How are you?)." Then, overwhelmed, she handed the phone to me, like I was the expert. And I was the expert all right.

My entire experience consisted of having seen Clark Gable, Claudette Colbert, Bette Davis, Cary Grant, and other stars of the silver screen adroitly handling that magical instrument in countless movies.

Actually, considering it was the first time I had held a phone in my hands, I thought I handled myself quite well, but I was quite excited also.

We just chit-chatted about this and that for a while; Mimmo asked me about school and stuff, I inquired about America, what it was like, what he did, how was the family, when he would come visiting, and so on.

As we talked, my sisters kept elbowing me to hurry up – they were waiting impatiently for their turn to talk. Just before passing the phone to one of them, Mimmo asked me the fateful question: *"Lillo, ti piacerebbe venire in America?* (Lillo, would you like to come to America?)"

Would I like to go to America? Does a bear shit in the woods? Is the Pope Italian? (Yes, in those days he was!)

"SI! SI! SI!" – I answered excitedly. And, I swear, I was ready to leave that same afternoon.

And now here I was, in America, with a telephone in my hands, and I could call anyone I wanted, assuming they had a phone, that is.

If truth be told, my brother's phone was a real antique. How antique was it? Let's just say Mama Bell hadn't reached that part of Maryland yet. In most other parts of the country, telephones had a regular dial and every telephone number had seven digits, with the first two numbers changed to the first two letters of a common sounding word, as in "Pennsylvania 6– 5000", Glen Miller's famous song.

Mimmo's telephone number was 14 K, I still remember it – that's how antique it was. To make a call, you first had to ring up the local operator with a hand crank attached to a box, and the operator would then connect you with whatever number you wanted. But why quibble? It was a telephone, another convenience; a convenience I didn't even dream of having in Italy.

Let's see, what else? The land... Ah yes! All that land... My brother's house was set on an enormous lot, just about as big as a real soccer field, and it had grass, beautiful grass, with lots of bushes, immaculately kept, so pretty I just wouldn't dare walk on it, much less play soccer on it.

The day I arrived, Mrs. Ravello – Mimmo's mother-in-law – had prepared an enormous dinner for us, and the night before Ange had baked this scrumptious strawberry shortcake that laid there on the kitchen counter, just waiting for me.

I should first mention that in Italy sweets were strictly in the realm of the gentry. The only time we common folks had sweets was at weddings, christenings, first communions, or special religious holidays like Christmas and Easter. And, even on those occasions, treats came in very limited quantities – the most we could hope to get was one thin slice of cake or maybe one pastry or a cookie.

After dinner, Ange served everybody coffee and a generous slice of that cake. What was left of it – about half I would say – just laid there on the kitchen counter and kept looking at me languidly, whispering softly, purring a seductive siren song. I kept hearing its melodious refrain, 'Come on, Lillo, I know you want me... Take me, I'm yours, I'm all yours...'

I was too shy and polite to ask for a second helping, but Ange either intercepted my glazed look or heard the same siren song I was hearing. She gave me another slice and then another. And then another.

That sucker was polished off before the evening was out, and if there had been another one it would have met the same fate. But I paid for it dearly, very dearly.

The next day my brother took me to Kennett Square, a small town in nearby Pennsylvania. Winter was at the door and I still had my short pants on, and he figured I needed some warm clothes.

We went to a couple of department stores – another first for me, I didn't even know what a department store was. There, he bought for me some long pants, a sweater, a heavy winter coat and other threads, stuff that my folks in Italy could have bought for me all at one time only if they had won the lottery.

On the way to Kennett Square I had been feeling a bit queasy, but I figured it was because of all the excitement of the previous day.

While shopping, my brother noticed I was somewhat pale and listless and asked me if I was feeling OK.

I wasn't feeling well at all but I was too embarrassed to admit it – I just lied and assured him I was fine. On the way home, however, all of a sudden I asked my brother to stop the car. He did, and I barely made it out the door.

And right there, on the side of the road, I barfed up all the cake and whatever else was in my stomach.

I felt like a piece of shit, plus mortified as hell, but Mimmo took it in stride. After making sure I was OK, he told me: "Don't worry about it."

He then advised me: "Sweet stuff here in America is very common, it's not as rare as in Italy. It's hard to hold back at first, it's a big temptation, I know, I went through it myself. You just have to learn to pace yourself. After a while, you'll look at it as ordinary stuff."

CHAPTER 6

Immediately after the war, strict restrictions on immigration quotas were in effect and only a very limited number of people were allowed to legally emigrate from Italy to the United States annually.

To bypass these restrictions and to give more credibility to my request for a visa, my brother had enrolled me at West Nottingham Academy, a private high school located in Colora, a small burg just a few miles from Rising Sun. It's the oldest boarding school in the United States, established back in 1744.

Armed with this West Nottingham document showing I'd been accepted as a student, we pestered the American consulate in Genoa. After some more wheeling and dealing on both sides of the Atlantic, they finally gave in and granted me a student visa.

West Nottingham Academy! Aaaaah!.... Sprawling fields, acres and acres of perfectly manicured green fields dotted with majestic trees, a tranquil fishing pond, and an atmosphere so quiet and serene that even one solitary car cruising by seems an intrusion. That's what greeted me when Mimmo first took me to my new school.

West Nottingham Academy! One look at that peaceful, pastoral setting and I was hooked. To this day, it still fills me with a sense of idyllic serenity whenever I visit.

But that wasn't all. In addition to a building with dormitories and classrooms, the Academy also had fabulous sporting facilities – a football field, a baseball field, a palestra for basketball, even a nine hole golf course – the kind of facilities that not a single school in all of Italy, public or private, could even dream of having. Even more remarkable, that entire godsend was for a student body of about 70 kids, all boys.

My scholastic career at West Nottingham Academy (WNA) began early in 1952, immediately after the Christmas holidays.

Most of the students at WNA were boarding students coming from all over the United States, a few even from faraway places like Thailand. I was one of only three students who lived nearby and commuted daily to school.

West Nottingham was only about 3 miles away from my brother's house. Mimmo drove me there every day in the morning and picked me up when school was out.

A few months later – when spring came – he bought me a bicycle that I used mainly to go to and from school, weather permitting. It was my first bicycle.

The good life can definitely spoil one's life – and fast. And the gift of that bicycle is a prime example.

My brother gave me that bicycle about five months after my arrival in America, just a couple of months before the end of the school year. If I had had that bicycle as soon as I arrived in the United States or – allow me to daydream! – if Mimmo had sent money to my mom to buy that bicycle for me while I was still in Italy, I would have been a hundred times, a thousand times, ten thousand times happier than when I got my soccer ball. In all honesty, if I had had that bicycle in Italy, I might not even have wanted to come to the United States, that's how complete my life would have been!

Holy baby Jesus! If I had had a bike in Italy I can't even begin to tell you how all my buddies would have literally kissed my ass just to touch it, just to be near it! Only my most trusted and dearest friends would have been allowed to ride it – a very short ride, of course – and for that ride they would have owed me. Big time.

Five months in the United States, and to me that bicycle was just a mode of transportation. I mean, don't get me wrong, I was glad to have it, but it really wasn't that big of a deal.

And the good life not only spoils you. As you absorb and digest it, it turns you into a world-weary, blasé, seen-it-all kind of individual, and everything that to you had been just a pipe dream, an impossible dream, just a few months before becomes common, everyday, dime-a-dozen stuff.

Allow me to explain. The America I imagined, the America of my dreams (childish dreams, admittedly, but still dreams) was an America that every day would have blown me away with an unending series of new emotions, astounding novelties, mind-shattering innovations and astonishing events.

And indeed, my first two, three, four, maybe five months in America were like that – the cars, the TV, the radio, the record player, the fridge, the wall-to-wall carpeting, the wide roads, the spacious fields, the hot water, the central heating and air conditioning, the neon lights, the stores chock full of merchandise, the overall efficiency of public and private services, the abundance of food, even the egregious waste of food, all of the above and more mesmerized me, left me literally open mouthed.

But in short order all those novelties were absorbed and digested – just like that. They quickly became common everyday things, they became a succession of *déjà vus*, even somewhat boring perhaps, the kind of stuff or events one would normally regard or look at as if they had been around forever.

Subsequently, just about all the novelties and innovations that followed were met with a brief, very brief burst of excitement and notoriety. And all the excitement and notoriety were always and inevitably followed by an almost immediate and quiet 'par for the course' shrug of acceptance. With, at most, a palpable sense of curiosity and anticipation for the next novelty that was sure to come in a not too far future.

Case in point: annually, sometime in October or November, all car makers came out with new models, and we all breathlessly waited to see the ads on television, in the newspapers and magazines, we marveled at the fancy new gadgets and literally went gaga over the stylistic changes, the wraparound windshields, the tailfins. In fact, I remember vividly how we used to compete – myself, my brother, Ange, even little Pete – to immediately identify the make, model and year of every car passing by. Damn! Ange was so good she could instantly tell, year, make and model of any car just by seeing a bolt!

By January or February at the latest the excitement was over, only to resurface the next October or November.

School was a breeze. I've already mentioned my lackluster scholastic achievements in Italy, and how I had promised myself I would become a model student in America. I had made a solemn pledge I would really hit the books, I would apply myself, and I would make my brother proud of me. Well, I did all that, and even more, and without even breaking a sweat.

Now, I'm not here to judge which school system is better, the Italian or the American, but I can certainly judge which is the most difficult – it's the Italian system, hands down!

The stuff they were teaching in the 10th grade at West Nottingham I had learned in Italy in the 5th or 6th grade. And while I was a dumb ass in Italy, or acted like one, at West Nottingham I was the best student in school, even though for the first year I spoke halting English. You be the judge!

To my pleasant surprise, I quickly integrated well with WNA students. In fact, I became quite popular for two reasons. First, in those days West Nottingham was one of the few schools in America that offered Latin as a regular course. I had studied six years of Latin in Italy, and even though I wasn't a brilliant student there – I had, in fact, flunked that subject several times – I still knew more Latin than the West Nottingham teacher.

When word got around that I was a whiz in Latin, students gathered around me by the dozens to get some tutoring or to get some help with their homework.

I never turned anybody down – in fact, I didn't mind doing that at all. For one thing, being sought after as an expert is a turn-on, in and by itself. Mainly, though, it was a great opportunity for me to interact with kids my age. As an outsider, I wanted them to like me. Furthermore, while helping them with their Latin I was also getting some much needed practice with my English.

My other path to popularity was soccer. West Nottingham had never had a soccer team, but they started one in my junior year just because there was this guy from Italy – yours truly – who knew how to play soccer.

Now, all modesty aside, I was a good player – a damn good player, in fact – but soccer is a team sport, a team made up of eleven guys.

The quickly formed West Nottingham soccer team was composed of 11 guys with only one – me – who knew what it was all about, and about two or three others who barely knew in which direction to kick the ball. All the others... zero, nada, zilch... no technical skills, not even a rudimentary knowledge of what the game was all about.

Our coach, Mr. Nillson – the history teacher and a native of Sweden – knew soccer quite well and understood the problems he faced. Knowing I had the knowledge and the skills, he asked me to be a sort of assistant coach. The two of us first tried valiantly to teach the other players the basic rules of the game and how the game is played.

We then undertook the task of drilling some technical skills unto them, but it took nearly two years before seeing some results.

I played for West Nottingham my junior and senior years, and our overall record was 2 wins, 4 ties, and about 10 losses, with the wins and the ties coming at the very end.

Still, I was the star of the team, and that made me popular.

At West Nottingham I learned first-hand an aspect of sports I had never considered before. I learned – and came to appreciate – that winning a game or, indeed, having a winning season isn't really all that important, at the amateur level anyway.

With a student body of only about 70 boys, all West Nottingham teams in every sport consistently had losing seasons, but that was OK.

Whatever sport we played – football, soccer, baseball, basketball, tennis – was against schools with a student body five or even ten times larger than ours and it was practically a given that we would lose. The student body and the followers, however, knew we tried our best and always provided strong support.

Talk about sports, my introduction to baseball was rather memorable.

In Italy I had heard of a sport called baseball, but had no idea of how it was played, what the rules were, what counted as a score, nothing, not even the most rudimentary knowledge of the game. In fact, I had never even seen a baseball before – I just knew that it was round and about the size of a tennis ball.

The only baseball-related spectacle I had ever seen in Italy was this Gary Cooper movie called *"L'idolo delle folle"* (The crowds' idol). I learned later that in America it was called "Pride of the Yankees" – it was Lou Gehrig's life story.

Watching the sport scenes of that movie, I kept wondering what the hell those players were doing with the bats, why they ran around the bases, why all the fans would go ape when the ball was hit out of the park, and all that stuff.

So I come to America and I go to West Nottingham. It must have been around March 1952 when they started spring training at the school. Classes were over, and while waiting for my brother to pick me up, I just hanged around the large lawn in the back of the dormitory when I saw these kids throwing a white ball and catching it with these huge leather gloves.

I just stood there looking at them, appreciating the fluid movements of the players as they threw the ball, the effortless way they managed to catch it with that rapid, nonchalant flick of the glove, enjoying even the popping, satisfying thud of the ball as it smacked inside the glove.

I was fascinated. What can I tell you, it's in my blood, I love all sports that need a ball to be played. To this day, every time I see guys playing with a ball I just naturally stop and watch. I would have liked to participate, but my English still wasn't all that good, plus I was kind of shy, so I just kept watching from the sidelines.

One of the players noticed me standing there and motioned me to join them. Not knowing exactly what I was supposed to do, I just shrugged and stayed where I was. Figuring I would have liked to play, he turned in my direction and lobbed the ball at me underhanded – since I didn't have a glove – and shouted out: "Here, catch it!"

Seeing that little white ball lazily arching my way, my soccer instincts took over. I positioned myself, timed it perfectly, and drop kicked it with wild abandon.

SONOFABITCH!!!

I had no idea that goddamned ball was as hard as a stone. As soon as I kicked it I yelled out in very serious pain while everybody laughed their ass off. I thought I had broken my foot, but thank God I just got a nasty bruise. My foot hurt for about a month, though, and I even had to miss some Phys-Ed classes.

And that was my first acquaintance with a baseball. Eventually I learned to love the game, but only as a spectator – in fact, I have never actually played the game.

Learning the language wasn't too big a problem. Having studied some English in Italy, I had a pretty solid base of grammar and syntax. It was just a question of getting some listening and speaking experience. And for that I had television plus a lot of help from many people, my brother, my teachers, the other students, and many others. Within six months of my arrival, I could communicate quite well.

Mimmo patiently translated for me most of the TV programming, especially the incredibly popular comedies of those days, "I love Lucy", the "Milton Berle" comedy show, and the wildly funny "Your Show of Shows" with Sid Caesar and Imogene Coca.

I still savor the towering feeling of euphoria I felt the day I actually understood a funny one-liner on my own – it was by Bob Hope, I remember. After that, it was like a domino effect – within a week or two, I understood practically everything on my own.

In my senior year, things really brightened up in a very special field – let's call it the human relations field. West Nottingham went co-ed.

During my first year in America, the opportunities for me to see, meet, or even talk to a girl were scarce for various reasons. No chance at all in school, of course, because it was all boys. Not many chances in Rising Sun either because I went there infrequently, only on those few occasions when my brother took me to see a movie.

In Rising Sun, the hangout place for all teenagers was *Poist's*, the local soda fountain. After school and on weekends, boys used to congregate at its long counter, sitting on rotating stools sipping shakes or malts.

The older guys – high school seniors or juniors – were usually accompanied by their steady girlfriend to whom, however, they seemed to pay scant attention. The younger ones just hung around together, noisily horsing around, trying to get noticed by unattached young girls who normally gathered by the jukebox pretending not to notice them. The magazine rack was the one obligatory stop for all kids, especially when the latest issue of Hollywood-related magazines arrived.

My brother used to take me to *Poist's* about once a week just to get a banana split or a soda. Mimmo was nearly thirty then. Understandably, he felt out of place staying with that young crowd.

He could have and would have dropped me off there to hang around and socialize with kids my age, but I wasn't too keen about it. My main stumbling block was shyness –additionally, I was self-conscious about my still uncertain verbal ability and my very noticeable Italian accent.

Let's just say that in that particular "human relations" field I wasn't all that chipper, all the more so because Mimmo had disclosed to me one aspect of American mores heretofore unknown.

He had quite casually mentioned something that I had found absolutely unbelievable, astonishing, something unheard of in Italy. He had told me that in America – are you ready for this? – in America boys and girls... **DATED!**

I had never even heard of the word 'date' used in that sense – in fact, I didn't even know what it meant – the only date I knew was the tropical fruit.

Mimmo explained to me that dating was when a boy asked a girl to go out – say, to the movies or to a dance – and she would accept. It was a perfectly normal occurrence here, he assured me.

"Ma va! Davvero?" (Are you kidding me?) – I remember exclaiming, seriously.

My brother had just smiled with amusement at my shocked reaction to this disclosure, but I was literally speechless. By American standards, my astonishment may seem to have been out of all proportions. But try to understand, please – I was a kid fresh from Italy and furthermore I had been raised in a Sicilian family. In Sicily, if it became known that a girl had had any type of private or unsupervised contact with a boy, she would have been considered practically dishonored, at best. At worst she would have been labeled a *puttana* – a whore.

Keep that in mind, and you can better appreciate my astonishment when I found out that in America a boy could brazenly ask a girl out without the girl's father actually killing him. Because that's what would have happened if you did that in Sicily. Well, OK, I'm exaggerating a bit, he would not actually have killed you, but he would surely have kicked your ass from now until next Thursday.

In Italy – and especially in Sicily – in those days casual dating just didn't happen, it didn't exist, it wasn't even in the vocabulary. The only time a boy went out with a girl was when the boy was a man, the girl was a woman, and the two were officially engaged to be married. And even then, they weren't exactly free to spoon or screw around. No sir! When they went out they had to have an escort, a chaperone.

The year before I came to America, two of my sisters had become officially engaged to be married, and my parents had made me the designated chaperone.

I wasn't too thrilled about it because chaperoning interfered with my free time, time that I would have rather spent playing soccer or hanging out with my buddies, but I learned to like it in no time at all. I got wise real fast that being a chaperone often meant free movies, ice cream cones, and even cold cash.

When my sisters and their fiancé's went to the movies, I had been instructed by my mother to sit right next to them – between them possibly! – but that never happened.

My future brother-in-law's saw quickly that I could be easily influenced – and I use the term 'influenced' only because it's less harsh than 'corrupted'.

Whenever I went out with either couple, my future brother-in-law would wink at me in a conspiratorial way, buy me a candy bar, and nudge me away to the balcony while he sat with my sister downstairs in the back row of the theater.

Once I looked over to where they were sitting and saw the two of them tangled up around each other like a plate of spaghetti. What was I supposed to do? Run over there, tap them on the shoulder, and say 'No, no, you rascals, that's a no-no and I'll tell on you?…' No way! *Gianni* and *Pinotto* were on the screen – that's what Bud Abbott and Lou Costello were called in Italy – and I was laughing my ass off at their antics. Who the hell cared of what they did?!?

Anyway, I was their chaperone every single time either couple went out, and… Oh! Yes! I just remembered where I got the 50 *lire* to ransom my soccer ball when the prick cops confiscated it. My future brother-in-law – I forget which one – had given me money to vamoose, once when he took my sister out.

Clearly, even then my Sicilian blood must have been quite watered down because I'll tell you right now that my sisters' honor didn't mean a goddamned thing to me. For all I cared, their fiancé's could have had their way with them and, for all I know, maybe they did. Just give me the cash!

So I discovered the existence of this dating bit, but the opportunities to actually put it in practice were scarce. When West Nottingham went co-ed, I finally had a shot at it.

In my senior year the student body included about twenty girls, and I had even managed to make a few friends among them. For one thing, I was the star soccer player, and jocks were always fawned upon by the female species, as they are today, I am sure. Soccer was not a major sport at West Nottingham, and I had nowhere near the adulation the star football or baseball players had, but still they at least had noticed me.

Looks-wise, I wasn't a Gregory Peck but I wasn't a Boris Karloff either. Furthermore, I did exude a certain charisma, I mean, after all I was a real, live Italian guy, and some silly girls equated anything Italian with continental charm, no matter what kind of a dolt the guy was.

There were opportunities galore, but I really wasn't all that good at capitalizing on them. What can I say, it wasn't just a question of shyness, and then again maybe that was part of it, but while here it was considered perfectly normal for a boy to ask a girl out for a date, to me it still seemed unseemly, and I just couldn't muster the nerve to do it.

Curiously enough, the very first time I went out on a date, it was the girl who actually asked me out. Her name was Janet Marshall – she was a schoolmate of mine who had transferred from Rising Sun High School to West Nottingham for her senior year.

Janet lived in a farmhouse about a mile outside Rising Sun and, just like me, she was a day student commuting every day to and from school. During the winter months, when it was too cold for me to ride my bicycle to school, her father would pick me up and give me a ride to school. When school was out, my brother would pick us up and drop her off at her home.

As a student Janet was just average, and I always offered to help her out when she had problems with her homework, especially with Latin. We had become good friends, but our relationship had always remained within the boundaries of plain friendship. I mean, I certainly did have a few impure thoughts about her – more than a few, in fact – but, what with my shyness plus maybe fear of rejection, our relationship had always remained a plain friendship, never blossoming to the 'friends with benefits' level.

She was one very attractive babe – slim, long blonde hair, the prettiest nose, kind blue eyes and a set of knockers to die for. She was so attractive that – just like me – most of the other students would have loved to ask her out but hesitated to ask. Just like me, they probably felt she was out of their league and would reject their advances.

The event that led to my very first date was a concert-dance in Oxford, a small town in Pennsylvania just over the Maryland border. The featured attraction was this new rock and roll group called "Danny and the Juniors", an up-and-coming quartet that was starting to get national attention.

Janet had managed to get two tickets to this concert-dance and she literally shocked the hell out of me when she asked me if I would please go with her. Yes, she even said please!

I was thrilled for the chance to go out with her, but not too crazy about the entertainment itself. My taste in music was still mired in the sentimental ballad category, and rock was too wild for me. Still, she had asked me and I had accepted. And off we went on that Saturday night.

I had just obtained my driver's license. Mimmo had let me borrow his car – a brand new 4-door Oldsmobile 98 – and I was programming a night to remember. It was my first date, after all!

Parents are more permissive nowadays, but back then dating teenagers had fairly stringent curfews. There weren't that many places in or around Rising Sun where you could justify staying out late – the last show at the only movie house in town ended at 10 PM, and the entire burg practically shut down immediately afterwards.

Dating teenagers usually had to be home by 10 PM, 10:30 PM at the latest. In view of the extraordinary occasion of a live concert-dance, however, Janet's curfew had been extended to midnight.

I had it all figured out – the concert would end around 10:30 PM, or we might even leave a bit sooner with the excuse of beating the crowd, and we would have about two hours to kill before I would return her safely home.

A lot could be accomplished in two hours – I thought – and I had all kinds of delightful visions of some *après* concert activities in the back seat of the car. No, not 'going all the way' of course! That was unthinkable, even then, especially on a first date – but certainly some heavy petting.

I came prepared: after taking a shower, I carefully selected and donned my sharpest outfit – khaki chinos, pale blue shirt, brown loafers and my most prized possession, a leather jacket Mimmo had given me for my birthday. After dousing myself with one quart of cologne, I promptly went to pick up Janet at 5:30 PM in that brand new Oldsmobile aircraft carrier.

I rang the doorbell and Mrs. Marshall let me in. Blushing slightly, I bashfully murmured 'Good evening' to her and her husband. Janet was still upstairs getting all dolled up for the big evening. When she heard me coming through the front door, she shouted a cheerful 'I'll be ready in a minute!'

A good half an hour later she came running down the stairs decked out in one of those popular pleated, wide-swinging, white skirts and a tight fitting, light green velour top, a perfect cover for a perfect set of boobs. Plus, the obligatory bobby socks, of course. Her long blonde hair was tied in a large ponytail with some kind of colored ribbon.

Jumping the last few steps, she gracefully landed right in front of me. She then made a pirouette, her white skirt rising in a perfect circle around her, exposing even the pink panties covering her pretty butt. And other stuff.

Her parents witnessed this brazen display of flesh and didn't seem to mind at all – in fact, they even laughed about it, but I swear I blushed. At the same time, I could also envision myself rummaging in there with my hands later on.

"How do I look?" – She asked flirtatiously.

"Janet *est tota pulchra* (Janet is all beautiful)" – I complimented her in Latin, the subject I most frequently helped her with. She liked that, and blew me a kiss.

When we climbed on the Oldsmobile, I immediately turned on the radio that I had previously tuned to her favorite station – one that played music I didn't like, by the way. She definitely loved it, however, and soon she was swinging and rocking on the seat to the beat of the music. Oh, yes! It was going to be a fun evening!

It was still too early for the concert-dance, so we made a quick stop at *Poist's,* where we had hamburgers, French fries, and a soda; my treat, of course.

And we then went to this concert-dance.

The event was held in Oxford's Fire Hall, a fairly large venue used for wedding receptions and sundry banquets. Its maximum capacity was about 300 guests but it looked like half the teen-agers of Pennsylvania, Maryland, and Delaware were there.

Christ! You could hardly walk in that place! In fact, while the occasion had been billed as a concert-dance, dancing was out of the question. The most you could do was jump up and down in place on your own. There simply was no room to move around.

We managed to squeeze our way close to the stage waiting for the show to start. The entire hall reverberated with the rollicking bantering and chattering of carefree gatherings of teenagers the world over.

We waited and waited for nearly half an hour past the advertised starting time, but nobody seemed to mind the delay at all – and for good reasons. Like it or not, everyone in there was practically glued together, and that crush was the perfect and most welcome excuse for couples to rub against each other. Like everyone else, I didn't mind the close quarters one bit, and Janet didn't seem to mind either because she never made any attempts to get away from my lecherous overtures.

Rubbing against her to the limits of impropriety – if not outright indecency – I was panting, salivating, and getting all aroused, while pretending of course that the tight body contact was an inevitable offshoot of the overcrowded conditions.

And there we were, laughing, joshing, and doing some discreet necking when suddenly Janet lets out this blood-curling scream.

My first immediate mental reflex reaction was: **"WHAT THE...!!!"** Or its chaste equivalent.

The word 'fuck' was not in my vocabulary yet – it entered some time later and stayed there for keeps, but I didn't even know it then.

Incidentally, apropos of nothing at all, I'm not an apologist for profanity but I consider "fuck' a very practical, very utilitarian word, and oh so fungible, so malleable, so versatile. Even essential, I would say.

Clearly, *tout le monde* must share my opinion – the English *monde* at least. There's got to be a reason why the word itself or, most commonly, its gerund form is undoubtedly the most used, the most useless and at the same time the most useful, the most ubiquitous modifier in the English language. The second most used – goddammed or goddamn –doesn't even come close.

From Animal to Zoo – and with 24 stops in between – the "F" word can and surely has been used as a modifier to every single noun in Webster's Dictionary – "Shut that fucking door!"… "Open that fucking window!"… "It's a fucking shame…"

But that's not all. It is also used as a modifier to an adverb – "Fuck, no!", and even as a modifier to a modifier! "Man! That's so fucking funny!" And then, implausibly, even as a modifier to a verb! "What did the Yankees do last night?… They fucking lost!"

And, of course, one cannot possibly ignore its most vituperative by-product: motherfucker.

Oddly, despite its clear etymology, this strangely entertaining insult is rarely used to explicitly indicate – or even hint at – Oedipal love between the insulted and his mother.

Another oddity about this incredibly flexible contumely is that its use and purpose vary widely along racial lines.

When spewed by Caucasians, it's almost always a serious invective, frequently even a fighting word. Blacks, on the other hand, are more eclectic in its use; coming out of their mouths "motherfucker" can mean literally anything. They use it mostly as a colloquial reference to whatever they are talking about, as a commentary to an event or just as an explicit interjection.

Ludicrously, when directed toward a person, "mothafucka" is frequently meant as a sign of affection, respect or admiration. Only on very rare occasions they will use it explicitly as an insult.

But think about it – what other language offers a comically inventive gem of a word like 'un-fucking-believable'? Or 'clusterfuck'? And in what other lingo could you find the terse, dismissive explicitness of a 'fuck off!'?   Or even the shockingly blasphemous oath 'Jesus! Fucking! Christ!'?

I don't remember where or when I first heard this last imprecation, or even who spewed it, but I still remember the intense jolt of 'shock and awe' I felt when I first heard it – and this was way before Operation Desert Storm! 'Shock' because, despite my less than sterling religious credentials, I do maintain a grudging respect for religious icons, and pairing "fucking" with Jesus Christ, especially as a middle name, was – well! – simply shocking and outrageous. And 'awe' because you got to admire the audacity – **THE BALLS!** – not to mention the originality and the inventiveness of whoever first sputtered that irreverent cry of exasperation.

I'm telling you, 'fuck' has it all! Curt, crisp, powerful – it's a word that in a way defines America. It's vulgar, of course – I am not disputing that – but its usefulness far outweighs its vulgarity.

Curiously enough, the only time its vulgarity hits me like a slap in the face is when it's used to describe exactly what it means, as in 'I fucked my girlfriend twice yesterday'. Used that way, I find it offensively degrading, demeaning, grating, it literally makes me cringe – I even lose respect for anyone who describes lovemaking so vulgarly.

Used any other way, as in 'Am I supposed to give a fuck about this entire dissertation?', then it is just a graphic expletive and, like all expletives, it becomes vulgar only when overused. When utilized at the appropriate times, it becomes a very effective, powerful, satisfying, indispensable tool. Frequently even mandatory.

But I digress – my second visceral reaction was fear. Honest to God, I was scared! My most immediate guilty thought was that I must have done something way, way, way too indecent.

This private acknowledgement of lascivious and immoral conduct on my part was promptly followed by the dread of the consequences of my dastardly acts, the shame that would be heaped upon me for my lewdness. Not to mention the reproach and retribution from her parents, or from my brother… Maybe even from the cops.

Alarmed, I immediately stopped my slow rubbing act and looked at Janet sheepishly, ready to mumble some pathetic lie or disclaimer about my conduct. She was now holding both sides of her face, pulling her hair up as if in agony. And she still screamed as if she had seen some slimy slug crawling up her leg.

In addition to fear, I now began to feel confusion, concern, apprehension, even a bit of panic. Yes, panic! Surely people were assuming I was responsible for whatever the hell was distressing her. I glanced around timidly, shrugging lightly, to make people understand I was just an innocent bystander. And all the while, Janet's screams kept increasing in intensity.

Somehow – and with enormous relief, believe me – I realized I wasn't the primary source of her anguish, and I began to breathe a bit easier.

Probably less than ten seconds had actually passed since Janet had started her banshee act, but even as I realized I wasn't guilty of anything, still I was totally clueless as to its cause. I finally noticed she was gazing at the stage with an indescribable look in her eyes, a look both terrified and mesmerized, as if she had seen an apparition or a ghost.

Following her gaze, I realized what had set her off – she had spotted one of the "Danny and the Juniors" singers peering through the stage curtain.

Janet's screams had alerted all the other girls that something big was happening and in no time at all the entire place literally went bananas.

And pandemonium set in, I mean, big, big time babel, pure bedlam, total anarchy, left and right, with a shrill chorus of ear piercing screams, girls pulling their hair, jumping up and down, biting their hands, some of them actually crying, I mean actually weeping, with tears in their eyes – **TEARS,** real tears, for Christ sake! – many of them holding their head with their hands, and shaking it in a 'No, No, No' motion, as if to dispel the ghastly image in front of them.

Again, **WHAT THE...!!!**

It was the first case of mass hysteria I had ever witnessed. And to my consternation, Janet – my girl! – had started that crazy shit.

Instantly, the relief I felt turned to irritation. I felt humiliated, like I'd been betrayed. You mean the girl I was with – **my date!** – was going fucking bananas over some young punks singing bad music?

True, every other girl was now acting exactly the same way. Still, I somehow felt Janet's outlandish behavior reflected badly just on me – I was embarrassed to be her date. I thought people surely were staring at me, wondering where I had found her, what circus she had escaped from and why I had brought her along as my date. Man, I thought she was acting so silly I actually considered going away and leaving her there.

But I didn't of course.

When the stage curtains finally opened, the crescendo of incredible, blood-curling screams reached dangerous levels for the eardrums. A two-bit announcer, an overweight geezer dressed in an ill-fitting tux and wearing a ludicrously noticeable toupee came to the microphone and began working the crowd into an even bigger frenzy.

After an interminable spiel of stale jokes mixed with the introductions of local dignitaries, the guy finally came to the actual presentation.

"AAAAND NOW... FOR THE FIRST TIME... HERE... IN OX-FORD... P... A... THE GROUP YOU'VE BEEN WAITING FOR... THE GROUP THAT'S REWRITING MUSICAL HISTORY IN THE USA... THE ONES... THE ONLY... I GIVE YOU... DANNYYYYY... AND THE JUNIORS!"

And four young kids came out scampering – two from each side of the stage – and gathered at the front, waving to a crowd so frantic and loud that it took several minutes before they could start their act.

At one point during their performance, they sang for what they claimed was the first time a song called *"Do the bop"*, a pleasant, bouncy tune, quite tame by today's standards, but very fast and provocative in those days. And that's when the place literally began to rock.

A couple of years later that same song – now re-christened *"At the Hop"* – did indeed become a humongous hit all over the world. And – big whoop-de-doo! – I can proudly say I was present at its genesis.

All the time they were on stage, Janet didn't look at me once – I wasn't even there, I was a cipher, I simply didn't exist. Along with all the other ditzy girls and steamed up youngsters parked around the stage, she stood there gazing adoringly at those four teenyboppers, screaming, jumping up and down and acting like a goddamned idiot.

Me? I felt so totally alien to that scene that I just stood there, barely off a corner of the stage, arms akimbo, watching that surreal spectacle.

At one point I began to purposely stare at one of the singers, and I kept staring at him until I finally managed to catch his eye. He realized I was staring at him, and from my body language and overall behavior he must have surmised I wasn't part of that scene.

Arms still akimbo and my face a mask of disbelief, I slowly shook my head as I silently asked him: "Can you believe this shit?"

Notwithstanding the ten thousand screaming idiots surrounding me, he must have understood my isolation, and I am certain he must also have understood and shared my disbelief and my alienation. He acknowledged my stare by looking straight at me for several seconds and then, even as he was singing, he laughed and shrugged his shoulders as if to say: "I can't believe this shit either."

During the interval, Janet continued to ignore me. She immediately joined a group of teenage girls, all of them having spasms, all wildly gesticulating and comparing notes about those young heartthrobs.

Realizing my chances of her paying any attention to me were sub-zero, I wandered around on my own. Soon I found myself right next to the steps leading up to the stage. Just out of curiosity, I inconspicuously climbed them and sneaked behind the closed curtain.

Nobody stopped me and I cautiously began meandering around the empty stage. Behind a back wall in a far corner, two of the singers were sitting on an elevated platform quietly taking a smoking break. One of them was the guy who had laughed at me, or rather with me. It was Danny, the lead singer.

He recognized me, motioned me over and I approached them.

"Pretty wild, huh?" – He said laughing.

We started talking, and it turned out they were pretty cool guys. To my pleasant surprise, both of them were Italian... Italian-American, that is. When I told them I was from Italy, one of them said his father or grandfather – I forget which – was from Sicily.

"Is that so?" – I exclaimed – "My folks are from Sicily also!"

We started chatting like we'd known each other forever. I asked him what he thought of all those girls out there, and these were his factual words: "Don't tell them I said this, but if you ask me, they are a bunch of *'puttane'*. That's what they are, whores. They got more cunt than brain."

My sentiments exactly, although at the time I wouldn't have expressed myself so crudely. I was still in the "altar boy" stage of my life, and the worst profanities that crossed my lips were "heck" and "darn it."

The word "cunt" definitely wasn't in my vocabulary. In fact, that was the first time I had heard it, but I had correctly guessed what it meant.

Without any prodding on my part, Danny then went on and casually volunteered that he and his three colleagues could get laid whenever they wanted, indeed after every performance – it was just a matter of choosing the prettiest and most available girls. And I knew he wasn't bullshitting by the way he said that, with a most casual tone of voice.

We chatted a while longer, then, trying to salvage what I could out of that miserable date, I asked Danny and the other guy if they would please say hello to the girl I was with.

"Sure, bring her over!" – they said.

Scouring the crowd from one end of the stage curtains, I finally saw Janet still talking animatedly with a bunch of other girls. Waving my arms and shouting her name, I tried to get her attention. It took a while, but she finally noticed me.

She looked at me questioningly, wondering no doubt what the hell I was doing up on the stage. I kept motioning for her to come over and finally, wading slowly through the crowd, she made her way to the stage followed by several other curious young girls. They all assembled at the foot of the stairs leading to the stage staring at me, unsure of what to do next or what was going on.

My main concern now was that, what with the throng of people jammed all around, someone would notice us and there would be a mass stampede up the stage. It turned out, however, that the overall bedlam provided our best cover – nobody paid any attention to what was going on.

I held the stage curtain barely open, just enough for them to glimpse the two singers waiting behind me. Trying to be as inconspicuous as possible, I just pointed at them and I then signaled the girls to come up the stairs quietly. Still, they wouldn't move, scared perhaps that climbing on the stage was a serious breach of security or etiquette.

I was pretty sure they would have given up even their virginity – assuming they still had it – to approach the singers, but they just were too scared or too shy to do it.

I kept encouraging them discreetly to come over, and went to meet them at the top of the steps leading up to the stage. Finally, one by one they quietly scampered up the steps and ducked behind the curtain, stopping right next to it and holding on to it, clearly excited to be there yet terrified to approach us.

The dazed look in their eyes and their tentative ways mirrored their anxiety and trepidation. First one, then another girl would start taking a few timorous and tentative steps in our direction, but just as they did one or more of the other girls in the group would hold them back, the way one would stop some other from approaching a dangerous looking dog, unsure of its tameness even as the owner has given them assurance it wouldn't bite them.

Smiling confidently, I encouraged them to come closer, even placing my arm around Danny's shoulder like I was tight with him and the other guy. Finally they scurried over all at the same time and crowded around us, wide-eyed and jittery.

I introduced a teary-eyed Janet to both singers. Danny first then the other singer hugged her, and Janet grabbed and held on to them and wouldn't let go of either one as she tearfully moaned her joy and disbelief. They finally managed to free themselves and then hugged the other girls also, each hug returned with an animal frenzy that nearly knocked the singers down.

And that's when all the girls started falling all over each other breathlessly asking stupid questions, questions the singers had surely heard hundreds of times before. And, of course, they breathlessly waited for the equally stupid and well-rehearsed replies.

A few minutes later the singers were called back to finish their act. They excused themselves and left, but not before being practically raped by all the girls.

For a short while I became a small celebrity and had my fifteen minutes of fame – I had actually shared confidences with Danny, the leader of the Juniors, and everybody wanted to know the what, the who, the where, the how, and every little detail of our conversation.

Oh! God! I was so close to spitting it out! You can't even imagine how much I wanted to just casually remark: "Oh! Yes! They are just regular guys… Oh! And by the way, Danny thinks you all are a bunch of whores."

God! How I would have loved to tell them! It was right on the tip of my tongue but I chickened out, I just didn't have the guts to do it. What I did instead, I began to improvise and told them we had talked about the evolution of musical styles in the United States over the past quarter century. They were all looking and listening to me with the same wide-eyed expression people have when they look at and listen to a politician, that is, hardly understanding one word the guy is saying yet nodding their approval because they figure he must be stating something important. And not realizing, of course, that he is spouting bullshit at best and wildly improbable nonsense at worst. Just like I was.

I had them in the palm of my hand, I could feel it, and I then began to enjoy myself. Shamelessly I began ad-libbing some cockeyed claptrap about how knowledgeable those guys were about music.

"I'm telling you, it's remarkable… such young guys… Yes! Danny is still a sophomore in high school in Philadelphia, can you believe it? And yet, oh man! You should hear him talk… He surprised the heck out of me. He knows his Vivaldi, his Pergolesi… He even makes a good argument that contemporary American music has been strongly influenced by African rhythm…"

I was brazenly lying my ass off, of course. So brazenly that even I thought I was laying it on a bit too thick, but they seemed to buy it.

They were all staring at me like I was some kind of musical guru. At the same time, despite their seemingly engrossed attention, I am certain they weren't really all that interested in what I was saying.

Without a doubt, the only things they cared about were the personal, insignificant details in their idols' lives, what they ate, did they have girlfriends, who was their favorite actor. Crap like that.

My celebrity was short-lived – fifteen minutes precisely. When the concert dance resumed, I once again became a cipher – it was like I wasn't even there. Janet was now practically bonded to the other girls, especially now that they had all been privileged to see, talk to and even hug the objects of their adoration.

To this day I have never been able to fully understand – and much less share – that kind of mentality, but I recognized it as the typical manifestation of immaturity of many adolescents. I remembered reading in Italy about a similar scene involving a young Frank Sinatra at some New York theater.

In the late 40s, in the immediate aftermath of World War II, the Italian bourgeoisie almost invariably frowned upon whatever happened in America – especially in the entertainment world. It was shameless! It was brazen! It was immoral! It was sinful! At the same time – *and for those very same reasons!* – it was even expected, and then accepted, approved and even emulated.

Everyone understood, it was a given, that America was an entity in itself, a world apart; it was a place – the only place on the planet – where everything could happen. Where indeed everything did happen.

Our burning fascination with everything American was in fact kindled by this expectation of outlandish behavior, of the bizarre, the shocking, and the kind of occurrence that in those days could never have occurred anywhere in Europe, Asia, Africa, and South America or even in neighboring Canada.

Any report from America of a brazen tweak of what was then the widely accepted moral code – a pending divorce, rumors of an affair, and so on – would make us gasp with incredulity. At the same time, it fascinated us and – yes! – even made us secretly wish we could emulate them.

That Sinatra bit and this one with Danny and the Juniors were the perfect examples. They are common occurrences all over the world now, even in Italy, but back then they could have happened only in America.

While I had come to understand and passively even accept the existence of that kind of mentality, I wasn't quite ready to forgive and forget.

I wasn't exactly pissed off at Janet, but I most definitely was disappointed in her. Let's pass on the fact that she should have been grateful to me – and only me – for her meeting and hugging her idols. And let's also pass on the fact that she had acted like a silly teenager, without one ounce of maturity. What really smarted was that throughout the concert she had not paid any attention whatsoever to me, she had totally ignored me. And that stung.

I can be a prick when I'm upset and – by golly! – I was upset! Under normal circumstances, my *après* concert plans were to park somewhere and do some serious necking. I mean, that was the only reason I had come to that stupid concert in the first place. But she had turned me off. Totally.

When the concert ended we just got in the car and I headed straight home, hardly saying a word. If she said something I just barely answered with a few words. And of course, I didn't lay one finger on her. I dropped her off at home without a hug, without a kiss, nothing. I just thanked her for the tickets, said goodnight and left.

Who knows, since I hadn't laid a hand on her, maybe she got the impression I was half queer, but I didn't care. My disappointment was so deep that after that dismal date our relationship actually cooled off and I only saw her for the occasional ride to and from school.

A few months later we both graduated and went our separate ways. For a long while we lost track of each other. Then, in a rather poignant aftermath, I saw her again at West Nottingham Academy, at the twenty-fifth anniversary class reunion.

She was still a great looking chick, a bit on the matronly side perhaps. She had put on a few extra pounds but was still quite attractive. In fact, she was much sexier looking now than when she was a teenager.

Gone were the long pigtails, the virginal look, the wholesome air, the sweet and innocent smile and the polite and gentle manners. Her kind blue eyes had morphed into knowing eyes, her laughter had a carnal, risqué undertone and she now had that 'been around' look, that experienced, sensual, revealing look some women have that tells a man they would know what to do in bed. And enjoy doing it.

Time hadn't been kind to me either, of course. The only resemblance to the flashy young kid who used to dazzle the sparse crowd dribbling down the soccer field was my still noticeable Italian accent. Everything else had changed, and not for the better – I had put on many more pounds than her, my hairline had receded considerably and the general signs of physical decline were evident all over my body.

I was married, she was divorced and we both had kids. As usually happens on those occasions, we started reminiscing about the good old days.

She was the one who brought up that famous episode. It must have been one of her most-cherished recollection because, grabbing my arm, she suddenly exclaimed with the surprised tone of voice of one who has just recollected a quirky event of long ago: ""You remember when we went to see "Danny and the Juniors" in Oxford?"

Of course I remembered. How could I forget? And, laughing sheepishly, I confessed how upset and disappointed I had been because of her immature behavior, and did she remember that? Of course she did, and she knew I had been upset with her and even acknowledged she had acted foolishly, like all teenyboppers did in those days. She also confided she would have liked to resume the friendship we had but was too proud to make the first move. At the same time, she said, she felt a bit intimidated by what she thought was my display of maturity.

We both laughed about it, that sweetly wistful, schmaltz-tinged laughter middle-aged and over-the-hill folks invariably laugh when they recall their youthful, scatterbrained antics. And then she suddenly hugged me, a long skintight embrace, as if we had reconciled after a long estrangement.

Pressing her voluminous and still magnificent bosom against my chest, she squeezed my hands tightly and then looked at me in a way that clearly was telling me she wouldn't have minded having a fling with me, just for old times' sake.

I read it in her eyes, her body language, the way she pressed her body next to mine several seconds more than was appropriate. And I was tempted – God, was I tempted!

I was certain that's exactly what was on her mind. Not one word had been spoken, but the message had come through loud and clear as if she had verbally propositioned me. That type of communication is transmitted telepathically; it is sent and received with the express purpose of being acted upon later on. But I didn't pursue it.

And no, not because I am a saint or immune to temptation. Far from it! It's just that I had a good marriage, and I'd made up my mind from day one that I wouldn't do anything to jeopardize it. I knew that if I had gone after Janet, I couldn't have looked at my wife in the eyes again; and so I chose not to.

I am also sure that if 25 years before Janet may have gotten just a fleeting suspicion I might have been half queer, she was now certain I was.

But sometime that's the price you pay for playing straight.

CHAPTER 7

I am now as bald as a bald billiard ball, but in those days I had a good, thick crop of hair. Unfortunately, it was brown and straight, straight as uncooked spaghetti.

So, what's wrong with straight brown hair, you ask? Clearly, you were not a teenager or a young adult in the mid-50s and early 60s.

My friends, those were the days of Fabian, Frankie Avalon, Bobby Rydell, Frankie Valli, Dion, Danny and the Juniors and all those rock singers who came out of Philadelphia and New York. Not to mention Mario Lanza, if you were into what Hollywood palmed off as classical music.

Those young troubadours were all Italian-American and had reached extraordinary nationwide popularity on the strength of a barely passing singing voice plus their "Italian" look, such look consisting of the typically dark and masculine Mediterranean features, but mainly a head covered by an Amazon forest of curly, oily, black hair. Very curly, very oily and very, very black hair.

In those days, if a boy had those features his chances of scoring with chicks were much, much better than average. And if he had those features and he was also Italian, his chances of scoring with chicks were cast in stone. In fact, there was no element of chance: he would score, guaranteed.

Well, I was Italian, I even had a pretty good singing voice, but I did not have the curly, oily, black hair. And I didn't score, of course. You don't believe me?

Case in point – let me introduce you to Johnny Catalano, a nephew of Mrs. Ravello, my brother's mother in law.

Johnny had come over from Italy about a year after I did. His first real job – when he was only 17 – was as a ship's boy on an Italian cargo ship. It was a job he had been dreaming of getting, but it had turned out to be a nightmare. Decent pay, but very hard work, mistreatment, and seasickness – after only two trips he couldn't take it anymore and had decided to jump ship. And he had done just that, literally.

When his ship docked in Philadelphia, he had been denied a pass to come ashore because his boss suspected he contemplated jumping ship. But that didn't stop Johnny: leaving most of his meager belongings on board, he had literally jumped overboard in the middle of the night swimming to the nearby dock. He had then somehow managed to contact his aunt, begging her to help him out.

My brother and I went to pick him up, and we had a hell of a time locating him because the only information he could provide us was that he was in Philly under some long bridge.

Johnny was a pint-sized kid, 5' 2" maybe 5' 3" tall, and just about my age. He was pretty good looking, I have to admit – he resembled Rock Hudson a bit. A nice, hardworking kid overall, a solid but also very stolid kid, the quintessential rube with an IQ like two plus two equals five.

In addition to his not-so-remarkable features and intellect, he also had very little formal education and zero knowledge of English, and I do mean Zero… Zip… Zilch. But he did have the "look". That he did! The Italian look **AND** the hair, the oily and very curly black hair. He had *mucho* galore of that.

Soon after he arrived, he started working for his uncle Nick in the mushroom houses. It was hard and tiring work, but he had plenty of energy left over for after-work activities and – oh, boy! – he had *mucho* galore of that also! And then some!

Guys, I'm not lying to you! American girls would come to pick him up at home, in their cars, two or three nights a week and every single weekend, and every time they did he would always come home weak-kneed and bleary-eyed from too much screwing. If there is such a thing as too much screwing.

I have no idea how he managed to communicate with the girls. Like I said, his English was practically zero, and normally you don't just get in a car and start screwing. Well, OK... I suppose it can be done, but in normal circumstances, between two ordinary people of the opposite sex, there's got to be some kind of verbal exchange... something – come **ON!**... – a greeting, how's the weather, something... anything... before you start grabbing each other.

But not Johnny! I swear, he started getting lucky the minute he showed his face in town. When he first arrived, I took it upon myself to take him around Rising Sun and vicinity just to show him the lay of the land, and I even introduced him to *Poist's,* where all the kids used to hang out.

OK! Every time we went there, the minute we entered that joint, girls would naturally gravitate toward him, even leaving the boys they were talking to, just to be near him. And they would ogle him, and fawn all over him, and talk to him, using me just to make rapid-fire translations.

Adding insult to injury, goddamned bitches used to ask **ME** to ask **HIM** if he would **PLEASE** go out with them. Can you fucking believe it?

"What am I, your damn pimp?" – I felt like screaming at them, even as I grudgingly related their messages to an eager and panting Johnny.

I swear to God, to this day when I think about it I get so mad I still feel like screaming and banging my head against the wall. I repeatedly told them he didn't speak any English, but they didn't care at all. And neither did he, of course.

Now, I swear, this is not sour grapes, but there I was, a star soccer player in school, first in my class, I could speak damn good English, I was a better than decent conversationalist, I was fairly good looking and I was Italian. What more do you want?

Did American girls ever beat a path to my door? Did they ever come to pick me up in their car? Did they ever beg me to take them out?

Not in your wildest dreams they didn't! Did I ever come home on weekends weak-kneed and bleary-eyed from too much screwing? Not in **MY** wildest dreams I didn't!

I know it was the goddamned curly black hair... Need more proof? Take the Ravello brothers, Joe, Jack and Tony – all of them Nick's nephews.

They had come over from Italy the old-fashioned way, by jumping ship, like my brother and Johnny Catalano. I swear, in those days Rising Sun had more illegal aliens than regular inhabitants!

The Ravello brothers – Tony my age, Joe and Jack a few years older – had settled in Rising Sun with their uncle, hiding out like Johnny Catalano actually, and keeping a low profile because of their illegal status. Nick had generously offered them also some work in the mushroom houses while they looked for some way to stay in this country legally, and they all lived for free in a small bungalow Nick owned.

That shack was usually a glorious mess, a sleazy dump, and understandably so. You know how it is – as for most Italian young men, housework had never been part of their job description. In those days – and even today, I suspect – Italian young men never soiled their hands with menial domestic labor, all housekeeping work always being done by their mom or by a sister.

Additionally, the three brothers worked very hard in the mushroom houses and, anyway, let's just say Oscar Madison – of "Odd couple" fame – would have felt right at home with them, and leave it at that. Beds always unmade, dirty dishes piled up in the kitchen sink, floors never swept, dirty underwear scattered all over the place, and so on – that's how their abode looked like.

They also knew very little English and had little formal education, neither one of them having gone past the fifth grade. Unlike Johnny Catalano, however, they had tons of street smarts and great adaptability and survivor skills. And, just like Johnny Catalano they had both the Italian "look" **AND** that goddamned mass of curly, black, oily hair.

Well, I know for a fact that within months – **WEEKS!** – of their arrival they had managed to attract and retain a sizable number of groupies, a veritable harem of American girls who used to sneak in that bungalow just to be with them. And while they were there, they would not only provide the brothers with fresh pussy on a silver platter, but also brought presents – shirts, ties, sweaters, even a radio. Plus they would perform all housecleaning, cook and even do laundry for them. And those solicitous bitches even made arrangements to take turns, so they wouldn't step on each other's feet!

Is that proof enough?

I'm telling you, it was the hair! Look, I am not embarrassed to admit that all of them – the Ravello brothers and Johnny Catalano – occasionally put in a good word for me with some of their surplus chicks. And I was damn grateful for it because most of the action I got in Rising Sun – oh, hell, why lie… **ALL** of it! – was with girls they had introduced to me, girls they got tired of after having previously worked them over.

One girl in particular I will always remember – Margaret Wood was her name. She was one of Johnny's leftovers, and I will always remember her name because Margaret was a historical first for me – I lost my virginity with her.

Margaret was a good old country girl, not an exceptionally brilliant conversationalist, but pleasant enough. She had a rather bland intellect, her favorite topic of conversation being pop music singers and Hollywood stars.

She talked breathlessly – and non-stop – about Eddie Fisher, Gary Cooper, James Dean and, of all people, Hopalong Cassidy or whoever played him. She absolutely adored all of them. Mind numbing conversation mostly, but now and then she also displayed a wacky sense of humor with uproariously ribald overtones. Despite her silly talk, I liked her, and we kind of hit it off from the word go.

She was the first girl I knew who used profanity.

"Shit or get off the pot, you asshole!" was her outraged comment to a slow moving motorist in front of us the first time I went out with her – and that kind of language shocked little innocent me. But she also had an incredibly bountiful set of tits, and that kind of equipment overshadowed whatever she lacked in social manners or intellectual capacity.

Johnny had bragged he had 'done the job' to her more than once, and he had repeatedly told me she was hot, hot, insatiably hot, she really liked to do it. He also mentioned she had been pressuring him to go steady and had even suggested marriage, an additional reason why he was eager to dump her.

"Why don't you take her out?" – He had suggested, and he had then introduced me to her. And I did ask her out, especially after Johnny guaranteed she would practically sexually assault me.

The first time I went out with Margaret my brother let me use his car. At her suggestion, we went to a drive-in movie.

Drive-in movies!... Are they still in existence?!?... The thing I remember the most about them is that hardly anybody went there to see the movies. You went there to make out, even the old folks I bet. If you looked around, you could see nothing inside the cars because all the windshields and car windows were always fogged up.

I had never been to a drive-in movie and – still wet behind my ears – I actually believed people went there to see the movie. Accordingly, when we got there I maneuvered the car front and center to get a good view of the screen, but Margaret – a veteran of the drive-in scene – coyly suggested we park the car in the far corner of the drive-in lot. And that – hint! hint! – was my cue that her suggestion to go to the drive-in was not motivated by her desire to see whatever movie was playing there. And we didn't in fact see much of the movie, if we saw any of it at all.

I don't mind telling you I was nervous. Every boy who goes out with a girl knowing he is going to get laid for the first time or – as in my case – even thinking or hoping there's a fair chance he'll get lucky for the first time is bound to be nervous. And I was nervous. Very, very nervous.

There are no 'self-help' or "Losing Virginity for Dummies" guides I know of that coach you on what to do 'that first time'. And it's just as well, I suppose – following a script would surely cut down on the excitement. You just wing it, and let nature take its course.

In my 'first time', being with a far more experienced girl made things a lot easier for me. Clearly, had she been as green as me, we would surely have wound up watching the entire movie, the cartoons and the scenes from coming attractions. And, just as clearly, two frustrated youngsters would have returned home sporting a few extra pimples on their faces. But I was well aware that Margaret wasn't exactly a chaste maiden – I knew she had been worked over by Johnny and almost certainly by others also. Something was going to give, I was sure.

While waiting for the movie to start and the lights to be dimmed, I bought sodas and French fries from the concession stand and we sat in the car just munching and jabbering – sort of like going through the boxing preliminaries while waiting for the main event to start. As I said before, there's got to be some sort of verbal exchange between two people of the opposite sex before they start grabbing each other. And that's what we did.

Predictably, she started babbling about what she knew best, actors and singers. I steered the conversation toward Eddie Fisher because I kind of liked him myself. He was then in his golden period and had had a string of hit songs. One of his minor hits, *"Green Years"*, was actually one of my favorite tunes. On the other hand, she was crazy about *"Oh, my Papa"*, a pleasant but rather bland cover of an old German tune. And she even sang it for me, way off-key and messing up the lyrics.

Soon after – thankfully – the movie started, and we quickly did start grabbing each other. Actually, she took the initiative. After some rather tentative and awkward attempts on my part to casually lay a hand on her shoulders, she just slid across the car seat and parked her voluminous and creamy soft breasts right under my nose.

I won't lie – I was literally trembling, trembling and panting, trembling and panting and fumbling my way trying to touch four, five, six different parts of her body at the same time. On such occasions, two hands are never quite enough.

We made out like bandits, hugging, kissing and touching each other but – alas! – I didn't score. She had her monthlies and, reluctantly, we could not consummate what we both really wanted to do.

The second time we dated we went basically through the same routine – this time, however, with a little less shaking on my part as I was certain she wanted it just as badly as I did. Regrettably, I didn't score this second time either. Stupid me, I hadn't had enough sense to bring any condoms.

"You got no goddamned rubbers?!?!" – She had protested grouchi-ly – "No rubbers, no nooky, buster… I don't wanna get pregnant. I don't want no goddamned kids!"

And neither did I, of course.

Third, fourth and fifth time I came prepared. 'Nuff said.

Even as I write, I can't help smiling wistfully as I recall the awk-wardness, the crisis, the anguish, the angst, the alarm tied to that "*came prepared*" operation. Let's just say that it was a far, far more difficult and complicated operation than losing my virginity, and leave it at that.

I am reminded of that awkward episode every single time I walk into "Walgreen" or any other chain drug store where, openly exhibit-ed on racks right next to vitamins, laxatives, cold remedies and sundry stuff, one can see a lavish display of condoms for all sizes and tastes. Small, medium, large, extra-large, ribbed, colored, lubricated and even flavored, take your pick!

It wasn't **quite** that easy the day I stealthily walked inside the lone, small Rising Sun pharmacy to "*prepare*" myself. No sir!

Embarrassment? Damn, I'm frantically trying to come up with a word to accurately describe what I felt – embarrassment just doesn't cut it. It went far, far, far beyond that. I even looked in Roget's The-saurus to find something, but I couldn't find a suitable substitute; no such word exists.

Nothing even comes close to describing how I felt, the embarrass-ment of course, plus the anxiety, the shame, the **FEAR**… Yes! Even the fear of being spotted in that place where I **KNEW** that customers would surely guess that I had come in there to purchase **THAT** shameful stuff.

And how does one describe the agitation, the jittery sensations, the jerky fidgeting, the tense feelings, the restless eye movements, the violent blushing, the incessant gulping, the infinite series of "hmmm's" and "aaaah's" while I spoke with the pharmacist?

I'm telling you, losing my virginity was a piece of cake.

Hell, I didn't even know the exact name of **THAT** stuff, the word "condom" was not part of my vocabulary yet. Margaret had called them "rubbers", and I knew of course what she was talking about, but I also instinctively knew that the word "rubber" was too harsh, too crude. And never in a million years would I have had the guts to use it.

Exactly how the transaction came to its conclusion is now irretrievably lost in my memory. Surely the pharmacist – a chubby, good-natured, elderly guy – must have had plenty experience in seeing embarrassed teenagers coming through his pharmacy's door and had guessed the purpose of my visit.

Whatever! After I blessedly managed to finalize my brown paper bag purchase, another equally critical problem arose – where do I hide **THEM**? I mean, can you imagine the shame, the jerky fidgeting, the restless eye movements, the violent blushing, the incessant gulping, the infinite series of "hmmm's" and "aaaah's" if my brother had somehow found those rubbers in my pockets, in my room or wherever? Or – Holy Mary, Mother of God, pray for us sinners! – if Ange had come across them?

Ah! Let's just forget about it! Like I said, the third, fourth and fifth time I came prepared. 'Nuff said.

That also brings to mind a consideration. In those days the back seats of cars were the equivalent of a matrimonial bed, for teen-agers at least – that's where most of the nitty-gritty action took place. To some extent, that's probably true even today, but in those days certainly more so.

While I never turned down an opportunity to use the back seat of a car, I was never really all that crazy about doing it there.

True, the immediacy of a back seat encounter added to the excitement, but I'm talking comfort here. Even in the largest back seat, you had to be a contortionist to perform, and then you had to spend half an hour defogging the windows and making yourself presentable.

Reminds me of the old joke about the very pregnant blonde who asked her gynecologist what position she would have to be in when she gave birth. The gynecologist told her it would be more or less the same position she was in when the child was conceived. And her comment?

"You mean I must lie in the back seat of a Buick with my legs propped up on the window sill?" – Ha! Ha!

Anyway, while I did manage to get on the scoreboard despite my lack of black curly hair, it definitely happened through the good auspices of someone blessed with that precious commodity.

June 1954 – Graduation Day. Got my diploma and much, much more than that – best senior student and class valedictorian, a stark difference from my dismal performance in Italy, where I was the class goofball.

With that track record, college was the next logical step and a bright future lay ahead of me. But it wasn't to be.

The Immigration Office threw a monkey wrench in my plans when it refused to renew my soon-to-expire visa. The original visa had been granted only to attend West Nottingham Academy and was valid only for as long as I was enrolled at that school. Bottom line – my days in this country were numbered and before the end of November I would have to pack my bags and return to Italy.

Return to Italy? No way! Three years in America were all I needed to decide my future was here, here was where I wanted to stay the rest of my life, and here I was going to stay, by hook or crook.

As my graduation gift, as well as for my outstanding performance in school, my brother had given me an even more outstanding present – a used 1951 Ford, a four-door, two-tone model with a great engine and lots of room in the back seat. It was my first car.

Any teenager will tell you – getting that first car is a unique experience. It's like getting laid for the first time, you just don't forget it. You can't forget it.

I have had dozens of cars since then, most of them brand new cars and certainly much better than my first one. I have practically forgotten most of them, but I can still recite by memory all the details of that first one – 1951 Ford Custom Deluxe, four-door sedan, Three-speed manual transmission with Overdrive, Flathead V-8 engine, salmon color with white top, with ribbed fenders and white wall tires. Plus radio and heater, of course.

One very happy camper I was! Hot damn! How many pictures did I take of that car? Dozens and dozens of them, with me at the wheel, next to it, in front of it, under it, climbing in, getting out, with the hood raised, whatever position I could think of. And, of course, I sent them to my folks, and especially to my friends in Italy, and I could envision them turning green with envy.

That Ford put me on top of the world, cloud nine. I had arrived and nothing could stop me now. I used to find all sorts of excuses just so I could drive that car. If I had to go to town to buy whatever, I would purposely forget to buy something just so I could get behind the wheel of that car again, gun the engine and drive back to town. Once there, I would park in front of *"Poist's"* and slowly make a seemingly nonchalant exit, all the while covertly scoping the territory behind my dark shades, checking to see if any teenage babes were around and looking at me. I felt like a man, **THE** man.

Hell, I even practiced – on the sly, of course – trying to imitate and master that quick, sure, assertive, sudden lowering of the right shoulder I had seen other youngsters execute so well, so damn confidently, as they downshifted. Total control of man over machine; better yet, pure symbiosis of man and machine, that's what I saw in that smooth, natural, almost imperceptible downward movement of the shoulder.

That first car was pure bliss, an unforgettable thrill. It gave me more joy, more pleasure, more pride of ownership than any other car I've had since.

Yes! One happy camper I was! Except for the constant preoccupation of my soon-to-expire visa.

Returning to Italy was out of the question. I had two choices – either going 'underground', like the Ravello brothers, or obtaining my citizenship by getting married to some American girl and start raising a family quickly.

Too young – and definitely not all that enthusiastic – to get hitched, becoming an illegal alien seemed my only plausible alternative. If the Immigration Office caught up with me, the worst that could have happened was that they would have sent me back to Italy. At their expense.

Then, by pure chance, like a gift from heaven, the opportunity to legally remain in the United States presented itself.

A couple of months after graduation, I returned to West Nottingham Academy to say goodbye to some of my teachers, Mr. Nillson, Mr. Bauer, Mr. Foutz and others.

They asked me about my plans and they strongly encouraged me to continue my education. They even gave me information on where I could apply for and almost surely receive scholarship money, based on my outstanding academic record.

I informed them that, regretfully, I couldn't go to college, not immediately anyway, because of my predicament with the visa. When I told them about my plans to go to New York, they gave me some advice, some encouragement, and even some names to contact in New York.

Then Mr. Nillson suggested: "Why don't you join the armed services?"

He explained that by joining the army or any of the armed services, I could apply for and receive citizenship within 90 days of enlisting; that's how he had become a citizen, he assured me.

I rushed home and told my brother what I had heard. The next day we went to the recruiting station in Elkton, and they verified that I could indeed enlist and then apply for and automatically obtain American citizenship. I enlisted on the spot.

Full disclosure – I should mention that an armistice had been signed in the Korean conflict not long before my enlistment. That made my decision to enlist much easier.

Would I have enlisted and risked being sent to Korea if the war had still been going on? Probably not; in fact, surely not.

Just the idea of bullets flying around, and me possibly being on the receiving end – or within a thousand miles – of one of them would have sent me scurrying back to Italy in a heartbeat.

CHAPTER 8

GREETINGS!

In the early 50s, mandatory conscription was still on. Most young men of draft age dreaded receiving an official looking letter that addressed you with that innocuous sounding salutation – it meant you were being drafted. The Korean War was still raging, and that surely didn't help assuaging the dread everyone felt.

Korean War apart, young men didn't like being drafted because the armed forces – and the Army in particular – had the reputation of being tough, no-nonsense, martinet organizations.

A private's pay was a pittance, and not many people consider-ed enlisting in any branch of the armed forces and make a career in the military.

Most draftees displayed their resentment at being drafted by showing an unspoken yet unmistakable disdain for all enlisted men. As a general rule, enlisted men – as well as all Army career men – were viewed as fuck-ups who had joined the military because they couldn't hack it as civilians; an accurate frame of reference in most cases.

I caught the drift of that sentiment immediately and quickly explained to my fellow basic trainees – most of them inductees – that I had enlisted only because I wanted to become an American citizen. They then accepted me as one of their own.

Most draftees dreaded in particular the harshness and rigors of basic training. I had known a few guys who had been in the Army, and they all were unanimous in saying 'man, basic training is a bitch'

– that was the general consensus. And it was tough, I must admit, but I managed to get through it fairly well.

The site of my basic training was Fort Jackson, South Carolina, just a few miles outside Columbia, capital city of that Dixie state.

Our drill sergeant was an Italian-American career man – his name was Sal Alessi. I still remember his name because an aunt of mine had married an Alessi. We did have a Sicilian background in common – he said his grandparents came from Milazzo, a small town about 20 miles from Torre Faro, my parents' hometown. So, who knows, maybe we were distant relatives.

He was one tough son-of-a-bitch with the kind of withering tongue that would reduce grown men to trembling puppets, but he took a liking to me.

Despite strict military standards that discouraged drill sergeants from fraternizing with basic training recruits, we chatted frequently. With me, he felt like he was connecting with his roots. When we talked he used a funny mixture of Sicilian dialect and Americanized Italian words, mostly food-related or cuss words.

He even worried about my welfare. One particular occasion comes to mind. We had done our "night firing" training, an exercise that required staying outdoors all night long firing at moving targets. It must have been sometime in late June or early July, when the South Carolina fields at night are full of goddamned mosquitoes, millions, gazillions of mosquitoes. And mosquitoes absolutely love me.

At dawn, when we returned to the base camp, my face looked like I'd done a few rounds with Rocky Marciano. When Sgt. Alessi saw my swollen face – I never called him Sal, even though we were almost buddies – he was furious.

"Who's the son-of-a-bitch done beat the crap out of you?" – He demanded to know. He actually believed I'd been on the losing end of a fight, and he was going to have the guy court-martialed.

I told him: "Fucking mosquitoes!"

Less than two months in the Army and I had already picked up that most functional American word. And made it my own.

He wouldn't believe me. I swore that was the case and he then sent me to the infirmary to get a malaria shot.

During basic training, most trainees would be lucky if they got one or two passes – free time to spend away from camp. I was a bit luckier. In eight weeks of basic training – with more than a little help from Sgt. Alessi – I managed to get six or seven passes, including a few for the entire weekend.

Weekend passes were joyfully spent in Columbia in the company of other trainees. We roamed around that charming southern city, usually spending the night at the "Wade Hampton" Hotel, right across from the Capitol building, two, three, sometime even four guys to a room.

Like all good soldiers, we weren't all that interested in local museums, Civil War artifacts, or any other cultural enrichment program. Like all horny soldiers, we were looking to have a good time. And having a good time meant one thing and one thing only: to score, to get laid, period.

Getting laid with traditional hookers wasn't all that easy for several reasons. To start with, we are talking what?... 1955 or 1956, when prostitution was still seriously frowned upon, especially in a genteel southern city. It wasn't like today where you can find hookers at well-designated spots in every city, town or even hamlet.

The word 'hooker' hadn't even entered the vocabulary, I believe. I'm not saying there weren't any hookers in Columbia or anywhere else in those days – hell, they don't call it the oldest profession for nothing! I'm sure the locals knew where to go to get laid – the males, anyhow – but we didn't. To start with, we didn't know the lay of the land, but mostly we didn't have all that much time in our hands, certainly not enough to find out where to go to get our rocks off.

Equally important – we didn't have all that much money. A buck private's pay was about 80 bucks a month, and even in those days 80 bucks didn't go all that far. Lots of guys used to blow that money in a day – in an hour! – just shooting dice. Luckily, I never had the urge, or the nerve, to try that type of gambling.

Surely a few recruits got lucky and did manage to score, but just listening to the guys talk you would think the entire city of Columbia was one big whorehouse.

On Saturday and Sunday nights, before lights out and even after, the conversation topic in the barracks was invariably the same – Sex! Women! Screwing! Booze!... Booze! Screwing! Women! Sex!... Never, ever varied.

In a rowdy, circus-like milieu, one act followed another, guys tried to top each other weaving wildly outlandish stories of improbable situations involving one, two, three loose women – plus the protagonist, of course. It was an endless drivel of tales seasoned with well-timed obscene gestures and winks, and this guy would tell about this great club or that wild bar where he picked up this hot chick and how he plied her with drinks. Not to be outdone, others would tell of drinking and dancing till all hours, and still others would brag about going into even wilder bars, getting into fierce fistfights, and how eventually all of them wound up screwing their brains out.

Invariably, there was also loose mention of someone slipping some "Spanish fly" in some girl's drink, and of how she had become so sexually aroused that she needed four, five, six, or even more men to satisfy her.

The stories were always the same, or variations on the same theme, but we all listened with interest as well as amusement, even though everyone clearly understood that most of the tales were wildly tall, if not pure bullshit.

In some cases the fighting part of the tale must have been true because the narrator did have visible marks of a fight – a black eye or a broken nose – but the rest of the story was at best improbable, and at worst full of shit.

I was more inclined to believe the stories when narrated by black recruits, or Negroes, as they were still called in those days – among a lot of other things. For one thing, black women had a reputation of being more sexually liberated than white women, meaning of course that most white folks believed black ladies considered chastity a nasty vice and were eager to offer anyone pussy on a silver platter. Mostly, though, black recruits sounded more truthful, more natural, and their stories seemed more believable and rich in those details that couldn't have been invented on the spot. Furthermore, the descriptions of their amorous adventures were always much, much funnier than the ones told by white recruits.

Blacks are natural comedians, I believe. I don't mean comedians in the sense of knowing how to tell jokes or even in having a good sense of humor. I believe blacks are naturally funny in the way they express themselves, the words they use, the cadence of their speech, the innovative ways they have of phrasing and even altering the language, frequently inventing new words or expressions that eventually enter the national lexicon. I always loved listening to them, even though at times I couldn't quite understand what they said.

During those verbal free-for-alls I was usually a listener. While I could hold my own very well with my English, I was still self-conscious about my accent and felt uncomfortable displaying it. Additionally, I didn't have all that much to contribute or to brag about – my erotic exploits were not exactly the stuff of legends. In fact, during basic training I managed to get laid only once.

It happened this one time after I attended some genteel afternoon dance where no alcohol was served. I don't remember how or why I even went there, but I do recall hooking up with this well-endowed young girl, not exceptionally good looking, a bit overweight but definitely worth pursuing.

I made a good impression on her because, just like me, she liked to dance; I'm a decent dancer and I made her spin like a top on the dance floor. Additionally, while doing the slow dances, I held her close to me and hummed in her ear whatever tune was being played, and she seemed to enjoy that also.

She even had a car and when the dance was over she invited me to go for a ride outside town. Hoping she might have ants in her pants – a cute expression I had recently learned from my fellow trainees – I eagerly agreed to join her.

She drove around for a while and we then stopped to grab a hamburger and a soda at some joint. She even paid for it against my not too strenuous objections.

Afterwards, I suggested we go to a movie, figuring I would have the opportunity to do some heavy petting in the dark. She agreed, but when we drove by the theatre she just looked at the marquee and said she had already seen the movie they were showing, so she just kept driving around.

I was pretty sure we were on the same wavelength when, without any prompting on my part, she parked the car in an empty parking lot next to an isolated grove just off some deserted road. True to my beliefs on dating etiquette, we didn't just start grabbing each other – we just chitchatted for a while about this and that.

She inquired about Italy, and I started telling her about the beauty, the mystique and romance of my home country.

Romance! That was the magic word!… As soon as she heard that word, she got a misty look in her eyes. Looking at me languidly, she whispered she had always dreamed of finding real romance.

"Real love, you know what I mean, don't you? The **real** thing…" – she kept saying over and over. But all her attempts to find that ideal relationship had miserably failed, she bemoaned.

She then switched gears and went into this long spiel, morosely complaining about the local boys.

"I'm done dating them." – She drawled haughtily. "All they want to do is get in my pants, without so much as a kiss, a caress… nothing."

Their only interests were cars, booze and sex, cars, booze and sex – she lamented. "That's all they talk about… when they do any talking at all…"– She mumbled, clearly miffed.

Her inner spirit needed some emotional nourishment, she kept whispering in a damned good imitation of Lana Turner at her worst; at heart she was a romantic, she was born a romantic – she sighed breathlessly, in comically melodramatic tones. Being born in South Carolina was an accident of birth, she actually said, she always felt European at heart.

And every now and then she would grab my hands and look at me with eyes that tried to but never quite succeeded in being sultry.

"You understand me, don't you?" – She would whisper. – "You are Italian, all Italians know what love, what **real** love is, Italians know how to treat women."

By then, of course, I knew it was time to turn on my Italian charm – brown spaghetti hair and all.

With a perfectly straight face, I told her I understood how she felt. Trying to infuse as much remorse as I could in my voice, I confessed that until a few years before I used to behave like the local boys, but I had finally learned that all women – Women! Not girls!... That's important! – all women had special feelings, that they **suffered,** that they needed to be understood... And I understood her, now.

Five minutes of that bullshit – both mine and hers – and I had already managed to remove her bra. Five more minutes, and we were in the back seat. And, for once, I had come prepared with condoms. I always carried two in my wallet, just in case I got lucky.

We had barely finished, and I had visions of at the very least a doubleheader when – talk about *"coitus interruptus"*, that had barely started – I happened to glance at my watch and I realized I had less than half an hour to return to base or my ass would have been on KP for the rest of my basic training.

"Please, honey, please drive me back to base." – I begged her. And she did, bless her little Dixie heart!

We barely managed to make it back in time. After dropping me off, she told me to make sure I'd call her next time I was in town. I got her address and phone number, kissed her goodbye, and that was it for that day.

Of course I called her the very next day to set up another date, and she eagerly agreed to pick me up that weekend, if I got a pass. Unfortunately, that weekend I was on guard duty and I did not get a pass. Reluctantly, I called her and cancelled the date. Ten days later my basic training was over, I was shipped out and I never saw my southern belle again.

The next eight weeks saw me in Fort Sam Houston, just outside San Antonio in Texas to be trained as a medic. As an Army base, Fort Sam Houston was pretty much like Fort Jackson but much more pleasant – the rigors of basic training were over. And, as a town, San Antonio was just as pleasant as Columbia.

I arrived in San Antonio just at the height of popularity of the Davy Crockett craze fueled by the wildly popular Walt Disney movie by the same name.

All the old fogies should remember it. Everything in San Antonio was Davy Crockett inspired. Everywhere you went, bars, stores, offices, in the street, absolutely everywhere, even in the bathrooms, you'd hear that familiar refrain blaring "Davy... Davy Crockett... king of the wild frontier" sung – if memory serves – by Tennessee Ernie Ford.

For once, even we soldiers were caught up in this "cultural" experience. And to enlarge this "cultural" experience, instead of looking for action, first thing we did as soon as we hit town on a pass we went to visit the famous Alamo where Davy Crockett and his troops put up a heroic resistance to the Mexican army before being massacred.

What a letdown!... Like fifty million other people, I'd also seen the movie and – on the screen at least – the Alamo looked like a very large fortress surrounded by high walls.

Maybe the original structure was more in line with what showed on the screen, or possibly Hollywood had done its usual aggrandizement, but what was actually there was a church– like front, and a rather small one at that. Inside, there was an area about twice as large as the average backyard in a middle– class housing development; with an annexed souvenir shop, naturally. And that was it.

A national craze just for that?... What a waste of time! I couldn't believe it, and neither could most of my fellow soldiers.

We made a smart 'About face' and left immediately. In typical Army fashion, we then started searching for entertainment more suitable to our immediate needs.

And guess what that would be?

CHAPTER 9

"Do you have any preference about where you could be stationed for the remainder of your Army hitch?"

That's the standard question all trainees are asked at the end of their final training session. In Fort Sam Houston we had been trained to be medics. Theoretically, if the location we chose had a need for medics they would try to accommodate us. Theoretically.

The US military had – and still has – bases in Italy and in most of Europe. Obviously, my first choice was to be stationed in Italy, with anywhere else in Europe as my second choice. It was a no-brainer. While there, whenever I had a leave I would get to see my family and friends whom I hadn't seen in over four years. And I wouldn't even have to pay for the trip.

My chances of getting there were pretty good, I thought. Surely the Army could have used me not just as a medic but as a translator also.

It didn't work out that way – not quite. When our definitive deployment orders came, I wasn't sent to Italy, or France, or Spain – it wasn't even to Germany or to any other nation in the Old World. Try the opposite side of the planet... Try a place called Korea!

Goddamned Army! Always doing things backasswards! And to further piss me off, a few guys in my unit did get to go to Europe while I, with a perfect knowledge of Italian and a working knowledge of French and Spanish, had been sent to some godforsaken place in the Far East where some sporadic shooting was still going on. Go figure.

After a brief stay in Olympia, Washington State, a troop ship took us to Korea. And it sure as hell wasn't a cruise. Another long voyage in another goddamned ship, and this time without any comforts whatsoever. Just an upper berth in the hold of this humongous troopship and with the smell of vomit – mine included – all around me.

And once we got to Korea things got worse. Chop-chop.

Korea! What a God-forsaken, miserable country! Jesus! You had to see it to believe it!

Villages marginally better than what we see today in documentaries about the most desolate parts of Africa; straw-roofed houses with dirt floors, unpaved streets, outdoor toilets, little or no electricity; the most abject poverty everywhere; little boys and girls running around dirty and half naked, wearing what could charitably be called just rags; adults walking slowly, slightly hunched, barely better dressed than the kids; not one single attraction, natural or artistic, in the entire country; most everyone seemingly resigned to their desperate situation. And with nothing, absolutely nothing to look forward to.

That's what Korea was.

I remember thinking – still do, in fact – you mean America sacrificed the lives of over 40,000 young men for this piece of shit? What did we gain from all that carnage? Unbelievable!

American troops were a glaring contrast to this all-around misery. Well fed, well dressed in our sharp military uniforms, we had most household comforts even in our cramped barracks. We even had money.

Yes! Even our pittance pay went a long way in Korea! American soldiers could hire a Korean to do their laundry, or whatever, for about 10 dollars a month. In fact, for that little money Korean houseboys – that's what we called them – would do laundry for two or three guys.

Worst of all, the most depressing sight of all, was the rampant prostitution.

In the States, everyone understood that young men – and soldiers in particular – needed an outlet for their raging sex drives. It was an established and widely accepted reality.

Like all GI's, I shared the constant preoccupation about looking for the next piece of ass, better if it was offered on a silver platter but – as a last resort – even in exchange of cold cash.

Personally, even under the best of circumstances, the idea of a direct exchange of money for sex never appealed to me. And no, not because I was a prude – I had in fact done it a few times myself, but I still didn't like it.

This aversion of mine, by the way, was a radical turnaround for me, and a perfect example of how quickly and how completely one's feelings or opinions can change when exposed to a different environment.

Allow me to explain. As a teenager in Italy, I couldn't wait to become of age so I could go to a *casino*. And no, I don't mean the Trump Plaza or Caesar's or any of those other horrors you find in Vegas or Atlantic City – c*asino* is Italian for whorehouse.

In Italy, the most common way for a young man to get laid – short of getting married –was by going to a brothel.

Everyone knew where *casinos* were located, and every john had his favorite one. The practice was regimented countrywide, and it was widely accepted as normal for most unmarried men – young or old – to patronize one. I mean, it's not like a young buck would announce at the dinner table: "Well, I think this evening I'll go to a *casino*", but every mom and dad knew their budding lothario would consort with some accommodating wench of ill repute now and then. It was understood and even tacitly approved – all young men were expected to do it, and in fact did it.

The practice was so standardized that when the Italian military got its meager pay most civilians didn't even bother to go to a *casino*. They knew you would literally have to wait in line to be entertained. Like I said, it was a widely accepted practice, and nobody frowned at it, not even the Catholic Church. Hell! It was no secret that many Catholic priests also discreetly patronized *casinos*! In civilian clothes, of course.

I then came to the United States where – what with the dating scene and all – there was certainly more opportunity for both boys and girls to... how can I phrase it delicately?... to experiment with sex, that's it! Dating was a normal occurrence here and – if you played your cards right – dating could and frequently did lead to sex.

Since there was this ample opportunity to 'experiment', my opinion changed drastically. 'Earning' whatever sex I got rather than purchasing it became my erotic goal.

I was well aware, of course, that trying to 'earn' sex usually translates into a considerable reduction in the amount of sex one gets. All the more so if one isn't blessed with a head full of black curly hair, but I was OK with that.

A decrease in quantity – I confidently made myself believe – will surely be offset by an increase in quality although, if truth be told, neither the quality nor the quantity of what I managed to score was something to write home about. Still, once I started dating, my mindset changed – quality, or the illusion of quality, supplanted the reality of quantity.

That's just my personal opinion, of course. I also believe in the maxim 'to each his own', so if one prefers quantity to quality, more power to him. Or to her.

Depressing and appalling as it was, the rampant prostitution in Korea was just the tip of the iceberg. Worse yet were the methods used for soliciting johns, methods that were for me downright mind numbing and inhibiting.

All right! All soldiers have a need for sexual relief; they need to get their rocks off, OK? I'll concede that! But somebody please explain to me, how in hell could a guy shack up with a woman when her little brother, or little sister, or even her little son or daughter – or even her mother, for Christ sake! – came and grabbed him by the arm in the village street – in front of friends and neighbors, for Christ sake! – and asked him, in fact, solicited him to go to their house and screw her? Somebody please explain to me how one could perform under those circumstances!

That's what I couldn't understand, that's what I couldn't accept and couldn't stomach. But that's exactly what was happening there.

Even as I write this, I worry that someone may view me as a sanctimonious, goody-two-shoes phony with lofty ideals about the purity of women or – worse yet! – one of those charlatans who feather their nests sermonizing about the sanctity of family and that type of humbug.

No, no, no! Let me introduce myself: Under ordinary circumstances, I would have had no qualms whatsoever – and I do mean zero qualms – about dipping my tool anywhere half-ass decent.

Most certainly, in those days one of my preoccupations, maybe even the main one – in fact, no maybe about it - was the same one of most other young men: sex and where I could find it. Free if possible but, if absolutely necessary, even if I had to shell out some cold cash. And no, I was not a sex maniac. I mean, it's not like I woke up in the morning and all I would think about was sex until I went to bed at night. Or even after that... especially after that. No, it wasn't like that at all! But sex was certainly on my mind, several times a day or night, and the idea of where, or when, or if, or with whom I could copulate was fairly prominent in my brain. And other parts of my body.

But the keywords in what I just stated are 'under ordinary circumstances'. To me, the idea of using children to solicit sex didn't even come close to being an 'ordinary circumstance'. No way! To me, it was – still is, and forever will be – plainly and simply immoral. I felt then – and still believe now – that that type of solicitation should inhibit anyone's desire to taste whatever fruit was harvested using that shameful tool. I'm not the least bit embarrassed to say that it certainly inhibited my desire.

A clarification – the word 'immoral' here is used in an ecumenical sense. I was well aware that morality, or lack of it, had nothing to do with the behavior of the Korean ladies and their family members. I knew damn well that hunger, plain and simple hunger, mixed with widespread destitution and desperation, can cause a moral breakdown even in the most puritanical society. Something very similar happened in Italy also, near the end of World War II, immediately after the Allied troops landed.

Appalling as it was, the outdoor flesh bazaar was just one disturbing aspect of Korea's deplorable state of affairs. There was also the blatant juxtaposition of an economic disparity so sweeping, so disproportionate as to be downright immoral.

Here I go again using the word 'immoral' in two short paragraphs, but I'm not trying to make a morality play here, honest! Just like with the prostitution, morality – or lack of it – had nothing to do with this lopsided economic condition. It was the inevitable postscript of a scenario that brought together two civilizations totally different in just about every measurable criterion.

What disturbed me the most was that America had not only contributed to the creation of that tragic situation by entering the war – or 'police action', as it was called – but that its troops were actually exacerbating it by displaying their affluent lifestyle.

In a nutshell, we had everything and they had squat. True, the conveniences we had in Korea were nowhere near what we enjoyed at home. Still, we did have plenty food, good health facilities, clothing, movies, money, and even the use of Korean boys to do our daily chores. In most cases, however, we didn't have the decency not to flaunt our superior lifestyle. In fact, we even had the nerve to complain because... well, because in the Army you were expected to complain.

I did my share of complaining – I'm embarrassed to admit – mostly about being there and wishing I were anywhere but there, but I did complain.

American people's most obvious good quality, recognized all over the world, has always been their kindness and generosity. A cursory look at our foreign aid budget over the years will clearly indicate that most Americans are really good-hearted and generous souls.

Most Americans would never intentionally hurt or demean the less fortunate ones, but Korea seemed to have soured all those good intentions and qualities. On several occasions I saw American soldiers treating Koreans like dirt, even making fun of the fact that little kids urged them to screw their sisters or their mothers.

I should add that the Army brass, aware of the inequity of the situation and its potential explosiveness, took steps to minimize this glaring economic disparity by placing strict limitations on our free time and even stricter rules on our behavior.

Whenever soldiers left their compound, they were allowed to walk in the village streets but were strictly forbidden from entering Korean homes. MPs (Military Police) kept patrolling all areas, and could even enter Korean homes at will to make sure no GIs were in there. Soldiers, however, always managed to find ways to sneak inside a house because… well, because that's where you could get laid for as little as five bucks.

Koreans, of course, were no fools. To counter those restrictions they managed to find ingenious ways to set up an alert system whenever the MPs were patrolling. Most village homes – shacks would be a more accurate word – had a built-in "sneaky boys' room". This aptly named room was actually just an alcove, about 7 or 8 feet long, about 4 feet wide and 4 feet high, its only furnishing a rudimentary straw mattress laid on the floor. This oversized coffin was the bedroom, the romantic *boudoir* where all amorous *rendezvous* were consummated. Cash up front, of course.

You entered – or snuck in, hence its name – through some kind of trapdoor hidden behind an easily removable piece of furniture. You then did your thing with the partner you had chosen and exited fifteen or twenty minutes later. And if you wanted to do a doubleheader – still cash up front – you exited maybe forty-five minutes or one hour later; or a bit longer maybe, depending on the individual stamina.

Strictly for the record, in the eighteen months I was in Korea I personally used a "sneaky boys' room" just once, as a birthday present to myself. I did not use the services of a young boy or a young girl as a pimp, though. Call it scruples or call it whatever the hell you want, but I knew I couldn't get it up if I had.

On that particular occasion I didn't even have to arrange for it. A friend of mine, a black corporal, made all the necessary arrangements through a steady girlfriend he had in the village, a former hooker that he in fact wound up marrying.

Aware of my aversion against seeing kids pimping, he had talked to his girlfriend, and she arranged my tryst with one of her girlfriend – a still practicing hooker – thus bypassing the sordid street scene. As an added bonus, as a birthday present for me he even paid for my dalliance.

Despite the freebie and the indirect route to that encounter, that particular mating certainly didn't rank among my most memorable ones, quality wise. In fact, the only thing I remember about it is that it actually happened. And that I wanted to get my ass out of there as quickly as possible.

I have read somewhere that when sex is good it's fantastic, and when it's not so good... well, it's still pretty good. On that particular occasion it was – how can I describe it? – just forgettable. And filled with apprehension. And not just because of the potential problems with the MPs, but because I had used a condom – the Army distributed them for free.

Talk about irony, or hypocrisy! The Army strictly forbade consorting with local women –if the MPs caught you inside a Korean home you could get court-martialed. Yet that same Army provided us with free condoms because it knew soldiers would do it anyway.

I had used condoms before and it had never bothered me. On previous occasions, however, I had used it mainly to make sure the girl I was with wouldn't get knocked up. On that occasion I had used it to make sure I didn't get the clap.

So what's the difference, you ask? A hell of a lot of difference, as far as this kid is concerned. During my eighteen months in Korea, I spent practically my entire time working in the base infirmary giving penicillin shots – dozens and dozens of them on a daily basis! – to my fellow soldiers. That's because many of them never used condoms because they foolishly believed that using one was – to use their colorful expression – like taking a shower with a raincoat.

Insanely, many of them actually viewed getting the clap almost as a badge of honor – it was *prima facie* evidence that they got laid, they were real men. And practically all of them foolishly thought of the clap as just a minor nuisance, like a cold, but I knew better. Let's just say I have always been pretty careful about that particular part of my body.

As an aside, had I been a frequent habitué of the local dating scene, I would never have worried about being caught inside a "sneaky boys' room" by the MPs. And no, not because I was a fearless, cocky, don't give a damn type of GI – far from it. It's just that I knew that MPs, like all other soldiers, also had physical needs, and when they had some free time they also patronized the "sneaky boys rooms", and some of them also were foolish enough not to take precautions. As a result, some of my best patients were members of the feared Military Police. If I ever got caught inside a "sneaky boys' room", I could and would have used that knowledge to persuade them to let me go.

The second and last time I got lucky in Korea was on a fortuitous but legitimate occasion.

Just before leaving San Antonio I had submitted to the proper authorities my request to become an American citizen.

My request had been accepted, of course, and had been sent through the usual channels. It was now just a question of waiting for the paperwork to be sent through the Immigration and Naturalization Office in Washington, and then for it to catch up with me.

It caught up with me while I was in Korea.

One day our company commander summoned me and told me to report to the American Embassy in the capital city of Seoul for the swearing-in ceremony of becoming an American citizen.

Man, was I thrilled! Not only was I going to become an American citizen but – better yet! – for about one week I would get to stay away from those depressing Army barracks stuck in the middle of nowhere.

Yup! That's what I said, better yet! Amazing how quickly one's priorities can change! Becoming an American citizen had been my ultimate dream. Hell! That was the only reason why I was in goddamned Korea in the first place. At that moment, however, the prospect of spending a few days away from camp seemed to me an even more desirable objective than becoming an American citizen.

I had never been in Seoul – I just knew it was a pretty large city, and I figured it had to be better than our Army post. It was, but not by much.

The city did have some war damage, but even the best-kept sites weren't much to write home about.

There was enough movement in the streets, with thousands of bicycles intermingled with few cars and even fewer buses, but it wasn't a dynamic type of movement. People seemed to be moving around only because they were forced to do so.

Few and unreliable facilities, limited transportation, half-empty stores with little of any value in them; old, decrepit buildings with a grim, unwelcome appearance; a cold, sullen and inhospitable populace; a place as dreary as any I had ever seen – that was Seoul in those days.

Seoul, a city without a soul – no pun intended.

After the swearing-in ceremony I was lodged for a few days in a huge Army compound, a very large facility, much better equipped than the Army camp where I was stationed. It had a full-fledged movie house, a nightclub for enlisted men and one for officers, a Post Exchange – a PX, as they called it – filled with all kinds of goods at half the price you'd pay in the United States. It even had tennis courts and other sports facilities. They had yet another, even more beguiling attraction there – they had women! They had American women!

Some of them were Army women and nurses, while others were Red Cross ladies, but they were women, ladies, females, maidens. And some of them not bad looking either.

I don't recall if my encounter in the "sneaky boys' room" had occurred before or after my excursion in Seoul, but I know I hadn't been with a woman in quite a while. And I will also acknowledge that a prolonged abstinence can make even a female gorilla look seductive, but I swear some of those ladies were quite attractive.

After the swearing in ceremony, four of us newly naturalized soldiers went to celebrate our newly acquired American citizenship at the base nightclub, not really a nightclub, more like a pedestrian social club, a place for GIs to hangout and relax, about ten tables, a jukebox and a rinky-dink bar where they served drinks. And there we met a group of young ladies stationed in that compound. Of course, we lost no time socializing with them. To celebrate our citizenship, the ladies even treated us to a round of drinks.

We kept feeding nickels and dimes in the jukebox and we danced and partied till all hours. I don't know what the other guys did, but I wound up with one of those ladies for my second and last intimate encounter in Korea.

This minor footnote, by the way, is strictly for the record and most certainly not to brag about my sexual conquests in the mysterious orient.

Hell! Bragging about getting laid a grand total of two times in 18 months is like bragging about having learned the entire alphabet from *A* to *C* in just one week.

CHAPTER 10

The Seoul Post Exchange (PX) wasn't as luxurious or as well stocked as your typical Macy's, but it did offer plenty of quality merchandise. Cigarettes, candy, games, bicycles, cameras, jewelry, sports equipment, radios – you name it – they had it. Best of all, everything you bought there was half-price, or even less, than what you'd pay in the States. And no state taxes either.

Despite our measly pay, I was flush with cash – and not because I am the parsimonious type, far from it. The reason for my affluent status was simple: at the base camp we had a mom-and-pop type PX with very little you could or want to spend your money on.

Most GIs blew their entire paycheck getting laid, gambling or buying cheap beer and liquor in the villages. I did drink, but the local stuff turned my stomach; I didn't gamble, and I've already mentioned my revulsion for the local dating scene. My only expenses were for laundry services by a Korean houseboy, and cigarettes. And that explains the unusually large amount of moola in my pockets.

As usual, it was burning a hole there. I had always wanted a good camera, and the Seoul PX had many different models at various prices.

I set my eyes on this luxurious Olympus model with all the latest bells and whistles, including carrying case, telephoto lens, flash, even the tripod, and I bought it. I forget how much I paid for it – around one hundred bucks, I believe – a pretty large sum in those days, more than one month pay, but I could easily afford it.

The guy at the counter somehow realized he was dealing with someone who, using today's terminology, was technically challenged. I won't hide it, I have always had this incredible resistance toward anything even remotely technical. Anything... even the language, especially the language, confuses me. When I open a simple instruction booklet for assembling whatever, it could just as well be written in ancient Mandarin Chinese – I am totally paralyzed with terminal ignorance.

With that particular camera, some hands-on instructions were necessary. Cameras in those days were not like today's totally automatic cameras. Today you just point, click, and you get a picture. Back then everything – distance, lens opening, focus, everything –had to be set manually, even with the most expensive cameras. You even had to advance the roll of film manually. And if you don't know what a roll of film is, I suggest you look it up on Wikipedia.

Patiently, the guy showed me how to load the camera, how to increase or decrease the lens opening, how to advance the film, how to focus and how to press the shutter, cautioning me to keep the camera still when I pressed the shutter. Just to be on the safe side, he also reminded me to remove the lens cap before taking a picture, but he did it in a nice way, not as a put down.

And finally he gave me another fundamental instruction, better yet a warning. He warned me that if I ever ventured out in the streets of Seoul with my camera, there would be a good chance somebody would try to rip me off.

I had to smile. Rip me off?... Rip **ME** off?... **ME?!?!...** Are you jesting?... Do I look like somebody who just got off the boat?

I thanked him for the friendly advice, paid for camera and film and went back to my quarters where I spent the best part of the evening trying to decipher the instruction manual.

By the next day I had it down pat. Or so I thought.

The next morning I got up, had breakfast in the Mess Hall and then headed out with my brand new camera in its leather case hanging with the strap around my neck. It was my next to last day in Seoul, and I was free to go anywhere I wanted. Why not take some pictures to send to the folks back home to show I had really visited the inscrutable orient?

And off I went, without venturing too far though – getting lost in the big city was a major concern. I wasn't exactly fluent in Korean – in fact, I didn't know one single word – and I didn't want to risk having to ask somebody for directions back to the compound.

Seoul was a war scarred, drab town with little or nothing memorable to photograph, but I did manage to take a few pictures of a couple of temples, along with some government buildings, to at least prove I had been there. I would have liked taking a picture of those places with me in the foreground, but that meant I would have had to ask some stranger to take the picture. And even I had enough sense not to do that.

The streets were crowded, and in some remote ways Seoul reminded me of Italian cities with its old buildings, very few cars and people just coming and going.

I had been wandering around for maybe half an hour when this Korean guy, a young man about my age, approached me.

"Hey GI! I give you two hundred fifty dollars for camera," he said in halting English. I knew immediately I was being hustled, of course. The guy at the store had warned me about it, but I would have known even without his warning. I mean, there was no doubt in my mind, I was fully aware, absolutely certain, beyond the shadow of a doubt that this guy was a con man trying to relieve me of my Olympus.

The best defense against a hustle is to simply walk away, but for some perverse reason I decided to amuse myself a bit.

Just for the hell of it, I decided to play along with this hustle, just so I would have at least one interesting tale, an amusing anecdote to entertain the guys back in camp or the folks back home. "Can you believe it?... That fucker actually thought he could screw **ME**..." Or something like that.

Please, don't misunderstand. My attitude had nothing to do with racial superiority, in the sense that I was not thinking there was no way a damned Korean could take advantage of an Italian. No, nothing like that, I swear... It was simply that I believed there was no way that this guy, who just happened to be Korean, could possibly make a fool of me, who just happened to be Italian. I was just curious to see what his hustle was, and I figured the best way to find out was by dickering with him on the price.

Clearly, assuming the offer had been made in good faith, any sensible person would not only have accepted it immediately, but would also have kissed the guy's ass in the bargain. I mean, I'd shelled out about one hundred bucks for the camera, the guy was offering me two fifty, that's a quick one hundred fifty dollar profit, almost two months' pay. A no-brainer.

Well, OK, it was against Army rules and regulations to sell PX stuff to the locals, but that was one of those rules and regulations expressly made-to-be-broken, the kind of rule hardly anybody paid any attention to. Hell! There were guys in my outfit who got rich running a small emporium in contraband trading of cigarettes, cameras, watches, radios and whatever stuff they could sell to the indigenous population.

Rules and regulations also forbade soldiers from consorting with local women, but that never stopped anyone from getting laid. Or getting the clap.

"Two hundred fifty?" – I said with some disdain. – "You must be jesting. Do you know how much this camera is worth, dear sir?"

Yes, I actually said "dear sir", and with a British accent to boot – me, with my thick Italian accent, but I figured the guy wouldn't know the difference.

"How much you want?" – He said with his thick Korean accent.

"Old chap..." – I said, really laying it on thick with my Lawrence Olivier act – "this precision built camera is worth no less than five hundred dollars."

I doubled the amount just to see what his reaction would be. There was none, so I went on: "But you seem to be an enterprising fellow, and I must say I jolly like that. And while it would grieve me to part with this sophisticated piece of equipment, I will consider selling it to you for just four hundred fifty dollars."

Man! I was having fun! Of course, I was expecting him to accept my offer, thus giving away his shabby game, but he surprised me.

"You GI crazy!..." – He said – "You keep fucking camera!"

And he started walking away muttering something in Korean.

This was also part of the hustle, I was sure, and I gave him twenty-five steps before he would turn around and make another approach.

Nineteen, twenty, twenty-one, twenty-two, twenty-three, twenty-four, twenty-five... He kept on walking. Twenty-nine, thirty, thirty-one, thirty-two, thirty-three...

"Shit! Is he for real?" – I thought to myself. "Have I just declined a fabulous bargain? Did I misjudge the guy?"

To my astonishment, the guy kept on walking away. O my God!... I thought alarmed – I had not only declined a fabulous bargain, I had not only misjudged the guy, but I had also insulted him, in my mind at least.

"**SIR!!!**" – I hailed, and I actually ran after him and grabbed his arm. "Please wait, wait just one minute, sir..."

He seemed annoyed, jerked his arm free and kept on walking. But then he stopped.

"About the camera..." – I stammered. God! Was I embarrassed!

"Don't want camera." – He said gruffly – "You keep camera. Koreans not fools."

My humiliation was now complete. I felt so bad I actually started apologizing to him.

"No, no, I don't think you are a fool." – I said with my legitimate Italian accent – "In fact, I'm the foolish one... and I must apologize to you."

"What mean apologize?" – He inquired curtly.

"It means... it means I am sorry." – I explained. "You see, I thought you were trying to hustle me out of my camera, and I just wanted to have some fun with you."

He seemed a bit confused, and I thought maybe he didn't understand English very well, but I guess he did.

"I no hustle, I want buy camera." – He told me.

"I know you do, and I'm really sorry I misjudged you." – I said contritely– "I feel very bad about it."

"It's OK, GI... I understand." – He said pointing a finger toward his temple, gesturing almost like an Italian, to indicate he had understood – "Lots young Koreans hustlers... you be careful..."

"Thank you!" – I said, "I mean it, thank you for understanding and for the warning. But I still feel bad... I acted like a fool."

And I did feel like an asshole.

My problem – and I'm even embarrassed to say this – is that there are times when I think I am smarter than others. Not in technical know-how, of course, witness the camera instructions and a million other things, but in general, in interpersonal relations.

This, let's call it superiority complex, is kind of hard to explain. It's a feeling, a belief that I'm always aware of what's going on, that I am on top of things, it's a cocky confidence that I get the drift of things immediately, that I'm with it, I'm hip, you don't have to explain things to me twice, that sort of stuff. You know what I mean?

I said 'there are times when I think I am smarter', but that's not quite correct – a more accurate way of phrasing it would be that there are a very few times when I **DON'T** think I am smarter than anybody else. And what's really awful and unforgivable about this superiority shit is that I keep reverting to this way of thinking even after I have been screwed, blued and tattooed. Repeatedly.

And every time that happens – and it does happen more frequently than I would like to admit – I feel like a piece of shit; perhaps because there's nothing worse than being reminded you are a common dickhead, like everybody else.

Just like with this Korean guy – I had acted like a pompous ass, and now I felt like a horse's ass and, as a consequence, I now felt the need to make amends. More than make amends, I felt the need to punish myself.

"Look," – I said – "I owe you an apology, but that's not enough. Why don't we have a drink first, and then I'll offer you a bargain."

"What mean bargain?" – He asked.

"Bargain means a good deal... for you." – I explained. "Do you know of any bars around here where we can have a drink?"

And with my right hand I mimicked the act of drinking.

"No want drink." – He said brusquely.

"Please!" – I insisted – "It's on me, of course."

He seemed to waver a bit, undecided about taking up my offer. After some more prodding on my part, he relented.

"OK, GI!" – He agreed and then led the way to a nearby bar, a rather sleazy joint, with a few rickety tables and chairs. A few bottles of liquor were displayed behind the counter, including some I recognized.

We sat at a table. When the barman, who also doubled as a waiter, came to our table to take our order, I asked my guest what he liked to drink. He said scotch, which happened to be my favorite drink also. I then asked him to order a double scotch for both of us –Chivas Regal, no less!

When the drinks came, not sure of what the local custom was, I raised my glass and said "*Salute!*" in Italian, then "Cheers!" in English for good measure.

This glass-raising bit must be a universal custom because he also lifted his glass and said the equivalent in Korean. I then raised the glass to my lips and downed half of my drink in one gulp.

"My friend..." – I said, the scotch working its way fast in my bloodstream – "like I said... like I was telling you, I thought you were trying to hustle me, to cheat me out of my camera, and I was trying to have some fun with you."

He looked a bit confused.

"I thought I was too smart for you," – I tried to explain – "and I was trying to play a cat and mouse game with you just to prove I was smarter than you."

"What mean cat and mouse?" – he asked.

"Ohhh..." – and I had to think about that – "It's like... it's like I wanted to play with you, to toy with you, just to have some fun."

His face reflected a whole spectrum of expressions, ranging from incredulity to perplexity, with touches of censure, even some diffidence.

Yes, diffidence!

For just a brief moment – and I really had to smile at this – the thought crossed my mind that he thought I was trying to hustle him.

"When I asked for 450 dollars," – I explained to him – "I thought for sure you would agree immediately and reveal yourself to be a hustler, but I was wrong."

"How much is camera worth?" – He asked bluntly.

"I don't know how much it's really worth," – I said – "but I know I paid about a hundred dollars for it, and if you want it I will be glad to sell it to you at that price."

His eyes popped open. Then, clearly surprised, he exclaimed: "You joke me?"

"No, I am not joking you... I mean, I'm not kidding you."– I said earnestly – "And besides, I can always buy another one at the PX."

"Look," – he said – "you make little profit, I give you one hundred fifty dollars."

But I was adamant.

"No, just one hundred... first because you deserve it, but mostly because I also deserve it." – I insisted.

He was clearly wavering between wanting to take advantage of a terrific bargain and not wanting to take advantage of my generosity.

"I not know what to say..." – He mumbled timidly.

I understood how he felt, and I tried to lighten him up a bit.

"I'll tell you what you can say... you can say 'OK, it's a deal!'" – I said with a smile.

He grinned engagingly then, bashfully, he said: "OK, GI... deal!"

We finished our drinks and he then reached in his pocket coming up with a thick roll of dollar bills. He peeled off five twenties, counted them again, then looked at me thoughtfully.

"You sure you sell for hundred dollars?" – He asked.

I nodded. "Yes, I'm sure." – I said. "OK, GI!" – he said.

My camera was hanging around my neck by its straps. I removed it, manually advanced the roll of film till the end, removed it from the camera and put it in my pocket. I then handed him the camera and he gave me the bills that I stuffed nonchalantly in my pockets.

I felt good, really good, at peace with myself, the way I used to feel when, as a kid, I used to go to confession to unload my conscience of all the little lies, disobediences and other minor and not-so-minor transgressions. I would then say my penance and walk away light-hearted with a full absolution.

"Thank you, GI!" – he said.

"Thank **YOU!**" – I said earnestly.

We both stood up and I shook his hand.

"It was really nice meeting you... It taught me a valuable lesson." – I told him. And I meant it.

"No, no, thank you!" – He repeated bowing in front of me.

I bowed to him and we both kept bowing to each other, me grinning foolishly and him backing up, bowing and thanking me until he finally was out the door.

I watched him leave. He took a few steps out of the bar and kept walking backwards bowing. He then suddenly turned around and sprinted like a madman across the street, barely managing to dodge a passing car and a few bicycles. When he got to the other sidewalk, he kept on running and in less than five seconds he was out of sight.

"What's the big hurry?" – I thought, a bit bewildered.

A red light flickered in my brain. Or whatever was left of it.

"Please God, no, please, please, God... **NO! NO!**" – I whispered.

Gingerly I fished out of my pocket the roll of bills he had given me.

The top bill was a fake one-dollar bill, all the others were battered pieces of newspaper.

Stunned! Floored! Speechless! That's how I felt for the first couple of minutes. After the initial shock, however, I started laughing so hard I almost choked. Guys, take my word for it, he had screwed me so skillfully that he deserved a standing ovation.

The guy had not only once again demolished the already shaky foundations of my self-assurance, but he had done it even while committing an egregious mistake. Yes!... As I went over the entire con,

I realized I should have picked up on the fact that the guy had flashed a huge roll of what looked like real American money. Hell! That alone should have raised a few alarm bells in my foggy brain.

I mean, a young Korean lad with that kind of dough? No way! But busy as I was doing my sanctimonious penalty act, I had ignored it – yet another puncture deflating the hot-air balloon of my vanity.

I did call the guy a motherfucker, of course, but in an affectionate way. Had I met him again on the street, I swear I would have wanted to shake his hand, congratulate him for a superb performance, and maybe I would even have advised him not to flash that roll of bills next time he tried his act. And then I would have treated him to another drink.

What I did instead, I ordered another double scotch for myself and drained it in one gulp.

The next day I went back to the Seoul PX and bought myself another camera. The guy at the counter looked at me kind of funny, but I told him it was a gift for my brother.

The tripod, the flash, the telephoto lens... there was no need to buy them. They were still safe in my duffel bag along with a couple of rolls of unused film.

CHAPTER 11

Aah! Home, home at last! And just in time for Christmas!

The euphoria of returning to civilian life lasted just about a month. After the holidays, some serious decisions had to be made. Just one, in fact: what do I do now?

Rising Sun offered few alluring career possibilities. It was – and still is – a farming community, and farming ranks right behind fishing in my personal classification of professions I have never had a desire to practice.

Despite my 22 years of age, I had quite irresponsibly neglected to give any thought at what career choice I wanted to make, I had never seriously considered how I was going to make a living. And, of course, I had never made any specific plans to reach a specific goal. In general terms, I knew I had no desire to make a living from the sea or from a farm. And I had also just deleted the military as a potential career choice.

The question still remained: what do I do now?

Nick Ravello very generously offered me an office job working with my brother, but I knew his firm didn't really need me. It was a clear case of nepotism. I just thanked him and declined it.

Since my discharge I had kept a steady correspondence with several Army buddies discharged at approximately the same time I was. One of them – John McKenna – lived in Wilmington, Delaware, about thirty miles from Rising Sun.

John was a bright, well-educated fellow of Irish descent who also happened to be an accomplished pianist. We had in fact hit it off because of his musical talent.

First time I saw him was at the local USO (United Service Organization). He was sitting at a piano playing *"Besame Mucho."* It was obvious he had real talent – he sounded just like a pro. Hearing that music, I just naturally gravitated there and stood right next to him. Knowing the lyrics well, I started singing, or rather humming, the song in Spanish.

Hearing I had good pitch and kept time well, he had encouraged me to sing the song out loud. I did and we both earned a nice round of applause from all present.

He thought I was of Latin-American descent, and when I told him I was Italian he started playing some Italian songs and arias. And a good friendship was born.

Our correspondence usually dealt with humorous reminiscences of our Army days. In between jokes, though, we also kept each other posted on job opportunities and plans for the future.

John was aware of my unsuccessful attempts to find meaningful employment in Rising Sun and elsewhere. In one of his letters he informed me he had found a job at a Delaware bank, adding that he worked in a branch located on Union Street, in Wilmington's Little Italy section. The entry-level pay was only fair, he said, but the hours were good and the job was rather easy and pleasant enough.

A large percentage of customers at that particular branch were Italian immigrants, he had informed me, and many of them spoke little English or no English at all.

"Why don't you apply for a job here?" – He had suggested, adding he was pretty sure the bank would have hired someone who spoke Italian.

"What have I got to lose?" – I thought. Still looking for a permanent job, I wrote back and asked him to send me an employment application.

Banking was *terra incognita* to me, and the prospect of finding employment in that field both intrigued and fascinated me. Banking in Italy – I clearly recollected - was considered an elite profession. I don't know what it's like today, but back then even getting an entry-level job in any bank in Italy used to be extremely difficult. Talent and knowledge in the financial field were essential, of course, but frequently even that was not enough.

Any rare opening for any type of bank job was always advertised in the papers, and they used to hold competitive tests with hundreds of qualified applicants participating.

In typical Italian style, obtaining the best score in the test hardly ever was the deciding factor on whether or not one would get the job. The backing of some insider, a powerful politician, an archbishop maybe, that would have strongly increased one's chances of getting the job. That, or maybe having a good-looking sister.

My Irish friend promptly sent me an application. Even as I was filling it, I didn't hold any real hopes they would even consider it, not if the banking employment scene here was similar to the one in Italy. All bankers had to have a college degree – I believed – maybe even a Master's degree, while I just had my two bits high-school diploma.

My friend John had a college degree from the University of Delaware – surely that had been taken in consideration when he had applied for the job. Still, I sent in my application, crossing my fingers and hoping for the best.

And here, once again, it's time to shout "**God bless America.**" I still say it, and will keep on saying it and even singing it after all these years!

Incidentally, apropos of *"God Bless America"* – I'm talking about the song now – I believe American-born nationals and foreign-born naturalized American citizens have different feelings about that tune.

I believe American-born people view and sing it strictly as a patriotic song, the way they view and sing the national anthem, *"The Star Spangled Banner."* Naturalized immigrants, on the other hand, sing it for what that song really is – a hymn of gratitude to a country that has given them all it had promised to give. At least this particular immigrant does.

Somebody may have already pointed this out, but I believe it's no casual occurrence that *"God Bless America"* was composed and written by

Irving Berlin, an immigrant. Only an immigrant could have composed such a rousing anthem.

And while I'm digressing, let me get this out of the way also. I have already used that patriotic expression several times, and I'll surely use it again. It comes straight from the heart – honestly! – but I am not, repeat, **I AM NOT**, a flag waving, 'America-first' jingoist. Far from it!

Just like your typical born-in-the-USA American, I have also loudly complained – and will continue to complain – about existing social inequities, government inefficiencies and corruptions, plus all other tangibles or intangibles that keep America from being Utopia. But unlike your typical born-in-the-USA American, I have a great advantage – I was **NOT** born in the USA, and I have first-hand knowledge of how the American system compares with other systems; in my case, the Italian system.

Let's just say that the American system is better! Much, much better! A hell of a lot better! So much better, that if your typical born-in-the-USA American knew, **REALLY** knew how better off he is compared to individuals in most other nations, he would be kissing politicians' asses in the street at high noon, publicly praise the IRS, throw flowers at the police, send monthly thank you notes to their public utilities, and shut the fuck up if he ever felt like complaining again.

What prompts this display of patriotism? Well, within a week of sending in my application I actually got a reply; and not just a simple reply, but a reply asking me to come in for an interview.

Is that it, you say? All that flag-waving just because they asked you to go in for an interview?

For crying out loud! You haven't been listening! That's **exactly** what I'm talking about! There is no doubt in my mind that, had I asked a bank – **any bank!** – in Italy to send me an employment application, I wouldn't even have received one. What with the Byzantine employment system they had there, I doubt if they even had employment applications.

And since it's still digressing time, let me get this out of the way also. Working at the bank, I got firsthand exposure to a business practice heretofore unknown to me.

I am referring to the way practically all American businesses – as well as all local and state governments, plus the federal government of course – always manage to maintain and foster an incredibly healthy relationship with their customers and/or constituents through the mail and/or the telephone. It's a practice that to this day I still find incredible, astounding, almost mythical, at times even exaggerated but always real. It's a practice that the typical American takes for granted and shouldn't.

In America, you... me... any interested or even an uninterested party can write to or call any company or government agency to express an opinion, to register a complaint, to make a suggestion, or even to tell a company president or his own congressman to go fuck himself, and he will almost certainly get a reply, a courteous reply.

Case in point – years ago I personally called the office of my state representative to complain about the shoddy repair work done by some road crew on the street right in front of my house. Even as I was making that call, the Italian in me was thinking: "Why am I bothering?"

I thought for sure my message would never reach his desk, my call was just an exercise in futility, a useless waste of time on my part, a way for me to vent my frustrations.

OK! At 9 PM that same day my phone rang. Yes! You read that right! At 9 PM! It was the representative himself calling back to express his regrets he hadn't called sooner, and to thank me for letting him know about the problem. Again! You read that right! He actually **THANKED** me for making him aware of the problem.

I swear to God, I thought it was some kind of a prank call! But no, it was he, and he was serious. And he got the problem fixed in less than a week. Needless to say, I voted for that guy every time he ran, and I would have voted for him even if he had run for the Nazi Party.

Try to contact your representatives in Italy or in most other European countries and let me know first if you can reach him, and then if he will call you back and thank you!

Does that warrant a little outburst of patriotism? I think so.

Enough already with digressing. I went in for my interview and they hired me on the spot. I could start the following Monday!

Man! I felt good about myself, even though my pay was a meager $55 a week! They'd offered me $50, but I talked them into an extra five bucks since I had a 60-mile round-trip daily commute and that – I felt – warranted an extra fin.

My idea of what banking was all about turned out to be way off base. To be a successful banker – I believed – one needed to be at the barest minimum an expert in accounting, and a whiz in esoteric financial erudition if one aspired to reach the higher levels.

After working at the branch for about a week, I discovered that the only technical knowledge one needed was to know that two plus two equals four.

OK, I'm exaggerating a bit, but take my word for it – good, solid banking is ten percent technical knowledge and ninety percent interpersonal skills. And one doesn't need to be a rocket scientist to absorb the technical knowledge required to do banking work, not at the branch level anyway.

Basically, if you can interact with the public and know some basic math, you can be a successful banker. In America, of course.

This is not bragging or bullshitting, but within a couple of months of my employment, I knew I could have performed the branch manager's job without any problem.

Why am I saying that? Because within a few short months, I **WAS** doing quite a bit of the manager's job. Mr. Guthrie – my branch manager – quickly saw that I had my act together. After a brief training period, he assigned me the task of "closing" the branch at the end of the day, a job normally performed by himself or his assistant.

I was just a teller and I had my own window to take care of customers, but I quickly learned how to open accounts, how to sell bonds, traveler checks and how to take loan and mortgage applications, all tasks also ordinarily performed by the manager or his assistant.

Word soon got around the community that an Italian speaking

person worked at WSFS, and within a few months hundreds of new customers started coming in.

Once again – I know… you are tired of hearing me saying this, but it's time to shout it again, and this time in capital letters.

GOD BLESS AMERICA!

Why? Because only in America hundreds – **thousands!** – of poor and simple immigrants could come daily to the bank to make sizable deposits, guys who – I swear to God – literally signed their names with a cross.

Did I say poor? Scratch that! I mean poor as in 'ordinary Joe Palookas, totally undistinguished nobodies who worked their ass off for a living'. Those same guys who hardly spoke English – and could hardly speak Italian for that matter – who had near zero education, practically no social skills, and had been here for a relatively few years… yes, those same guys all had bank accounts in the low-to-middle five figures. And that's before the decimal point, of course. And I'm talking dollars, of course, not *lire*.

I saw first-hand what America was all about, and it was like an epiphany for me.

By then, of course, I had lost all my childhood illusions of instant riches. I had come to understand that one's chances of achieving financial success in America are definitely much better than anywhere else in the world, but I had also learned that financial success can only be achieved through hard work.

My brother and Nick Ravello were my most visible mentors. They were not exactly millionaires, but they had done quite well for themselves.

The only break they got – or needed – was coming to America. Once here, nothing was ever handed to them – like millions of other immigrants, they worked hard, very hard. And like millions of other immigrants, they understood that their workweek could but didn't necessarily have to end after 40 hours. And like millions of other immigrants, they were glad to have the opportunity to work longer hours and be compensated for the many hours they worked.

I had just entered the labor market. Except for my three years in the Army I had never broken a sweat in my life. Now, my new line of work put me in contact with hundreds of plain, simple immigrant folks who literally laid the steel and concrete foundations that sustained the mythical allure of America around the world.

Those folks were the same folks I had seen vacationing in Italy, the same folks who had a second or third grade education, the same folks who could hardly speak Italian, the same folks who – big, dick-headed me! – I foolishly thought I could wrap around my little finger just because I had had a few more years of school.

By God! I learned to look at them in a new light as I realized they had managed to achieve a comfortable middle class status against all odds, in a foreign environment, with enormous sacrifices while having to fight latent and not so latent prejudice. And they had managed to accomplish all that with just one weapon – their willingness to work, to work hard; very hard.

My hat was off to all of them!

I was a natural at selling bank products and quite good in public relations, pretty damn good in fact.

Public relations skills require talent in placing your company in a favorable light through interpersonal relations with customers. To be successful in selling, one needs to believe the products he is selling will benefit both his customers and his employer. Equally important, one needs to transmit this enthusiasm in a sincere manner **AND** mainly by always treating his customers as his equals or betters.

This last part is vitally important. I have known many bankers with far better selling skills than mine, yet not as successful as I. Why? There was always something in their presentation that didn't ring true, customers could sense they were being patronized or just regarded as sales targets.

I was good at public relations because there was nothing faked about my attitude. I **HAD** tremendous admiration for all those people who came to my branch every Friday night and invariably deposited a fair portion of their paycheck in their savings account.

And quite naturally, my feelings of respect for them soon evolved into a mutual admiration society – my customers thought very highly of me also.

They viewed me with Italian eyes – that is, they saw me as a member of an 'elite' profession. To them I was a banker, a man of knowledge, someone who handled a great deal of money. And they also thought of me as a man of letters, one who could read and write fluently both in English and in Italian. They saw me as a role model, someone they could point out to their kids as an example of what one can achieve in America by studying.

Me? I would gladly have traded my two-bit high school diploma for half of what they had in their savings account.

There was no question that they had accomplished a hell of a lot more than I had in the same amount of time or even less. Bottom line – I honestly believed they were better and more deserving people than I was. But there was absolutely no envy on my part, I'll swear to that – just plain and simple admiration; plus a desire to emulate them, of course.

I became their friend, advisor, confidant, and all-around helper. I made myself available to them even for non-job-related matters – translations, help or advice for US and/or Italian government matters, etc.

I even had a few customers who used to bring me letters for me to read, letters they had received from home in Italy, letters they couldn't read because… well, because they did not know how to read, letters that frequently had been written for their loved ones by someone else.

The content of most letters was the usual rundown of daily occurrences – our health is good, hope your health is good, the weather is bad, the crop doesn't look promising, your cousin Filomena had a baby girl… that kind of stuff.

Reading those letters, it wasn't hard to imagine a faraway wife or mother dictating her message to a semi-literate relative or friend who would then scribble her words on paper. And somehow, those illiterate phrases, those misspelled words, those uneven lines slanting downward near the right side of the page lent even more poignancy to their long-ings, to their sadness and to their hopes to be soon reunited.

And it was touching, and sometime even embarrassing, to oc-casionally read some intimate detail, the lament of a wife missing her husband and wishing to embrace him. But I did it for them and, on many occasions, they would also ask me to write a few lines for them because... well, because they did not know how. And I did that also.

One minor detail is worth mentioning, a detail that never failed to happen and always touched me – I could always tell when they came to my branch just for this type of favor.

They would enter the bank with an air of circumspection and uncertainty and they would then sit down in the customers' waiting lounge, hat in hand. Invariably, they would have a brown paper bag or a wrapped little package containing a bottle of homemade wine or cookies. It was their way of repaying me for the favors I did for them.

To be sure, all of them had at first offered to compensate me for my services, but I had always refused to accept any type of hono-rarium. Still, they felt they owed me and expressed their appreciation by bringing these little gifts that I accepted warmly. I knew they were given with heartfelt gratitude, and for that very reason they meant more to me than any monetary compensation.

They would then sit and wait quietly. Even if they were next in line, they would always give precedence to other customers with le-gitimate bank business. They would approach me with their personal requests only when they were certain there were no more customers with bank business.

Very few of them spoke even passable Italian. Mostly they spoke a dialect – usually Abruzzese, Neapolitan, or Sicilian – but so what?

I could name dozens of these illiterate or semi-literal folks who not only had very healthy bank accounts but had also managed to pur-chase a house with a WSFS mortgage. And that's not all – while most mortgages were initially set up for terms of 20 or 25 years, I don't re-call a single one that wasn't paid off within 10 or 12 years. And I know for a fact that not one of my Italian customers ever defaulted on their mortgage. And this, by the way, was true for customers of other ethnic extractions – Polish, Irish, German, etc.

One amusing offshoot of my admiration for these Italian immigrants – and my resulting popularity among them – was that several of my Italian customers began to view me as promising in-law material.

They first discreetly inquired about my marital status, and I would tell them, of course, that I was still a bachelor and looking for the right one to come along.

I soon noticed that while before they used to come to the bank on a Friday night by themselves, they would now come accompanied by their daughters or sisters, and they would of course introduce them to me.

And soon came the first invitations to dinner at their houses. At first I begged off or found excuses for not going, but eventually – not wanting to risk offending them – I accepted a few. Additionally, it became a sometime convenience for me.

The few dinner invitations I accepted were always on Friday evenings when the bank closed at 3 PM and opened again from 6 to 8 PM.

I still lived in Rising Sun and on Friday evenings I would usually grab a bite to eat at "Mrs. Robino's," an inexpensive but quite good Italian restaurant about two blocks away from the bank. Accepting their dinner invitations not only saved me some money but it practically guaranteed an even better meal than I used to get at "Mrs. Robino's".

I was then about 24. The idea of getting married was definitely on my mind, but there was no urgency to it. It was something that sooner or later had to be attended to, but I didn't actively pursue it mainly because I was having a hell of a good time as an unattached bachelor.

Most Friday nights, immediately after the bank closed, I would hop in my car and head to New York to visit my friends Jack and Tony Ravello who now lived there, still as illegal aliens. Their older brother, Joe, had returned to Italy to marry the girl he loved.

I kept in touch with Jack and Tony by letter and occasionally by phone. They now worked as waiters in a small but celebrated

Italian restaurant in mid-Manhattan, made damn good money between salary and tips and scored heavily with the ladies, or so they told me.

This last part got my attention, and I had every reason to believe it was true. They still had the black curly hair and the Italian look, and I was well aware of how well they had performed in Rising Sun.

Christ! They had left that small village four or five years earlier, and I swear some of the chicks who used to entertain them were still asking me about them. And they wouldn't just ask me about them – the bitches! – they even had the cheek to ask me to 'please remember me to Jack and Tony', or to 'please tell them to look me up if they ever come visiting'.

"Goddamned bitches! What am I, chopped liver?!?!" – Was my silent comment, even as I assured them I would deliver their message.

Once a pimp, always a pimp, I guess.

Start spreading the news! I'm leaving today! I want to be a part of it... New York, New York!

Good Lord! Is it still the same today as it was back then? I'm waxing nostalgic, I know, but – Jesus! – I can still feel the surge of adrenalin I would get every time I hopped in my car on most Friday nights.

The surge would steadily escalate as I crossed the Delaware Memorial Bridge and hit the New Jersey Turnpike; and it would practically explode to orgasmic intensity as I dove into the Lincoln Tunnel and surfaced in Manhattan.

The anticipation of forthcoming excitement was so intoxicating and, on the downside, the prospect of returning to the daily drudge was such a bummer that – word! – on the way to New York the smell of the refineries around Elizabeth NJ was like Chanel N. 5, while on the way back on Sunday nights or, more frequently, in the wee small hours of Monday mornings it smelled like... well, like gasoline.

The Ravello brothers worked every weekend – that's when they made some real dough in tips – and didn't get off work till after midnight, around 1 AM or even 2 AM. But that's when life started in New York.

They both had steady girlfriends, Italian girlfriends they would eventually marry, but their girlfriends' parents would never allow their daughters to be out past 8 PM. It was perfectly natural for both brothers to look for entertainment, to seek some kind of outlet or relief elsewhere.

I don't know about their girlfriends, but surely even their future in-laws understood that. Anyway, they did look, and they always managed to find someone, for themselves and for me also.

In New York you could find girls by the dozens. Not hookers in the traditional sense of the word – that is, there was never a direct exchange of money for sex. I've already mentioned my aversion to pay for sex, but during my New York excursions there was no need for that. In their line of work, the Ravello brothers managed to hook up with dozens of ladies, swingers who – just like us – were out to have a good time, the kind of girls an Italian boy wouldn't even dream of taking home to meet his parents.

One unforgettable highlight of my forays in the Big Apple was the implausible occasion when we managed to sneak inside the famous *"Peppermint Lounge"*, in those days the pantheon of the Twist, the new dance craze that was sweeping America.

Keep in mind that at the height of its fame only the upper crust, the social register VIP's could get inside that joint – I'm talking folks like Jackie Kennedy, Marilyn Monroe, Frank Sinatra. And even they had to have ironclad reservations.

But we got in, and without reservations. We managed to be admitted on the strength of the Ravello brothers' amazing skill and aplomb in coming up with a likely story.

It just happened that during one of our forays in downtown Manhattan, as we were passing by pure chance in front of that nightclub, I made a comment to the effect that to get inside that joint you needed to make reservations months in advance. That's all the Ravello brothers needed to hear. Just like that, for sheer bravado, they said we would get in that same night.

A lighted display case near the entrance announced that "*Joey Dee and the Starlighters*" were the featured attraction at the Lounge. The Ravello brothers went straight to the usherette checking the reservations and had the nerve to tell her, with a perfectly straight face, they were Joey Dee's agents. Joey Dee had made an emergency call to them – they explained. One of his musicians had called in sick and he needed a substitute. And they had come with the replacement – me.

Aghast at such brazen audacity, I was ready to bail out of there in a hurry if they ever checked out that story, but the young usherette actually bought it. She eagerly and cheerfully gave us directions to Joey Dee's dressing room and we got in. Once inside, we just mingled with the crowd and that was that.

No question about it – one ounce of well-crafted bullshit is worth more than ten pounds of unvarnished truth.

That was one exploit we bragged about for months. What a night! Unforgettable!

We were by far the youngest – and indubitably the poorest – customers in a crowd of mostly well-heeled, elderly ladies who had left their respectability at the door.

Within five minutes of our entrance the Ravello brothers were practically ravished by a horde of wealthy dowagers looking for one last wild fling. Me? As usual, I tagged along hoping to get lucky. And I did.

The two brothers weren't very good dancers, but they did have the Italian look and the curly black hair. And that's all they needed.

I became a minor hit on the strength of my dancing – I could shake my ass with the best of them, and those ripe ladies wouldn't even let me take a five-minute break. Two, three, even four of them sweet young things – the youngest about 40 – would prance all around me at the same time, gazing with ravenous eyes as I gyrated my hips wildly. And... oh! How they squealed with obviously fake shock and very real pleasure whenever I intentionally banged my well-muscled rump on their voluminous and soft derrieres!

On that unforgettable night we got a glimpse of what a gigolo's life must be like. And let me tell you, it has its perks. Suffice to say it didn't cost us a dime, not even to pay for our first drink.

At closing time, two groups of ladies got in a bit of a squabble – on account of us. One group wanted us to join them because they had seen us first while the other insisted we belonged with them because we had stayed with them the longest.

We remained strictly neutral but – a wink here and a nudge there – we had a pretty good hunch that if we played our cards right we could have a great time, and possibly get something out of that.

Jack and Tony, who could charm the bark off a tree, told them graciously "we enjoyed the company of **ALL** you beautiful girls..." and suggested we could perhaps continue to party at someone's house. There was a loud chorus of agreement.

Another mini squabble arose – at whose house should the party resume? Once they got that settled, they all agreed to hire Joey Dee and his group to play for them at the hostess' house. Poor Joey Dee and his group were visibly tired, but they must have thrown a ton of money at them because they readily accepted.

We wound up somewhere on a cliff on the Hudson River in a mansion with a long, winding driveway nestled in a park-like setting with majestic trees, fountains, and beautifully clipped hedges and topiaries.

I don't mind admitting to an initial feeling of inadequacy, of not belonging with that crowd, especially when I parked my five-year old Studebaker with a noisy muffler in the midst of chauffeur-driven Rolls Royces, Cadillacs, Mercedes, Packards and Lincolns.

To quote Sophie Tucker (or was it Mae West?): "I've been rich and I've been poor and, believe me, rich is better."

No truer words were ever spoken.

Damned if I know how the hostess managed to do it, but the party was ready to start by the time we got to her mansion. In a hall about as big as a basketball court, tables had already been set up with a staggering assortment of hors d'oeuvre, soft drinks and alcoholic beverages. We partied till about 4 AM, eating, drinking and shaking our collective asses to Joey Dee's music. And then we finally hit the sack.

And there, for the first and only time in my life, I wound up in bed with two women. It wasn't exactly a full-scale orgy – but close enough.

Was I embarrassed? Did I feel any shame? No, not really. *Au contraire…*

Just before leaving the next day, somebody actually pressed some money in my hands, two $100 bills, to be exact. Was I embarrassed? Did I feel any shame? A bit, perhaps… But I got over it real quick. The Studebaker did need a new muffler, after all.

That, of course, was the exception, not the rule. Most other times we simply winged it… Brooklyn, Queens, Astoria, the Bronx… wild forays in places where the Ravello brothers had heard there was action, fast action. Together, we would hit some nightspots, always searching for a certain atmosphere, always looking for a particular something that would excite our senses in different ways, something that would provide new and stimulating experiences, and we would stay out till 5 or 6 in the morning.

And that didn't come cheap, by the way, it did cost quite a bit of money, probably more than it would have cost to hire a legitimate hooker, but we didn't care. We figured we had busted our asses all week long – well, at least the Ravello brothers had – and we deserved having some fun, having a ball. Quite simply, it also allowed us not having to think about the upcoming Monday morning.

Usually, by the end of the night – or, more accurately, in the wee small hours of the morning – we managed to wind up in the back seat of the car, in a motel, or in somebody's pad, which was the ultimate reason for going to New York in the first place. Furthermore, it helped maintain the tender illusion that we had actually scored, that we had made a conquest, that we had added another scalp to our belt.

Life was so good! So damn good! How does that song go?

"Those were the days, my friend, we thought they'd never end……"

Ah! Blessed youth!

PART II

A MAN

CHAPTER 12

Yes!… Life was good! And when it's that good you think it will last forever. You **want** it to last forever.

Young! Healthy! A decent job! A bright future! No family responsibilities and all kinds of opportunities to enjoy life! What could possibly happen to disrupt my very own *"dolce vita"*? Or to fundamentally change my sweet life?

Dramatic life changes usually occur as a result of sudden, unexpected, totally unpredictable events. You win the PowerBall lottery, you are a key witness to a Mafia hit, you are momentarily distracted and inadvertently cause a fatal accident, and you can be sure your life can and will change dramatically.

Occasionally, though, radical life changes occur as a result of an ordinary event, an insignificant event, an everyday occurrence.

My brother's life changed drastically because a store clerk in Norfolk gave him some books of matches. A simple gesture like that made him decide on the spot to jump ship, and it entirely changed the course of life he had programmed for himself.

And an ordinary event, a chance event, a most common everyday event occurred to me also, fundamentally and irrevocably changing my life.

It came in the form of a letter, a letter from my mom in Italy.

I could always count on my mom to fill me in on whatever was happening in Italy, whether I cared to know or not. Even the most insignificant events were important to her, and her rambling letters always ran three, four, even five pages.

Typical of most young people, I was somewhat remiss in my letter writing, always procrastinating two or three days, sometimes even a week or longer, before answering one of her letters – but not my mom. The minute, make that the second she finished reading one of our letters she would grab pen, paper and ink, sit right down and reply.

We got one such letter sometime in the summer of 1961.

All her letters were always addressed to my brother, but since I lived with him, they were also meant for me. Mom was writing from Torre Faro, in Sicily, where my folks vacationed every summer since my dad retired.

After filling us in on what was happening back home, she inquired for the umpteenth time when I was going to visit them in Italy, reminding me she hadn't seen me in nearly ten years, and that it was high time for me to go back for a visit.

Her signature ending was invariably '*Saluti e baci, Mamma*' (Greetings and kisses, Mom). This time, however, she also added a Post Script: "Filippo '*U Rizzu*', and his daughter Rosa also, asked me to send their best regards to Lillo."

That cryptic tag line puzzled me. 'Cryptic' because mom never used a Post Script when she wrote – whatever she had to say was always in the body of the letter; and 'puzzled' for two reasons: to start with, I had no idea of who this Filippo '*U Rizzu*' guy was, and much less his daughter Rosa. And then why would they send their best regards to me just like that, out of a clear blue sky?

A brief explanation is in order: in Sicily everyone has a first name and a last name, like everyone else, but quite a few folks also have a nickname. '*U Rizzu*' is Sicilian for 'the curly-haired one', which is not an unusual hair type in Sicily – after all, the island is only about 90 miles away from Africa. If this Filippo guy got stuck with that nickname his hair must have been like frizzy steel wool.

Nothing doing – I just couldn't remember anyone with that kind of pompadour, and he still remained a cipher to me.

Puzzled, I asked my brother: "Who is this Filippo '*U Rizzu*? Am I supposed to know him?... Is he related to us?"

Surely Mimmo would be better informed. He was born in Sicily and he had lived in Torre Faro until he was thirteen years of age, when our family moved up north to Genoa. As a result, he knew most of our Sicilian relatives and still kept in touch with some of them. Furthermore, he had a good memory about people, names and things.

Of course he knew who that guy was.

"You don't remember him?" – He said, a bit surprised. "Are you kidding me? He's Filippo Donato! His grandfather and dad's grandfather were first cousins... What do you mean, you don't remember him? He's the one who takes care of our house in Torre Faro when mom and dad are in Genoa... He lives in that large villa, right by the beach, about four houses down from Uncle Nunzio's house."

And on and on he went with other small details that, presumably, should have jump– started my memory.

Nothing doing, I still couldn't remember him. I had only been to Sicily three or four times in my life, always for brief vacations, the last time about 11 years before, when I was only 15, the year before I came to the United States. The few relatives I did remember were the very close ones – aunts, uncles and my first cousins, and not even all of them.

Surely, while in Sicily I had met this guy at some point because over there even distant relatives are like family, but kids usually don't pay much attention to distant adult friends and relatives – at least, this kid didn't. When we went to Sicily, most of my time was spent hanging out with friends and relatives around my age, going to the beach or playing soccer.

Mimmo provided a few additional details but then seemed to give up and just stopped talking. Much as I tried, though, this Filippo guy just didn't register with me. Still puzzling and shaking my head, I turned and told Mimmo I definitely couldn't place him and much less his daughter Rosa.

But Mimmo, waving his hand, silently motioned for me to wait a second. He was now re-examining that letter with an absorbed look on

157

his face, as if something wasn't quite clear. Suddenly the beginning of a faint smile appeared on his lips, an odd smile followed by a slight snort. He then began nodding his head several times, smiled again – this time knowingly – and then openly began to chuckle, clearly amused by what he had read. Really puzzled now, I asked him to let me in on the joke.

Still chuckling, he gave me an amused glance.

"You really don't get it, do you?" – He then said, teasingly.

I felt silly and confused, not unlike the guy who is the only one in a crowd who fails to get the punch line of a joke.

"No, I don't get it," I said, a bit lost, still trying to figure out what I had missed. "What's so funny?"

He saw my bewilderment and stopped chuckling.

"Ah! You city boy..." he exclaimed.

He then cut to the chase: "Bet you ten dollars mom is laying the groundwork to arrange a marriage between you and this Rosa girl. Want to bet?"

No, I did not want to bet because I knew I would lose ten bucks. My brother knew what he was talking about, and my hat was off to him. He had immediately seen through that seemingly innocent greeting, while I had been puzzled by it, but hadn't picked up on it.

You know how you feel when you see a sleight of hand trick performed by a magician? You are amazed, and you wonder how in hell the guy managed to do what he did.

What most people don't realize is that the whole point of a sleight of hand trick – the intriguing part if you will – is not the trick itself, it's the performer's legerdemain.

In most cases the trick is ingenious but relatively simple to explain. Once the trick is revealed, you'll probably let out a long "Oooooohhhh...", and realize you have been rather gullible in not seeing through it immediately. Well, that's exactly how I felt.

Of course, Mimmo had picked up on it because he was born in Sicily and had lived there for quite a while. Even after my family moved to Genoa, he still maintained close contacts with Sicilian friends and relatives.

Sicilian to the core, he not only spoke the Sicilian dialect perfectly but was also savvy with the local customs. In pointed conversations he could immediately grab those little nuances that would be missed by a greenhorn like me. He knew that, to a Sicilian, words have different meanings when spoken with a certain intonation or in different settings. Mostly, he had mastered the art of drawing perfectly logical conclusions from just a few seemingly unrelated words casually uttered or written, or even from the body language of the person who is speaking them.

On the other hand, I was a city boy from Genoa, and all of the above went right over my head; I was an innocent abroad, so to speak.

I mean, I'm not totally simpleminded, but I just didn't have that Sicilian knack to 'get it', to 'understand', to 'grab' an idea, to 'read' a hidden meaning, a secondary message, or an ulterior motive in someone else's conversation or writing – and, quite honestly, I still don't have it and probably never will.

That knack, that talent – because it is a talent, undoubtedly – is primarily found in plebeian folks, people who have suffered or have been oppressed a lot, people who had to learn to live by their wits. And Sicilians are at or near the top of that list.

That kind of skill is honed by being around people who are masters at that game, people who are cynics, people who understand that cynicism is a necessary, even a vital tool that helps you survive in a hostile world. And, of course, it's perfected by careful observation, it's absorbed even by osmosis, and it's constantly sharpened by years and years of practice. And I had had nothing of the sort.

Now that my brother had pointed it out, I could begin to intuit the logic, the thread of what he was saying, but I certainly hadn't grasped it when I first read the letter.

In addition to his Sicilian background, there was yet another compelling reason why my brother had quickly picked up on that hidden message – he was also well aware that our mom had a solid reputation as a marriage arranger. But so was I, for that matter. I was well aware, for instance, of a recent such episode.

Only six months earlier my uncle – her brother – had lost his wife of over 50 years to a heart attack.

Zio Ciccio was a portly older man of 75 who had been totally dependent on his mate for all home-related activities: cooking, cleaning, ironing, sewing, grocery shopping, everything.

With his life companion gone, he had literally found himself to be like a fish out of water, totally unable to cope with simple, everyday activities, incapable of feeding himself, to take care of the house, or even to get a clean change of underwear – this, in addition to his sorrow and the inevitable loneliness.

A couple of weeks after his wife's death, my desperate uncle contacted his sister – my mother – and asked her to start looking around and find him a mate. No subtle hints, no nothing – just a desperate and direct plea: "Please, Nella, find me a wife!"

My sisters laughingly still recall my mom's shocked comment upon receiving his request.

"Jesus Christ!" – She had sputtered – "If they dig her out and prop her on her feet, she'll walk home, and he's already looking for a new one."

Still, she couldn't let her own brother down. She immediately started looking around and found him a suitable mate – within one month!

My uncle remarried about two months after his wife died. In those days people did not shack up – they got married. For all her salty tongue, my mother was very straight-laced about this, and she would never have even considered finding a mate for anyone unless the union was blessed by Mother Church.

My uncle's new mate was an old maid, 67 years of age, of impeccable character, whose only defect or handicap was being nearly deaf – definitely a blessing, for her at least, because my uncle's snoring could be heard across the Strait of Messina.

They married in a private ceremony and with very little fanfare. She provided what he needed: companionship, a clean house, cooking, sewing, shopping, and everything a good wife was supposed to provide, while he provided her with companionship and security.

As for sex, I don't even want to think about that.

My brother and I had even laughed at this rapid marital turnover, but it had not been laughter of derision, of course. We understood and sympathized with our uncle's plight and immediate needs – it was rather an amused appreciation of how quickly and efficiently our mother had managed to resolve a critical situation.

So, yes! – I was also well aware of my mom's penchant for arranging marriages, but just that knowledge hadn't been enough for me to arrive at that same conclusion as my brother's.

It's not easy to explain how my brother "got it", but let me give it a try, using that letter as an example.

He gets the letter and reads it. At the very end, he reads this Post Script: "Filippo 'U Rizzu', and his daughter Rosa also, asked me to send their best regards to Lillo".

So far, so good – a perfectly innocent remark – **ASSUMING I KNEW WHO THIS FILIPPO 'U RIZZU' GUY WAS, AS WELL AS HIS DAUGHTER ROSA.** Are you still with me?

While that innocent looking Post Script had puzzled me, it never entered my mind to read into it anything other than a casual greeting. I mean, the above assumption went right over my head. But not over my brother's head.

Mimmo knew – or accurately guessed – that my mother also knew I would not know who this guy was, and much less his daughter. And, of course, that got him thinking.

And the next logical question in his chain of thought was: "If mom knows Lillo does not know who these folks are, why did she even bother to add that Post Script? I mean, it's not like those folks would ever find out she hadn't sent their greetings. So why **DID** she add that Post Script?"

What gave the scheme away was our mom specifying that they were sending their regards just **TO LILLO**. Surely mom knew that this Filippo 'u Rizzu' knew my brother far better than me. And since he knew Mimmo far better than me, why would he send the greetings just to me and not to him, or at the very least to both of us?

Clearly – to my brother, once again, but certainly not to me – there had to be a reason, and the reason was revealed in that throwaway line, "**and his daughter Rosa also.**"

Following this line of reasoning and, of course, once you factor in the knowledge that our mom had a penchant for arranging marriages, then it becomes reasonable to discount other possible explanations.

In fact, it becomes reasonable to assume that the only possible explanation was that my mom was subtly trying to plant in my mind some seeds that eventually would bear fruit.

Once you have established that premise, it doesn't take a rocket scientist to assume a marriage arrangement was in the works. A simple, everyday, ordinary Sicilian will do.

My brother was like Sherlock Holmes to my Dr. Watson – he deduced what was going on by simple observations and deductions, while I understood it – and marveled at his brilliant discovery – only after he opened my eyes.

Once I realized what game was afoot, I laughed along with my brother and tried to make light of that matter.

"Oh! Great!" – I exclaimed, and I then jokingly asked him: "And what will your wedding gift be?"

"Hey! You could do worse..." – Mimmo said, suddenly quite serious – "I don't know what she looks like, but I bet you she is very beautiful, very intelligent and has a good education. Plus I assure you her family is top of the line."

His comments were both typical and surprising at the same time. Typical because his Sicilian upbringing espoused the premise that arranged marriages are perfectly normal and acceptable occurrences; and surprising because, despite his Sicilian upbringing, he was also very liberal and open-minded.

He viewed many old Sicilian customs – marriage arrangements, the sacred relationship of a godfather to a godson, or the defense of family honor – with a mixture of respect and detached amusement. He could laugh at the idea of a marriage arrangement, but he also recognized its valid points; and so do I, by the way.

In fact, let me go out on a limb and hazard a guess – I believe arranged marriages have a far better chance of survival than conventional ones. It's just a gut instinct on my part, and I may be way off target because I have no statistics to back me up, but if it's true that nearly two out of five conventional marriages end in divorce, my guesstimate is that less than one in twenty arranged marriages end up in a divorce court.

My conclusion is based strictly on personal observations. I am acquainted with or I know of at least two dozens couples whose marriage had been rumored to have been arranged either by my mom or some other busybody. In fact, I am even related to a few of those couples. All of them have been married for over ten years and all of them are still together.

Are they happy? Damned if I know, but they are still together.

Admittedly, these personal observations do not constitute a valid statistical sample, but they must count for something. If I am right – a big if, I'll admit, as I have no empirical data – why is it so?

I believe it's because arranged marriages are based mostly on solid, concrete, no-frills foundations. In an arranged marriage there is little or no room for the ephemeral joys of a conventional courtship, and even less for the passionate longing to possess or to be possessed, the kind of romantic stuff that precedes the nuptials of a couple in love. Or in heat.

In fact, a conventional marriage differs from an arranged one in precisely this one aspect: conventional marriages are based on the premise of a man and a woman falling in love with each other. As a direct result of their feelings, they then come to the realization that they will be happy only by spending the rest of their lives together. And they decide to get hitched.

A few months, or years, or maybe even a few weeks after they tie the knot, they realize that getting hitched had been an ill-advised move and that spending the rest of their lives together would mean a world of grief for both, and they decide to split up.

Arranged marriages, on the other hand, are usually based on the material needs of the individuals, on the obvious conveniences of having someone running a household – not to mention on the immediate effect of tempering one's loneliness.

Obviously there is also the assumption – or hope – that love, or an acceptable facsimile, can come after the couple has been together for a while. But even if Cupid doesn't show up, it wouldn't necessarily be the end of the world – or of the marriage.

And those very same important considerations – plus others both of an economical and of a practical nature – are what hold arranged marriages together. Even if their marriage is not exactly made in heaven, couples know there are some benefits to their staying together – at the very least they will keep each other company, he knows someone will do the housekeeping, she knows someone will be the provider, it's better to be a couple in society, etc.

Most important, there is the common realization that, if they broke up, hooking up with another partner wouldn't be too easy for both spouses. They are both well aware that their marriage came about only because of an arrangement – a last resort, in and by itself – and where would they find another partner?

And then, of course, there is sex. And sex, with or without love, cannot be ignored.

Most people don't quite understand how arranging marriages works, in Italy at least. They believe it involves long financial negotiations between the two families. Do the prospective bride and groom come from the same economic class? Does the girl have a sizable dowry? Does the guy have a good, secure job? And so on.

Sure, some of that stuff goes into the equation – clearly, if you are arranging a marriage for a girl whose family doesn't have a pot to piss in, you wouldn't expect her to be able to hook up with a Bill Gates.

The basic idea behind arranged marriages, in fact, the main reason why arranged marriages exist – once again, in Italy – is the belief that it's unfair for anyone to go through life alone, and that everyone on this earth needs – or deserves to have – a mate.

First of all, as President Nixon used to say before obfuscating any issue, let me make one thing perfectly clear: in Italy a marriage arranger is an unpaid position.

To the best of my knowledge, my mom was rumored to have arranged some two or three dozens marriages in her lifetime and never got paid a dime. In fact, it probably cost her some dough because, having played Cupid for the couple, she would be invited to the wedding and would have to spring for a wedding gift.

Her marriage arrangements were done simply out of a desire to see two people of the opposite sex "*sistemati*", that is, settled down together.

If truth be told, in my mom's case there was also an inclination on her part to meddle in other people's affairs – my mom was pretty good at that. If anybody pointed this out to her, however, her perfectly logical reply was that a little meddling is not such a bad thing if done for a good cause. And to her, getting two people together was a good cause.

One can rightly ask – why can't two people get together on their own? And the answer is very simple – because they either don't know how or they cannot do it, for various reasons. They may lack interactive social skills, they may be too shy, they may not be bright enough or good looking enough, they may have some slight handicap, or whatever.

Bottom line – they have reached the age of thirty-five, forty, or even older, and they are still single. They may still be looking – openly or covertly – and they are still hoping, but they are getting slightly desperate by the minute.

A marriage arranger knows such a situation exists, she knows a relative – or a friend, or an acquaintance – who is single and could be, or should be, or would like to be married. So she starts looking around to see who, of the opposite sex, could benefit from being married to that person. And there are always plenty of candidates.

Arranged marriages do not necessarily come about because of a specific request by a bachelor, an old maid, a widow or a widower.

Frequently, a dropped hint here, a casual remark there, or even just the personal knowledge that a friend, a relative, or even an acquaintance is still single at an age when he or she shouldn't be, is sufficient reason to put a marriage arranger in motion.

Say, a relative or a friend, fast approaching middle age and still a bachelor makes a strictly legit social call at our house. His jacket happens to have a button hanging from a thread and the button just happens to fall off – all on the level, nothing arranged. My mom would immediately offer to sew it back on, the guy would remove his jacket and she would do the work.

He would of course say thank you very much, and he might then casually remark how nice it would be if he could find a wife who could have done that little job for him.

This comment could be a perfectly innocent statement. Or it could be a hint – most likely the latter if the guy knew my mom's reputation as a marriage arranger.

Either way, my mom would be alerted to the fact that the guy had clearly indicated he wouldn't mind getting hitched. So she would start making a mental list of all the females she knows who either are old maids or pretty close to that undesirable state.

This list – made up of unmarried women or widows – is then narrowed down to one or two very suitable candidates, such suitability derived from several factors: similarities in age, looks, education, social class, and other tangible or intangibles.

Usually, it's relatively easy to influence the final candidate because in Sicily, as in many other parts of the world, no woman really relishes the idea of remaining an old maid.

Most old maids – and Sicilian old maids particularly so – are very realistic women. They know that if they haven't been able to sink their talons on the man they care about by the age of twenty-five, thirty at the very latest, their chances of ever hooking up with someone – much less someone they really pant for – are slim or none.

To a potential Sicilian old maid, the idea of remaining "*cu i radichi 'o suli*" (with the roots exposed to the sun) – a Sicilian expression used to describe a woman who will never bear children – is a curse worse than death.

To avoid that curse, they understand and accept the obvious fact that they can't be too choosy, that some allowances, some small sacrifices will have to be made in the choice of a prospective mate, some minor physical imperfection will have to be accepted.

So the guy is not exactly Cary Grant, so he is about 30 pounds overweight, so he has a big nose, so he's missing a couple of teeth, so he has a receding hairline, so what? If he has good character, if he has a secure job, if he comes from a good family, it will all work out in the long run, you'll see...

And the same, of course, is true from his point of view – so she has the faint beginning of a mustache, so she is flat-breasted or pretty broad in the hips, so what?

And that's how it goes – once the two parties seem to be agreeable to a union, marriage usually follows quickly with little or no courtship. And in most cases, they live happily ever after.

By the way, I'm sure you have noticed that in referring to a marriage arranger I've always used the pronoun "she". That's because, to the best of my knowledge, marriage arranging is like giving birth – it is done only and exclusively by women. I have never ever heard of a man being known as a marriage arranger.

And basically, in most cases, that's what marriage arranging is all about – a condition exists and such a condition is resolved.

'In most cases', I specified – but there are always exceptions to the rule. And I was certain I was such an exception.

Why would my mom be trying to arrange a marriage for me? I was only 26, I was not a cripple or handicapped, I was not a social nitwit or a Quasimodo look-alike, and while I certainly wished having more action, I was also doing fairly well with the opposite sex. Furthermore, as I had humorously mentioned to her several times in my letters, many of my banking customers were trying to hook me up with their daughters or sisters.

She knew I was not desperate to find a wife, she knew it was just a matter of time before I decided to get hitched. So why was she trying to arrange a marriage for me?

Elementary, my dear Watson! In this particular case she was trying to arrange a marriage, yes, but that wasn't all. She was also doing her subliminal best to corner the market, so to speak.

Allow me to explain. If a marriage arranger knows there is a super-duper, cream of the crop, top notch, good looking, intelligent, up and coming, sure-fire, can't miss young girl or boy, the kind that will be snatched off the market and into a marriage in a heartbeat, it's only natural that she will try her damnedest to make sure such a prize will be landed by someone in her immediate family.

Clearly, my mom had seen a superb female prospect and she was making sure someone in her immediate family – me, of course – would get dibs.

While I didn't remember that Rosa babe at all, the fact that my mom was trying to hook me up with her told me several things about her.

Sight unseen, I knew she must have been a real looker, an absolute knockout; I already knew she was from an exceptional family – my brother had mentioned that, but my mother casting her eye on her confirmed it; I could be sure she was intelligent, well-educated and virtuous; and, last but not least – in my mother's eyes at least – it was an almost sure bet her family was pretty well off.

Yes! Sight unseen, I was sure my proposed bride had all those highly desirable qualities. But while all of them were most certainly qualities I would have wanted to find in any future wife of mine, still, I wasn't interested.

My exposure to the American way of life had so totally emancipated me, so totally freed me of old world concepts, standards, customs, and beliefs that I couldn't even fathom the idea of marrying a girl suggested by someone, anyone.

Just the concept of being united in holy matrimony with a woman I had not even met, much less courted, made me cringe. More than that, it actually made me outright refuse to consider the candidate as a prospective bride, even if she was a look-alike of Sophia Loren, at whose altar I used to worship in those days.

In my mind, the idea of someone trying to arrange a marriage for me was borderline insulting – it implied an inability on my part to find a mate on my own.

Bottom line: the way I felt, any girl recommended, or even barely suggested, to me by someone else as a potential bride automatically disqualified her for consideration.

Call me a romantic, call me a dreamer, call me a fool, but I always believed that prior to a marriage there had to be some kind of spark, on both sides – call it physical attraction, call it passion, call it a crush, call it love, call it whatever the hell you want to call it, but I always believed there had to be something to justify the union of two people.

In my mind, the fact that a marriage would be a convenience for both parties never even entered into the equation of what constituted a successful marriage. Or even a bum one.

Those are very trite remarks – I am well aware of that – inspired no doubt by my having seen too many bad Hollywood movies. But that's how I felt and that's what I believed.

Subsequent letters from my mom confirmed my brother's intuition – Rosa's name kept propping up with alarming regularity, along with repeated requests for me to make a return trip to Italy.

Soon, mom's letters began containing at first subtle, then not-so-subtle hints, and finally even spelled out wake-up calls about this once-in-a-lifetime opportunity to latch on to a young lady whom she described as *bella e virtuosa* (beautiful and virtuous). And she kept urging – insisting – that it would be a good thing for me to return to Italy to see what it was all about; so much urging and so many hints that in August 1962, nearly eleven years after I left my home country, I finally decided to return to my homeland for a vacation.

CHAPTER 13

Did I say for a vacation? Hmmm.... Totally emancipated... Totally freed me of old world concepts... I said that also, didn't I?

Whom am I kidding? Just a wee bit emancipated, maybe, and just a wee bit freed – that's probably a more accurate evaluation.

Those previous statements need some doctoring because whenever I think about those days – and about that first trip back to Italy in particular – the strongest recollection I retain is that I had very little desire to go to Italy in the first place. I didn't feel this need or urge to see my folks, my friends, or my homeland.

Why this lack of desire, this apathy on my part? I don't know and I can't provide any rational explanations but – I'll state it again – the plain and unvarnished truth is that a trip back to Italy was not a top priority for me at that time. And since there was no real desire to go, there surely had to be some other motive.

In one of his letters my dad had talked about having a grand family reunion. Mimmo had already eagerly agreed to participate and had also repeatedly urged me to go solely for that reason. But the very fact that he had to urge me several times – "Come on, what kind of family reunion would it be if you aren't there also?" – was a clear indication of my lack of desire to go.

I did agree to go, officially because of the family reunion, but in my heart I knew that was not the catalyst, the main motivating factor.

What was it then? Clearly, there had to be some other motive, and the only one I can think of had to be a not-so-latent curiosity about this potential mate.

Was it my Sicilian blood? Was it an implicit blind trust in my mother's track record as a marriage arranger? Who knows?... It could even have been some worry on my part that I might be missing out on a terrific opportunity. And then again, it could have been a desire to see what it was all about just for the personal satisfaction of scorning this proposed arrangement, just so I could tell myself and others – my mom included – that I could do better on my own.

Conjectures are pointless. But I admit that most probably the main motivation for going to Italy was my curiosity to see what it was all about. A perfectly justifiable curiosity, by the way; I mean, seeing for the first time the woman proposed to be your wife is not exactly a daily occurrence.

That lack of desire, incidentally, was a one-time thing. I have since gone to Italy dozens of times, and every single time my desire, my sense of anticipation has been so strong that, to this day, I can't wait for the plane to take off. But not that first time – my brother practically shamed me into going. He was going himself with his entire family that consisted now of three kids – Pietro, the little tyke who was already here when I came over, plus Nick who was born in '52, and Leo – named after me – born in '58.

August 1962: The New York to Milan trip took about nine hours, an incredibly short time in those days of the emerging jet age.

Time plays funny tricks. For the first time in my life I had the unsettling experience of seeing for myself how perceptions vary, how dramatically people change, how even memories are distorted after a long absence!

When I left Italy, I was a clueless sixteen-year-old kid at the threshold of puberty – I wore short pants, was barely 5' 3" tall, and weighed maybe 135 pounds.

When I returned I was a fairly well put-together grown man of 27, standing tall at 5' 10" and weighing a well distributed 185 pounds. And while my folks had seen pictures of me, still I'm pretty sure they half expected to see little Lillo emerging from that plane.

Same thing on my part, of course – I remembered my father 'towering' over me at 5' 6", and that's what I expected to see. But when I spotted him, I could hardly hide my surprise when, standing in front of me, I saw a wrinkled, stooped, gray haired old man of 65 who actually had to raise his head to look in my eyes.

With him were my sister and her husband, Gianni. They had come to pick me up in Milan in his car, the latest model of a Fiat 500, the first car anyone in my family – on the Italian side – had ever owned. It was a brand new car, and to this day I don't know how we managed to squeeze four people in that mousetrap.

My suitcase had to be tied on the roof rack, of course, because the Fiat's trunk could hold a briefcase at best. As for the trip to Genoa, we tooled along at a brisk 50 miles an hour, the top speed for that car.

At that time, my car in America was a '60 Ford Fairlane, a sporty looking 4-door job I had bought when the old Studebaker was just about ready to give up the ghost. My new car could easily accommodate six people, three suitcases, golf bags and assorted junk, went from 0 to 60 in a heartbeat, and could reach well over 110 miles an hour.

Still, that little Fiat fascinated me – brake, clutch and gas pedal just about the size of a credit card, one rather small round gauge on the dashboard, no radio of course, and God help whoever had to climb in the backseats. That's all it was, yet I kept gawking at that miniature subcompact with the same amazed fascination that makes one stare wide-eyed at the accurate reproduction of a model train with all parts working.

First impressions of Italy, eleven years later: first and foremost, where did all those cars on the roads come from? OK, small cars, but many, many, many more than I remembered having seen in the first sixteen years of my life in Italy.

And what about the zillions of scooters and motorcycles doing a crazy tarantella around, in between, in front and behind all those cars?... Where had they come from?

We had to stay in Genoa for three days – that's how long it took to get train reservations to travel down to Sicily where my mom had already gone and where the family reunion was going to take place. I used that time to catch up with most of my old buddies, all of them grown up men like me, some of them now married and with kids.

God, how they had changed! And no, I am not talking about the normal physical changes brought on by post-pubescence. That I expected. The most striking and unexpected change was sartorial.

When we were kids, our clothes were – how shall I phrase it? – barely enough to cover our privates: underwear, undershirts, short pants and some kind of top, all fairly clean. Plus a pair of shoes or sandals, of course; and socks, in wintertime only.

Today? Dapper! Stylish! Those are the words that best come to mind to describe them. One or more pieces of their attire – be it *pantaloni a zampa d'elefante* (bell– bottom trousers), shirts with meticulously hand sewn collars, V-necked sweaters of luxurious cashmere, elegant shoes, fashionable neckties or even a simple belt – was a *firmato*, **HAD** to be a *firmato*, that is, made by some prestigious firm. Clearly, anyone not wearing something *firmato* was a social outcast, a nobody.

They all smoked, of course, and *sigarette americane* of course. Nobody would be caught dead smoking those dreadful *Nazionali*, the best known Italian brand.

Oh! The watches! I almost forgot about the watches... When I was still a kid, I vaguely remembered that just having a wristwatch, any kind of wristwatch, was a big deal. It meant you had big bucks, or *lire*. But now, I was astounded not only by the proliferation of that now very common instrument, but by the prestige it had been accorded by practically all Italians.

Watches apparently had become some kind of status symbol. Just three days in Genoa, and easily a dozen times someone 'casually' asked me what type of watch I had. And they all seemed to be incredulous, dumbfounded, when they saw that my $20 Timex simply kept time.

And then – still very 'casually' – they would compare their watch to mine pointing out one or more of their useless features. Their time-pieces – they would condescendingly state – were not only waterproof, but also had chronometers. And the date! And luminous dials! And – hear, hear! – they were guaranteed to keep on ticking even if you dove in the ocean to a depth of God knows how many meters. As if I gave a shit!

Still, it was great seeing them again. Having the advantage of knowing who I was looking for, I didn't have much trouble recognizing them. But none of them knew I had returned for a vacation, and they sure had problems recognizing me.

Some things never change. As in the good old days they still gathered at our old stomping grounds – *I Giardinetti* – and that's where I went to see them again.

Every reunion with my old friends followed the same pattern. I would approach them smiling and looking straight at them, and they invariably held the uncertain demeanor of one who isn't sure if a stranger is looking at him or at somebody behind him. They would quickly and hesitantly glance once or twice behind them until they finally realized they were indeed the ones I was staring at. They would then look at me quizzically, sensing a vaguely familiar face. Yes, I was someone they knew from some distant past, someone they couldn't quite place.

As I neared them, I would then start shaking my head in fake disappointment. Pretending to be somewhat offended, I would then blurt out: *"Belin! Ma dai!.. Ti sei già scordato di me? Sono Lillo!"* (Dick! Come on!... You already forgot about me? I am Lillo!).

"LILLO!" – They would shout. And immediately there would be open-mouthed amazement and joyous shouts of recognition, followed by long, warm embraces. And they would then cheerfully drag me to surprise other old friends also unaware of my return.

Barely able to hold in their laughter, they would ask pointing at me: *"Lo conosci 'sto tizio? Dice che ti conosce..."* – (Do you know this guy? He says he knows you...).

More staring, more indecisive glances and then, after the re-introduction, more joyous shouts of recognition and amazement, and more long, warm embraces.

They were all delighted to see me again. With the warm hospitality typical of Italian folks, they wasted no time inviting me for dinner or taking me all over town, proud to show me how Genoa had changed. And my Genoa had changed quite a bit, with traffic a glorious mess, and with an enormous expansion in high-rise constructions in the suburbs.

Places in the mountains just outside Genoa, boonies where – as kids – we used to roam about exploring, sites we used as picnic grounds, hinterlands where we would hunt for frogs or pick wild mushrooms, they had now been transformed to urban sprawls with eight, nine or ten story condos lining both sides of streets carved on the mountainsides and twisting to follow the mountains' contour.

Most of my buddies were now motorized, some with a Vespa or a Lambretta scooter, a few of them even with small cars.

I will never forget my first exhilarating ride on the back seat of a Vespa with my best friend Luigi, as he zipped along at about 50 miles an hour on city streets about as wide as my living room and as busy as an anthill. Exhilarating and terrifying!

"*Vai adagio, Luigi!*"– (Slow down, Luigi!) I would say – no, make that scream. Yes, scream! Scream as in absolute terror because I knew I would never get back home alive. And he would laugh explaining that's the way they all drive in Italy, and – Holy Mary, Mother of God! – he wasn't lying! Man, those crazy bastards are either absolutely insane or totally deranged, take your pick!

The most obvious sign of newfound affluence was that everywhere we went, or whatever we did, they wouldn't allow me to even reach for my wallet. They absolutely insisted on treating me to drinks, coffee, even dinners at delectable '*trattorias*'. Quite a change from the days, a short eleven years earlier, when returning '*Americani*' were always treating.

More first impressions... All right, I had grown quite a bit since the day I left, but how was it possible that the streets had shrunk?

When I left, 'Via Ambrogio Spinola' – the street where my family lived – was a large tree-lined boulevard about as wide as 5th Avenue in New York. Eleven years later it had shrunk to a 10-yard wide road lined with the same six-story high buildings.

And 'Via Napoli', the street right around the corner where we played soccer all the time – our own Yankee Stadium! Yes, that was wider than the street where I lived – by about two feet maybe – and it now had cars parked and even double-parked on both sides of the street. And of course nobody played soccer there anymore.

But even without the parked cars, how could it have been possible for us to play with wild abandon on that narrow stretch of road? But we did, we surely did, hundreds, thousands of times, and with little or no interference from traffic.

Still more first impressions... I remembered Italy as a relatively quiet country, but it was now round-the-clock pandemonium with the discordant clamor of horns blowing, the rumble of engines gunned, the racket of people talking at the same time and the loud blaring of music all over – surprisingly, even lots of American music. Ye Gods! How could people live in all that bedlam!

Even more annoying, you couldn't escape that Babel by staying indoors because Italian homes – mostly built with solid materials with little or none noise-absorbing capability – have poor acoustics that frequently intensify that maddening outdoor cacophony.

And then, the rediscoveries! First and foremost – espresso coffee! I used to drink some coffee as a kid, mostly 'caffelatte' – espresso coffee and milk – with just a few sips of strong espresso now and then. I don't even remember if I used to like it or not – espresso coffee was just a drink adults seemed to savor after every meal – and I had literally forgotten about it.

Espresso is now popular in the USA (Thank you, Starbucks!), but in the 50s and 60s it was still relatively unknown. I had become used to the watery American coffee and I had even come to like it.

Three days in Genoa – about a dozen cups of espresso, minimum! Strong espresso! Pure, distilled, delicious, sensuous espresso! Every reunion with my old friends was invariably celebrated with a cup of espresso coffee followed by a shot or two of Sambuca or Anisette (their treat, of course!). Suffice to say I didn't get much sleep during those three days.

I don't think they even had decaffeinated espresso coffee in those days. They do sell it in stores now and, regretfully, even coffee bars will brew it. Back then, however, decaf was considered a sacrilege.

Another rediscovery – *farinata*! *Farinata* is a baked thin layer of batter made with chick-pea flour, water, olive oil and seasoned with rosemary, salt and pepper. That's it, you say? I know, it doesn't sound like much but – trust me on this! – when it comes out of the oven, its fragrance is beyond heavenly.

I rediscovered it the day I bought that infamous pair of shoes, socks, shoestrings, etc. There I was, window-shopping in my beloved *Via Napoli* – formerly our Yankee Stadium and now a mini-mall – when suddenly my nose detected a pleasant fragrance in the air. It was an aroma, a bouquet that triggered awake a memory that had lain dormant in my brain for years. It was the fragrance of *farinata* just coming out of the oven of some nearby bakery.

That strong, overpowering fragrance immediately summoned up rare and long forgotten moments of my impoverished adolescence, the gratifying savoring of one of the few treats us kids indulged in now and then – a slice or two of cheap *farinata*.

I know, I know, I am waxing sentimental again, but that memory – I swear to God! – brought tears to my eyes, literally. And it's hard to believe – I know that also – but that reawakening to me was just as joyous an event as seeing my parents, my sisters and all my friends after eleven years.

Sniffing like a hound dog – again, literally! – I just followed my nose, discovered where that heavenly scent came from, went inside the bakery, bought 2 *etti* (about half a pound) of *farinata* wrapped in oily brown paper, and wolfed it down. Even peeled my palate, the damn thing was so hot... but who cared? It was worth it!

More rediscoveries, still of the olfactory variety... Ambling aimlessly through the "*carrugi*," those dark, sordid and incredibly fascinating alleys in Genoa's *Centro Storico* – Historical Center – alleys so narrow you can easily touch the buildings on both sides with your arms extended, I wound up in *Via Prè*, the street where I was born.

While drifting around, I decided to make a brief stop at *salumeria "Da Ernesto"* – a cold cuts store – to say hello to Signor Fibrini, my buddy Luigi's father, who owned the place.

Holy prosciutto! Walking inside that store was like being enveloped in an invisible cloud combining all the distilled aromatic essences of mortadella, salame, prosciutto, soppressata, parmesan cheese, provolone, capocollo, caciocavallo, pecorino, olives, gorgonzola, ricotta, mozzarella, and the dozens – hundreds! – of other delectable cheeses and cured pork meats made all over Italy.

One has to experience that aroma to appreciate it. Its effect is immediate – you just take a whiff and you work up an appetite, even if you have just finished eating a sumptuous meal. Guaranteed!

And how can one convey in words the overpoweringly ambrosial redolence, the bouquet, the irresistible fragrance emanating from the *pasticcerie* (pastry shops) in Italy? O sweet, sweet Lord! How does one describe that aroma? Once again, you have to experience it to appreciate it. It's like a drug, a mind-altering drug! Just sniff it and you will feel mellow and at peace with the world.

Sweet refers to the sense of taste, right? Yes, but not always! When you walk into an Italian *pasticceria* you will **smell** sweetness. It's in the form of a celestial scent created with a primary base of vanilla extract infused with delicate doses of chocolate, whipped cream, candied fruits, honey, and other mouth-watering tidbits that are sure to add inches to your waistline, but who cares?

Yes! My first visit to Italy was a dazzling, glamorous, and overall positive event fraught with open-mouthed astonishment, joyous reunions, and pleasant feelings of rediscovery, rekindling of youthful memories and exhilarating excitement. But there was also a vague, blurry downside to it, a daunting dismay, a disturbingly melancholy sensation and – deep down – a pervasive sense of sadness, of things lost, of longing for a simpler, uncomplicated time.

179

Despite my still youthful 27 years, for the first time in my life I had the unsettling and somewhat disquieting experience of feeling myself growing old.

The highlight of my three-day stay in Genoa was an evening I spent with my buddy Luigi at a *"balera,"* an outdoor dancing hall carved out in a recessed alcove on the rocks by the seaside. To this day I still feel a vaguely sensual shiver when I recall that warm summer evening refreshed by the gentle breeze of the Mediterranean Sea.

Picture an enchanting, incredibly romantic setting – an outdoor, horseshoe-shaped courtyard surrounded by hedges and maritime pine trees on three sides, about two dozen small tables set around a dimly lit dance floor, a small band playing the latest Italian hits, all of them luscious songs I had never heard before. And, as background, the shimmering undulation of the ocean and the rhythm of the waves crashing on the rocks below.

The hall was actually a youth-oriented discotheque, a sharp contrast from the old *"balere"* (dance halls) once patronized by entire families.

With amused surprise, as well as a vague sense of bewilderment, I noticed that Luigi and I – both 27 years of age – were among the oldest patrons in there.

We had gone stag. Luigi had informed me that many girls now went to these dances unescorted – something absolutely unimaginable eleven short years before.

We managed to hook up with a couple of girls and we got to dance with them as well as with other girls, but never even got to first base, possibly because we were too old for them. They really were the same nice girls I remembered, only less inhibited, perhaps a bit more "Americanized."

That evening is still etched in my mind and for many years remained one of the most precious memories of that first trip back. To this day, it's a fading but still pleasant memory, a memory that haunted me for a long time, a memory that made me wish I could have stayed in Italy forever; in fact, a memory at times so obsessive that made me wish I had never left Italy in the first place.

A few of my unmarried buddies tried to talk me into visiting a private *casino*, but I found some lame excuse and declined to go.

In 1962 prostitution in Italy had already been outlawed but – my friends explained – there were now more hookers than ever.

When I left Italy, prostitution was still legal, and a young man's journey to manhood began with his first visit to a *casino*. As teenage kids, we used to listen with undisguised awe and envy to the exploits – real or invented – of the young adults who said they had patronized those places. Even my brother used to speak with reverential tones of those celebrated houses of ill repute where most young men lost their virginity and got their first taste of intimacy with the opposite sex.

I had never been in a *casino*. For one thing, when I left Italy I didn't have the... how can I phrase it delicately?... I didn't have the complete equipment yet – I was still a pre-pubescent young kid not fully developed into a man. Additionally, the legal minimum age to enter a *casino* was 18. I wasn't 18 yet, and I couldn't even bluff my way in because I didn't look anywhere near that age – I was sixteen and looked thirteen.

I still remember how anxious I was to develop and become of age, so I could go to a *casino* and become a 'made man', so to speak.

Some well-meaning but not very farsighted communist lady senator decided that legal prostitution was a shameful exploitation of women. She introduced legislation to outlaw the practice, and all houses of ill repute in Italy were shuttered on Sep. 20, 1958 – on my birthday, no less!

That, of course, wasn't the end of prostitution. While before 1958 there was an orderly exchange of sex for money, with fairly stringent physical examinations mandated by local health authorities, hookers were now working off the streets or in very private clandestine homes under the iron fists of pimps.

The real reason why I declined to go with my buddies was because goddamned Korea had ruined it for me.

Tragically dismal stat – I was in Italy on vacation for a full six weeks and I didn't get laid once! This in the land of love and romance... Ha!

We finally went down to Sicily and we had our family reunion, a glorious daylong affair right on the beach with close to one hundred people present, all of them wearing bathing suits and/or suitable beach attire.

With my brother's help, my dad had arranged to rent and erect a large tent to protect guests from the blistering sun. Tables and benches for all the guests had been set up under the tent and they had even hired a catering service with food, beer and soft drinks. Additionally, food-loving Italians never go to a party empty-handed, and every table overflowed with cakes, pastries, plus a vast assortment of wine and liquor bottles.

And that's where I met her.

The only thing I can say is that if twelve years before she had looked any way near the way she looked now, I very seriously doubt I would have forgotten her.

This has been said before – I am sure – and it's absolutely true. Many pre-teen girls – say, from the age of eight until the age of twelve or so – are at an awkward age. Really! They are mostly homely, with bad teeth, bad complexion, gawky and ungainly. Soon after they enter puberty, however, they blossom out and become much more attractive. A few will become outright beauties.

Rosa must have been one of them. There is no other explanation, because what I had in front of me was an absolutely gorgeous knockout babe, a drop-dead beauty, the kind of woman any man can't help staring at. With dirty thoughts in mind.

I knew it was Rosa even before somebody introduced us or, I should say, re-introduced, since supposedly I had met her some twelve years before. And I knew it was she because, as this beautiful, smiling girl glided forward to greet me, I had the eerie sensation that everybody was looking at us.

It was more than a sensation actually – it was almost a certainty.

In Sicilian circles, news of an arranged marriage – real or potential – travels fast, with or without verbal communication. It's just like the event that sets the marriage arrangement in motion – a dropped hint here, a casual remark there, and a marriage arranger knows that a situation exists. Similarly, the news that a marriage arrangement is in the works travels from family to family without a specific announcement.

While my mom was most definitely the meddling type – par for the course for a marriage arranger – I am certain she never uttered a specific word to let anybody know she was trying to hook me up with Rosa. In fact, she almost certainly never even explicitly discussed that possibility with Rosa's parents, except perhaps in making some casual but pointed comment like 'I hope that someday my son will be lucky enough to find someone like Rosa.' And without a doubt she hadn't specifically or even casually talked about it with Rosa.

Like I said, a dropped hint here, a casual remark there, and everybody knew exactly what was going on. It goes without saying of course that, though she had never explicitly reached an agreement about this proposed marriage with Rosa's parents, my mom was pretty sure they would have been absolutely and totally in favor of such a union. Mom was sensible and realistic enough to somehow test the waters before committing herself.

In my case, a blessing from both families was easy enough to assume. The Donatos were one of the most respected families in town, openly acknowledged by the entire community as being top of the line, and so was my family.

My dad was the silent type, but when he talked people listened. Mom was known as a great wife who had done a great job in raising five kids during the difficult war years. Her propensity for marriage arranging was certainly not looked askance at by anyone in town.

Economically, the two families were pretty much on the same level. Furthermore, the two families were distantly related – in short, there was no doubt both tribes would have welcomed seeing us united in holy matrimony.

People were looking at us – I could feel it – not openly staring, but looking at us, and absorbing all the delicious details. To all appearances, they may have looked like they were engaged in a private conversation, or they may actually have been chatting with others, but they were surely looking at us.

I could feel their non-staring gazes and I even thought I detected an almost imperceptible lowering in the buzz of their conversations as Rosa approached me.

Those folks are so skillful that, even as they continue to chatter privately with others without interruptions, they can still scrutinize you and monitor all your interplays, even your body language, to see what develops. **AND** they can even accurately divine what the outcome would be.

Nobody actually introduced us – she just came over and introduced herself.

"*Ciao Lillo, come stai? Sono Rosa, Rosa Donato, sono sicura che non ti ricordi di me* (Hi, Lillo, how are you? I am Rosa, Rosa Donato, I'm sure you don't remember me.)" – She said disarmingly, using the familiar '*tu*' instead of the formal '*voi*' – "*Sono la figlia di Filippo 'U Rizzu'. Sono tanto contenta di rivederti dopo tanti anni.*" (I am Filippo 'U Rizzu''s daughter. I'm so happy to see you after so many years.).

She offered me her hand and then kissed me on both cheeks, a very normal custom in Italy. She spoke perfect Italian, her speech surprisingly free of any Sicilian accent. Her voice had a pleasant and frank cordiality, totally devoid of the reticence or shyness one would feel when addressing a stranger or – as in my case – a near stranger.

Do I lie or do I tell the truth? Honesty is always the best policy, I always say, especially if you can match it with a compliment.

"I'm embarrassed to admit it but no, I do not remember you." – I said, with an appropriate smile. And then, without the trace of a leer: "But I'm sure I would have if you looked then the way you look now."

She blushed a bit, I could tell, more through her expression than by a change of skin color. Her skin was tawny brown – a bit lighter than a cappuccino is what comes to mind – and I could tell it was a year round brown, not suntanned.

It set off marvelously her sparkling green eyes and a glorious mass of honey blonde hair cascading freely to just below her shoulders. Her lips were russet colored, glossy and perfectly shaped. She wore large, round gold earrings, gypsy-like but not vulgar at all. An emerald green one-piece swimsuit covered by a brightly colored transparent silk blouse with flowing sleeves couldn't hide a splendid hourglass figure.

Everything absolutely outstanding, physically. But there was more: she had that confident, self-assured bearing, that sophisticated and yet so plain look in her eyes that tells one at first glance that whoever has it is no dummy. Better yet, it tells you loud and clear that whoever has it is exceptional, period.

"Thank you for the compliment." – She said smiling – "You have changed quite a bit too since I last saw you."

A bit of self-deprecating humor was in order.

"I guess I have, but not like you unfortunately." – I said, shrugging my shoulders. – "I've gone the other way. I used to be a good-looking kid, or so they tell me. And look at me now; I have turned into a toad."

She laughed – a good sign, I thought.

"You must be a hopeless case." – Was her quick riposte. – "I already gave you two kisses and you haven't turned into Prince Charming yet. What else can I do?"

I burst out laughing – she had a quick wit and I appreciated that also. Yes, I liked her, I definitely did like her. And the ice had been broken.

"What is America like?" – She asked me in English.

"Do you speak English?" – I asked her, pleasantly surprised.

"Not much well, but I understand enough." – She replied, still in English – "I have studied English for my last two years in school."

Her grammar and syntax were pretty good. She had a faint British accent – her teachers had probably learned English in Great Britain – and the cadence of her speech had the halting uncertainty of the typical foreign language student, each word individually enunciated rather than fluently melded together.

"From what I've heard so far, you are doing quite well." – I said in English – "The only thing you really need is practice."

"Thank you." – She said – "It is my hope you will present me with the opportunity to practice when we converse together."

"I'll be glad to *give* you that opportunity." – I told her, stressing the *give*.

She immediately caught the slight correction and, blushing slightly, she first thanked me.

"And please, do not have fear to correct if I commit errors when we converse." – She then added.

To make it easier for her to understand me, I intentionally began slowing down the cadence of my speech, pronouncing each individual word separately.

"OK, I will correct you if you make a mistake," – I said, spacing each word – "but please do not be bashful..."

I immediately noticed her puzzled look at the word 'bashful'.

"Bashful means '*timida*'..." – I quickly explained – "Do not be bashful, and please feel free to ask me anything you want, OK?"

"Oh, thank you very much." – She said with genuine pleasure – "I hope I will not become to you too much... oooh... how do you say '*fastidio*' in English?"

"Trouble. Either trouble or bother." – I explained – "No, no, Rosa, it won't be any trouble at all, I mean it. I'll be glad to converse with you in English any time you want."

Without realizing it, I had already resumed talking with a normal cadence. She gestured for me to slow down a bit, and I did.

Resuming a deliberately slow cadence I told her: "Look, when I went to America I was just like you, and I know I was a pain in the neck..." – again there was a puzzled look on her face – "I was a pain in the neck literally means '*ero un dolore nel collo*'. It's an American expression that means I was bothering, or giving *fastidio*, trouble to somebody. Anyway, I was bothering a lot of people... my brother, my sister-in-law, and the students in school. But if you want to learn a language well, you must get help from the people who know the language well."

While talking with a deliberately slow cadence I was also unwittingly raising the tone of my voice to emphasize each word, and that was definitely attracting attention from bystanders.

We both suddenly realized we had been engaging in a private conversation in a foreign language at a social gathering where practically nobody else could understand what we were telling each other. Looking around, we noticed with some embarrassment that several people were now staring at us.

"I think maybe we should continue this conversation later." – I murmured with a smile, gesturing with my head toward the rest of the folks gathered around us.

"That is a very good idea." – She said smiling. – "I think I shall go and get something to eat."

She turned as if to leave. She then quickly turned again to face me, tapped my arm and said: "*E grazie, grazie ancora* (And thanks, thanks again)."

It was a grand family reunion. While I was not specifically the guest of honor, it felt like they were all treating me as if I was, perhaps because they hadn't seen me for the past dozen years or so. I suspected, however that it might also have been because they all believed the announcement of an engagement would soon be forthcoming.

Much as I liked Miss Donato, I wasn't quite ready for that yet.

The next time we were together was at her house. The Donatos had invited me for dinner, along with my brother and his family.

Mr. Donato – a tall, portly, well-groomed man, deeply suntanned, with the no-nonsense air of somebody who is used to being in authority – looked to be in his mid-50s.

He was dressed impeccably in dark blue pants, an open-necked striped shirt and an elegant light blue sport jacket. Despite his authoritarian bearing, he displayed genuinely friendly manners and an easy cordiality that made guests feel at home immediately.

The day was quite warm and air-conditioning hadn't yet been introduced in Sicily. Mr. Donato soon shed his jacket and invited all to be comfortable and do likewise.

The nickname '*U Rizzu*' may have been appropriate when he was a young man, but he now had a receding hairline, with only some very wavy salt and pepper hair around his crown testifying to its former glory.

In the typically warm Italian way of showing closeness or affection, he spontaneously reached for you and touched your arm, or placed his arm around your shoulders when talking to you.

Mrs. Donato – Lucia was her name – was a very attractive matron in her late forties, just a bit on the heavy side. She wore a pink dress cut low, with short sleeves. A white pearl necklace with what looked like a cameo hung around her neck, the cameo resting right in the cleavage and drawing attention to her ample bosom.

Clearly Rosa had gotten her beauty from her, the green eyes, the shape of her nose, the splendid figure, even the color of her hair – although I was pretty sure Mrs. Donato's had been touched up.

Just like her husband, Mrs. Donato also had that same natural warmth that made guests feel welcome. She attentively listened to what one had to say, and her questions or replies expressed sincere interest in the matter being discussed.

Also impressive – and rather touching, I thought – was the palpable affection she showed for her husband as she instinctively took care of his every need, refilling his drink, positioning an ashtray or just listening attentively whenever he talked. It was also plain, however, that whatever she did for him was not in the role of a servant, but rather because she deeply cared for him.

Rosa wore a plain light green frock, a simple dress with spaghetti straps and no discernible waist, a "sack" dress I believe it was called – a type of fashion still quite popular in those days. I used to detest it exactly because it concealed the contour of a woman's body, but I had to admit it looked damn good on her. Its plain and understated elegance highlighted her beautiful green eyes. She wore very little make-up and no jewelry, not even earrings. And she looked gorgeous.

At the dinner table I was seated right next to her, and it crossed my mind that it was not just a casual occurrence.

As we sipped a *"Campari"* aperitif, she again asked me what America was like, this time in Italian. It was the same question she had asked me when we had first met at the family reunion, a question I had never answered.

A satisfactory answer would have required a long and almost certainly boring analysis of what America is all about, an analysis I did not feel qualified to provide in the first place. Furthermore, it would also have required me to monopolize the conversation for a while. I therefore limited my answer to a cursory listing of some of America's advantages, vis- à-vis Italy, but also mentioning what I considered to be its shortcomings.

"You have been there for how long now? About ten years, haven't you?" – Her father asked me. "Have you ever given any thought about returning to Italy?"

"Eleven actually, and no! Not at all! I like living there very much." – I said without hesitation – "I like it so much that I even enlisted for three years in the American Army just to become a citizen."

"But don't you ever get homesick for Italy?" – Rosa asked me.

"I really don't know how to answer that..." – I replied – "I didn't feel like coming at all. My brother here can tell you he practically shamed me into coming. I came mainly because of the family reunion, but now that I'm here I'm glad I came, and I'm sure I'll be back again."

The dinner proceeded beautifully with several deliciously different antipastos, a pasta dish with lobster sauce, veal scaloppini, roast pork, several side dishes, salad, espresso coffee, and finally... Ahhh! Sicilian *cannoli*. Oh, yes! And wines and liqueurs.

We started at about 1 PM and finished sipping the last espresso well after 5 PM

Every dish prepared was simply superb, both in taste and presentation, and I had to compliment the chef. Mrs. Donato just happened to mention that Rosa had done most of the cooking.

"And how did you learn to cook so well?" – I asked her admiringly.

"*Mamma* taught me most of the basics," – she said, blushing slightly and shrugging her shoulders to indicate she didn't think her dishes were all that great – "and I just kind of make up some of the side dishes and the antipastos."

"*Beato chi ti sposa!* – (Lucky whoever marries you!)" I remarked – not too tactfully, I realized immediately – as I saw her really blush this time.

My six-weeks' vacation was nearing its end rapidly, and the only other times I saw Rosa was at the beach, and always in the presence of friends and relatives, hers or mine.

On those few occasions, I reluctantly but deliberately refrained from making any type of private contact or conversation that could be interpreted as leading, or even just ambiguous. Reluctantly, because I was definitely attracted to her – she was gorgeous, obviously intelligent, witty and, additionally, an all-around nice girl. I could see with my own eyes she had all the attributes that had made her a top-notch prospect as my future wife in my mother's eyes.

And that was exactly the problem, damn it!

If my mother's eyes had strayed anywhere else, I most definitely would have tried to make some kind of a move, some direct or indirect action to show I was interested in her. True to my beliefs, instead, I intentionally maintained a behavior of studied casualness. Reluctantly.

The only time I made a gesture of open admiration for her – or what could be interpreted as one – was the night before I was scheduled to leave. It happened at the beach where a group of about thirty relatives, friends and acquaintances had gathered.

It was a gorgeous night with an indigo, star-filled sky, the silky sand and the shimmering sea illuminated by a full moon so bright we could easily see each other.

Talk about an appropriate setting for *amore* – a full moon, a star-filled sky, softly murmuring waves rhythmically washing ashore and a fresh breeze gently blowing in from the sea. Hollywood couldn't have come up with anything more romantic.

We had been on the beach since mid-morning. During the day, some of us young guys had marked off a small soccer field with lines in the sand and kicked a ball around. Several young ladies stood at the sidelines rooting us on while others played "*tamburello*", bouncing a little ball at each other with leather-covered round tambourines.

Now and then, when we felt fatigued or overly sweating, we would all find relief from the hot weather by diving in the sea – me too although, unlike everybody else, I merely dipped in the water and stayed close to shore, trying hard not to display my lack of proficiency in aquatic sports.

As dusk fell, we just sat on the beach talking, laughing, eating sandwiches, drinking beer, wine or soda, swapping stories and jokes and simply enjoying each other's company.

It had been a pleasant and spontaneous get-together, nothing organized. A chummy crowd of young men and women, all acquainted with or related to each other, had just happened to meet on the beach and had banded together into a congenial, stress-free gathering, a get-together made to order to forget about tomorrow. No one seemed willing to be the first to break up that pleasant and peaceful party, least of all me. It was the last day of my vacation and that gathering was exactly what I needed to make me forget I would have to leave soon.

Someone in the crowd asked Pippo Longo – a second cousin of mine and an accomplished accordionist – to go home and get his instrument to brighten up the evening with some music. He good-naturedly agreed and soon returned carrying a huge *"Soprani"* accordion. After practicing a few chords, he began playing some old Italian songs, the ones I love most.

Music is the universal magnet, and in no time several in the group gathered around him. Soon a young man burst into song singing in what was clearly the style of Claudio Villa, a well-known Italian singer.

The guy had good pitch but his rendition was weakened by his frequent stops and starts due to unfamiliarity with the lyrics and his inability to keep time with the music. Trying to help, others jumped in providing the correct lyrics, and soon there was a raucous but gloriously happy sing-along. And that's when my brother nudged me and urged me to go and sing a song.

"Dai, Lillo, vai a cantare tu... fai sentire a 'sta gente come si canta.. (Come on, Lillo, you go and sing... show these folks how to sing...)" – He asked me repeatedly.

191

Mimmo loved and was very proud of the way I sang, and always coaxed me into singing at every social occasion with music.

I tried to shush him because – yes! I do love to sing, and I am pretty good at it – but I always worry that people might look at me as a show-off. Additionally, when asked to sing I do get a bit of stage fright, and I usually need some "fuel" to relax me.

I had sung in public in America several times before – at weddings, dinner dances or other festive get-togethers – but on every occasion I'd had a few glasses of wine and other stuff before they could convince me. On that particular day, because of the very high temperature I had limited my imbibing to cold sodas.

Despite my repeated attempts to beg off, Mimmo kept insisting, telling everybody I was really good. Soon everybody joined in a chorus, asking please, please, come on, don't be bashful. And then even Rosa asked me. And how could I refuse her?

Reluctantly, I approached my cousin and asked him if he knew "*Mamma*", always a crowd pleaser. Of course he knew it – it's almost the second Italian National Anthem.

We isolated ourselves for a couple of minutes while Pippo played some chords for me so we could agree on a key. Meanwhile I drained a glass of red wine to clear my throat and to relax myself. Once we agreed on a key, we then chose a beat, settling on a moderate beguine tempo.

Finally he gave me an intro and I began to sing. Just as I started the first few notes, however, I began to feel uncomfortable, and for the silliest reason – I didn't know what to do with my hands.

Whenever and wherever I had sung in public before – dinner dances or weddings – I always held a microphone in my hands. Here on the beach there was no mike of course, so what do I do with my hands? Just standing there with my arms hanging at my sides felt unnatural and… well, uncomfortable.

A few feet away, next to my brother, I spotted Ange with her three kids, the youngest one already napping – she seemed to be the only mother there. The best solution to my temporary discomfort was to ham it up a bit –Italians love schmaltz, especially in the form of a show of affection for dear old *mamma*.

I ambled over near her and sang the entire song to her, occasionally even theatrically kneeling in front of her and rising to my feet only for the high notes. Ange beamed at me throughout, and at the end of the song she gave me a big hug.

Considering the song had been done impromptu, I thought I'd performed it well enough, but I wasn't sure how it had been received.

When the last note sounded, I jokingly made a deep bow to the audience. Then, grinning a wide, obviously fake grin – a clownish grin – I spread my arms and shrugged my shoulders to indicate I was just an amateur. I then turned to Pippo and complimented him for his excellent playing.

There were at first a few seconds of silence. Then I began to hear here and there some vague, unintelligible murmurs followed by individual exclamations. Then – to my astonishment – there was an enthusiastic, rousing, thunderous round of applause, with repeated shouts of **"Bravo!"** and *"Bis!... Bis!"* – which is Italian for encore.

Rosa seemed the most ecstatic one in the crowd. Rushing to my side, she complimented me and asked me in English: "Do you sing professionally?"

Not quite sure if she was serious or just teasing me, I laughingly told her: "Yeah! Sure! I'm undecided if I should sign a contract with RCA or Columbia... They both offered me very lucrative record deals."

Realizing her comment could have been interpreted as a joke or mockery, she assured me she was serious and asked me if I had taken singing lessons.

"No, I haven't." – I told her truthfully. – "As a matter of fact I can't even read music. I know what they mean by a musical key, but I couldn't recognize one. I have no idea if a song is in the key of C, B flat, or whatever. I can only tell if that key suits me or not."

"You are very good." – She told me in English – "You really sound like somebody who sings professionally, like you had musical training."

"Grazie." – I told her. "What little talent I have is that I sing in tune, or at least, I think I do. Knowing the lyrics of a song is also very important and – believe it or not – I know by heart the lyrics of over 500 songs, Italian, English, Spanish and a few French ones also. The most important aspect of singing, in my opinion, is having a feel for the beat, and that may be the only small gift that I have – I know I can keep time well. Also, I always try to interpret a song my own way. Mainly, though, I just love to sing."

And it was at this point that – fueled I'm sure by the wine I'd just washed down – I added: "Rosa, may I sing a song for you?"

I could tell she blushed, even in the tenuous moonlight. But she quickly said she would be honored and delighted.

I already had in mind the song I wanted to sing for her. It was *"Scrivimi"* (Write to me), a very popular and delightful tango from the 40s.

I had purposely selected that tune for a privately humorous reason. The song's lyrics start with *"Quando tu sei partita, mi hai donato una rosa"* (When you left me, you donated me a rose), and they happen to contain the words of both her first and last name, Rosa Donato.

I asked Pippo if he was familiar with that song. Of course he was – it's in every Italian accordionist's repertory.

I sang the song without looking at her directly – I was pretty sure she would have been embarrassed. But as I sang the words *'donato'* and *'rosa'* I intentionally stressed them and quickly sneaked an amused glance at her. I saw her smile a smile I couldn't quite decipher, but I was pretty sure she was pleased.

That song went over very well also. Surely nobody had missed that bit about her name and surname in the lyrics of the song, and almost certainly every one present must have thought it was my declaration of love for her.

There was another great round of applause, and Rosa came over and kissed me on the cheek. And this time I blushed.

Now they wouldn't let me stop singing and just about everyone had a special request. Soon two other guys in the crowd rushed home and got a guitar and a mandolin, and a pretty decent trio was quickly formed to accompany me.

I must have sung well over twenty songs, but by then I didn't mind singing at all – I had had a few glasses of wine and felt totally relaxed. Furthermore, once I start it's pretty hard to shut me up.

It was now nearly midnight. Despite the late hour, Mimmo sent somebody to Nick Ravello's house to tell him about the party at the beach. Old Nick had permanently retired in Torre Faro with his wife a couple of years earlier.

They probably had to wake him up but – like me – good old Nick wasn't one to miss an occasion with music and songs. Soon he was there also and he began singing some of the old songs, individually or with me.

He was then around seventy and didn't have the lung capacity of his younger years. Still, he could belt them with passion, hitting at full tenor voice high notes that I could only reach singing falsetto.

I don't know if other parts of his body were still functioning as well as his voice, but I swear the old goat still had an eye for the ladies and, in his own charmingly rascal way, he even tried to hit on Rosa who, just as charmingly, pretended being impressed by his interest in her.

Couples began dancing on the beach. Soon, hearing the sound of music, even people who lived in nearby houses came out to see what it was all about. And one by one, they left their houses and ambled down the beach, joining us in singing and dancing despite the late hour.

I love dancing just about as much as I love singing, and I would have loved to dance at least once with Rosa, but people kept pressuring me and Nick to sing and I didn't get to dance with her or anybody else. I noticed, however, that Rosa didn't dance with anybody either. And I was kind of pleased about that.

What a night! Marvelous! Magical! Absolutely unforgettable! So pleasant, so relaxing, so congenial, so totally carefree that to this day I still treasure it as one of the most memorable moments in my life.

I had to leave the next day – in fact, that same day. When the party finally broke up I said my goodbyes to everyone there on the beach.

195

Italian folks are very emotional, and Sicilian folks particularly so. Handshakes, kisses, warm embraces... everyone there, some of them with tears in their eyes, told me how happy they were to have seen me again.

They all wished me a good trip back and they all urged me to return as soon as possible. I assured everybody I would be back soon. And I meant it.

I said goodbye to Rosa last. She seemed to be in high spirit, but even as she smiled her eyes seemed to be welling up with tears.

She first shook my hand, then hugged me and kissed me on both cheeks. She repeatedly thanked me for singing the song for her and she then asked me in halting English: "It is much bother to you if I shall write to you sometime?"

Her request pleasantly surprised and, at the same time, vaguely bewildered me. Trying to conceal this curious uneasiness, I just held her hands for a while even forgetting to correct her grammar.

I finally managed to mumble: "Of course you can, Rosa...", then quickly added almost as a joke: "That's why I sang *"Scrivimi"* (Write to me) for you."

Then, for a just few moments there was an embarrassing silence between us. Realizing I was still holding her hands, I abruptly let go of them, as if holding them had been a too intimate gesture. Still trying to hide my embarrassment, I clumsily looked around and pretended to wave goodbye to other departing friends.

That disquieting feeling finally faded. Turning my attention to her, I talked to her seriously, speaking slowly.

"Please do write to me, Rosa, and write in English if you want. It will not be any bother at all, really. In fact, if you don't mind, when I write back I will return your letters marking any mistakes you made. Is that OK?"

"Please, please, yes, return them. I shall not mind at all." – She exclaimed with clear pleasure – "It shall be of much help to me with my English. And *grazie, grazie* again, Lillo. It was so nice seeing you after all these years."

And she then hugged me again. Did she press her body to mine just a bit closer than was appropriate?

That's what it felt like, and it felt awfully good. But it might have been wishful thinking on my part. Or just my imagination.

CHAPTER 14

Her first letter, written in English, arrived about two weeks after my return to the States.

Dear Lillo,

How do you do? I hope that I am not being bother you. I write to you because you said you shall like to receive letters from me.

I hope your voyage to the United States was good. All we feel very much your absence because we enjoyed very much when you stayed here in Torre Faro. We was so happy to have you and the family of your brother at our house for dinner, and I shall not forget that beautiful night at the beach when you sang so many songs.

You have changed very much since the year when I remember seeing you, I believe in 1950. You was a young boy still and when I have seen you after you returned, you was a big man. I was very surprised the day that you returned because I remembered a young boy. I am certain you were not surprised when you saw me because you said you did not remember me.

The weather in Torre Faro is still very hot. How it is in America?

I hope you have heard the record of Claudio Villa that I have given you, and I hope you like it. He is my favorite singer. I also like Domenico Modugno and a new singer, his name is Adriano Celentano. I do not believe you shall like Celentano because he sings rock and roll, and you said you do not enjoy rock and roll.

Please salute for me your brother and his family as well as the Ra-vello family.

Cordial greetings,
Rosa

Somewhat stilted English, some obvious syntax errors, but not too bad overall, and her spelling was fine. Maybe she had a dictionary next to her. I delayed only a few days in answering her letter.

Dear Rosa,

I received your letter a few days ago. I did not reply immediately because I have been a bit busy at work. Upon my return, there was a lot of work accumulated on my desk, and I had to take care of it.

First of all, I want to congratulate you because your grammar and your spelling are very good. Your English, however, is a bit stilted, which means 'forzato'.

It is not quite conversational English, and you can only learn conversational English by practicing it, by talking with somebody who knows it well. Also, the tense of the verbs sometimes is not quite correct, and I believe it's because you literally translate from the Italian equivalent of what you want to say.

You must keep in mind that, American English is not quite the same as the English they speak in England. Basically, the language is the same, but the intonation and the accent are quite different, and also some of the words are not quite the same. Additionally, Americans have a way of abbreviating some words, and even creating new words. It's hard to explain, especially in a letter, but I am sure your English will improve if you have the opportunity to practice it, and of course you can continue practicing it with me.

I told you I would return your letters with any specific corrections, and I am returning this one listing what I believe would be a more fluid way of phrasing.

My trip back was uneventful, which means 'niente di speciale'. I started the same life I had before, going to work, and back home.

I am a bit bored because I just returned from a wonderful trip to my home country and I wish I was back there, but all vacations come to an end. I really enjoyed myself, and I can't wait until I can come again.

I have listened many times to the Claudio Villa records you gave me. He has a beautiful voice and I also like the songs he sings.

I remember him from when I was still a young boy in Italy, but his voice is different now. He used to sing 'falsetto', but he seems to have acquired a more robust voice now.

My brother and his wife Angelina asked me to say hello to you and your parents. Please do write again. I will be glad to receive your letters.

Please give my regards to your parents who were very kind to me while I was there.

Best regards to you too.

Lillo

There! A friendly reply to a friend's letter!

I received her next letter, still in English, eight days later.

Hmmmm! She must have answered immediately because it took four days at the most for a letter to cross the ocean.

Dear Lillo,

I was so happy to receive your letter because I did not believe you will answer mine. Thank you very much for the corrections you made. I hope I will make profit of your suggestions.

All my family are in excellent health, and I hope the same is for you and the family of your brother Mimmo.

I am curious to know about America, how life is different from Italy, if political affair – how do you say 'fanno schifo'? (they stink) – like they do in Italy, what kind of music they have, and what kind of music you like to hear.

They play much American music in Italy and it is very popular here. I have heard on the radio songs of Elvis Presley, Pat Boone, and Paul Anka. I have heard one singer I like very much, his name is Johnny Mathis, he is a Negro and he has a beautiful voice like Claudio Villa. My friend Mariangela received a record from America with all songs of Johnny Mathis. I like very much a song titled "Chances are", a song titled "It's not for me to say", and another one song titled "Wonderful, wonderful".

I am not capable to understand all the words, but the music and his voice are phenomenal. I hope I will (shall?) receive your reply soon. I am always confused if I have to use will or shall in the future tense.

Cordial greetings,
Rosa.

I replied immediately also. I found her comments about American music very interesting.

Or at least, I told myself that was the main reason.

Dear Rosa,

I was glad to receive your letter, and I answer immediately.

I am at the bank right now, and I am taking advantage of the fact that I am not very busy. You want to know about America and how it is different from Italy.

It is not a very easy question to answer because there are many differences in just about every field. Overall, I believe things are much better here, but there are of course some areas where Italians are superior.

The first thing that comes to mind is the cuisine. American cuisine stinks, which is an expression that literally means "puzza", but it is also used to mean "fa schifo." And that, by the way, also answers your question about politics.

In regards to that same question, I personally believe that all politics in every country "fanno schifo.. From what I remember, however, and from what I read about Italian politics, it probably 'fa schifo' more in Italy than in America.

Here there are just two major political parties, and they really are not much different from each other. In Italy, instead, there are too many parties and that, I believe, confuses the electorate. Italians, however, are much more interested in politics than the American, and they are very knowledgeable about it.

The average American is interested in politics only when there is an election, and while most Americans know the names of the President and the Vice President, most of them don't even know the names of the Secretary of State, or the Secretary of Defense, or other important politicians.

Italians are also very knowledgeable about the leaders of other countries while most Americans have no idea of who the leaders of Italy, or France, or England are. At the most, they know the name of the leader of Russia because of the Cold War.

In your letter you mentioned some American singers. As for Johnny Mathis, I am so glad you like him because he is also one of my favorite singers.

I enclose the lyrics of the songs you like so you can follow the songs better when you listen to them. I strongly encourage you to use songs as a tool for learning the language. I assure you it helped me learning English.

Finally, the difference between "will" and "shall" is a bit difficult to explain in writing (actually, I am not sure that I know it myself). I can tell you that "shall" is used very infrequently and that most of the times people use "will". I know that is not a very good explanation, but it's the best I can come up with now.

> *Please extend my greetings to your parents,*
> *and cordial greetings to you also.*
> *Lillo*

I eagerly waited for her next letter, which arrived exactly eight days later. Hmmm!...

I do believe the lady seems to be very interested in me... Totally discounting the fact that I had been eager to receive it.

Dear Lillo,

I was so happy to receive your letter, especially since you answered so quickly this time. I know you are a very occupied person and you do not have the necessary time to devote to writing letters.

I wish to thank you so very much for sending me the words to the songs of Johnny Mathis I understand most of the words of "It's not for me to say" and "Wonderful, wonderful", but I do not completely understand all of the words of "Chances are."

What does "chances are" mean? And at the end he says, "you think my heart is your valentine", I do not understand what it means, maybe it is a idiomatic expression, can you explain?

The winter is almost here, and Torre Faro is a very silent town, not the same as when the summer is here when our small town becomes very occupied with many people who come here for the beach and for swimming.

I like the summer because there is more amusement (fun?), but I also like my little town when it is more calm, as in the winter.

I hope your health is good and I assure you our health is very good also. Are you still very busy with your work? It must be very interesting working in a bank.

Please extend my regards to your brother and his family and to the Ruello family. My parents asked me to send their regards.

Cordial greetings.
Rosa

I waited a few days, about two weeks actually, before answering.

I hadn't been doing well at all. Damned Italy had messed up my life – big time. Since returning to the States, my life had been a bummer, an absolute disaster.

At home, at work, in the car, all day long, all night long, just about every single minute of every single hour, my mind was occupied and preoccupied by one thing and one thing only – Italy, Italy, **ITALY, ITALY.**

So many pleasant memories... the evening at the 'balera' in Genoa, the boisterous gatherings with friends in charming *trattorias*, the exquisite food and wine, the ribald exchanges, the carefree days at the beach in Sicily and, last but not least, that memorable last night on the beach, with all the singing and dancing... A flood, that's what it was, a runaway flood of marvelous and nostalgic memories.

And every single memory filled me with a languorous feeling that just wouldn't quit, a nostalgia so deep that it had become an obsession, an obsession that wouldn't leave me for one single minute. Day after day, night after night.

The unpleasant moments – what unpleasant moments? – were somehow forgotten and relegated in the dustbin. The incessant noise, the maddening traffic, the unbearable heat, the flies, and the lack of running water even – it was like they had never happened. Well, yes, they had actually happened, but they really weren't all that bad, were they? Certainly not bad enough to count.

At home after work my ears were literally glued to the record player. I kept listening through the late afternoons and into the nights to several records of the latest Italian hits, some Rosa had given me plus others I had purchased in Philadelphia since my return. I was constantly filled with this unbearable longing to go back to my homeland and to stay there forever. And that intense desire literally obsessed me, confused my thoughts and altered my moods. As a result, I always felt sulky, sad and dejected.

At work I couldn't concentrate on what I was doing. To my dismay, I realized that this lack of concentration was responsible for my making mistakes, foolish mistakes I had never and would never have made before.

Since my return from my vacation – just in the first couple of weeks – I had screwed up on at least four occasions. Three mistakes were venial ones and one not so venial – I had forgotten to include the punch tapes of the daily transactions in the branch bag we sent daily to the Main Office.

It was a routine but very important task I was required to perform before physically leaving the branch. It consisted of simply making a visual inspection to make sure the branch bag contained all the stuff that had to be sent to the Main Office. I just had to look on all desks and on all teller counters, and I had failed to do it. It was the most easily preventable blunder, yet I had managed to muff it.

I got lucky because on that particular day my boss, Mr. Guthrie, had stayed behind to make some personal calls, and just before leaving the office he had spotted the manila envelope containing the punch tapes. It was in plain view on the teller counter and I hadn't seen it. He just inserted it in the branch bag that hadn't yet been picked up by the bank courier.

He called me in the next day and told me about it. He did not give me the dressing down I deserved because he was more surprised than upset. He knew I was as efficient as they come, and that was in fact the very first time he ever had to call me in for a mild reprimand.

I apologized for my oversight, and promised him it wouldn't happen again. I finally found the time to answer her letter.

Dear Rosa,

Please excuse me if I didn't answer your letter sooner.

I really haven't been myself lately – in fact, to be absolutely honest, I haven't been myself since I returned from Italy.

My trip to Italy has been both a blessing and a curse – a blessing because I got to see my parents, my relatives, my friends, and my home country, and a curse... for exactly the same reasons. Sometime I ask myself, how is it possible that the same event can affect a person in diametrically opposed ways, how it can uplift or upset one's state of mind, one's view of the future, one's very life.

And yet, that has been my experience. I am talking about my coming to America eleven years ago and returning to America now.

Eleven years ago, just the idea of coming to America was the most I could aspire to, was the dream of my lifetime, my road to success, all I ever wanted in life.

Returning to America now, after my vacation, meant instead returning to my dreary job, returning to the daily routine, commuting to and from home. Worst of all, it meant being awake on endless, sleepless nights remembering enchanting Italy and the wonderful times I had there.

I am telling you all this because I consider you my friend, and I really need to talk about it with somebody before I go crazy.

I have mentioned it to my brother, and he says he felt the same way after he visited Italy the first time, seven years ago, but it will pass, or so he says.

I can't understand why I feel like this because, when all is said and done ('when all is said and done' is an expression which means "tutto considerato"), as much as I liked Italy, there were times when it was quite unpleasant while I was there.

The weather was unbearably hot, especially in Torre Faro, and nobody has air conditioning. I was sleeping in a very uncomfortable cot, Torre Faro had no running water, there were flies all over, the train rides were long and uncomfortable – like I said, it was not all that good, when compared to what I had left in America.

Still, I miss everything about Italy, even the unpleasant parts, and I constantly have this unbearable longing (longing means "desiderio" or "nostalgia") to return and to stay there forever.

This crazy feeling has affected my work also – since my return I have made mistakes that I never made before. I have improved on that, but once I am out of the bank the Italian siren song starts playing again and keeps repeating Italy, Italy, Italy – in fact, Italia, Italia, Italia.

I hope you don't mind my burdening you with this – I just needed to unload myself with somebody. I hope my brother is right and I'll soon be OK.

As for your questions about Johnny Mathis' song, "Chances are" literally means 'le probabilità sono', but it can best be translated as 'c'è una buona possibilità.' And then, here in America, on Feb. 14 they celebrate the feast of St. Valentine, who is supposed to be the patron saint of all lovers. On that day, it is customary to give your loved one a heart-shaped box full of chocolates.

The words 'Chances are you'll think my heart is your Valentine' can best be translated as "c'è una buona possibilità che tu penserai che il mio cuore sia il mio dono d'amore per te."

As for being busy at work, it depends on what day of the week or what day of the month it is. Fridays and Mondays are always the busiest days. Banking work in itself is fairly interesting, but the part I like the most is dealing with customers.

Once again, please forgive me if I have bored you with my problems. I hope you do not mind, and I have done it because I consider you my friend.

I already feel better for having talked to somebody about it.

Best regards to you and to your parents.

Lillo

It was an awfully long and very private letter. I realized that even as I was writing it, but – what the hell! – I had been down in the dumps, way, way down in the dumps, and I needed somebody to dump on, so why not Rosa?

But then another thought crossed my mind, the other side of the coin. Why Rosa? OK, I knew my mom – and maybe her parents too – were trying to get me hitched with her, and maybe she wouldn't have minded either. Still, why Rosa?

I asked myself that question more than once, but no clear answer was forthcoming.

She certainly was a very attractive woman, quite smart, well-educated and, from all indications, also a down-to-earth, nice all around girl. But – come on, now! – I had only seen her and talked to her maybe a dozen times while I was in Sicily, including a few times when I just said "Hi" to her. And all our casual or formal meetings were always while in the company of others.

True, I had also encouraged her to write to me, but I would have done the same with anyone else – girl or boy – who had an interest in learning English. She was not a total stranger, but she really wasn't a very close friend or a confidante; at least, not yet.

So, why Rosa?

The best explanation I could come up with was that I was suffering from borderline depression, and she just happened to be there.

Her next letter came awfully fast. Again, eight days.

Dear Lillo,

I received your letter today, and I want to answer immediately because I have the impression you are in an anxious state of mind.

I do not know if it is natural to feel the way that you do about Italy. In a certain way, maybe it is natural – last year I went with my parents for a little vacation to Tremosine, a pretty town on Lake Garda in North Italy.

It was so very beautiful that when we returned to Torre Faro I cried for a week just thinking about it. But after one week I was all right.

But you are saying that you have been feeling this incredible nostalgia since you have returned to America, nearly four months ago, and I do not believe that it is normal.

I am so sorry because you say you are suffering, and I hope you will soon overcome this.

If you do not mind that I give you my opinion, please do not be offended if I say that your feelings about Italy are not very realistic.

Yes, it is true that you amused yourself very much while you were here, but all those other things you mentioned in your letter, no air conditioning, no water from the tap, many flies, etc .are also true, and you should not forget that.

If you think about it, the bad parts are probably more than the good parts, and it will continue this same way for a long time, at least here in Sicily.

Unfortunately, Italy has many, many more problems than those small ones you have mentioned. It is not my intention to talk badly about my home country, because I love Italy the same that you do, but I live here, and I have lived here all my life, and I am more familiar with the problems of Italy than you are.

One thing is to come to Italy on vacation, but it is much different, and much difficult, if one comes here to live.

It is true that emigration from Italy is not the way it was until ten or twenty years ago, but nobody comes here to live, they just come on vacation.

It is my belief that if you look at Italy just as a location where you can have a nice vacation, you will have a different idea of our country, and it will help you cancel the nostalgia, and enjoy living in America like before.

It is strange you feel like that because I feel the opposite way, I wish I could visit other countries, especially America.

I sincerely hope that this letter will find you in a better humor.

Please do not permit this bad feeling to affect your health. Let me know if you have improved.

I want to wish you and the family of your brother 'Buon Natale e Buon Capodanno' (Merry Christmas and a Happy New Year). *And also to the Ravello family.*

Cordial greetings also from my parents.

Rosa

A good, sensible head on her shoulders! Yes! Add that to all her other attributes! That was my first comment after reading her last letter.

It gave me a new perspective about my fixation with Italy and all things Italian. Most of all, it made me feel much better.

And, of course, I wrote right back.

Dear Rosa,

Thank you for your very thoughtful letter. I dare say it was exactly what I needed, and it helped me realize that this Italian fantasy of mine is probably just a pipe dream (a "pipe dream" is an expression which means 'una fantasia irraggiungibile').

You are really a very mature young lady, certainly more mature than me, because I still have these pipe dreams, and I am five years older than you.

I have some good news to give you. As you know, I have been living with my brother Mimmo ever since I came to the United States, except for the three years when I was in the Army.

My brother has been like a father to me, and he has never asked for or accepted any money from me because he considers me part of his family.

I have decided, however, that it is time for me to live on my own, and I will soon be buying a house in Wilmington, in the state of Delaware, near where I work, about 50 kilometers away from my brother's house.

I have already put a down payment (that's a 'caparra') on a three-bedroom rancher (a rancher is a house on one level), with two bathrooms, living room (salotto), dining room, recreation room (soggiorno) in the basement, and a one-car garage, all on a lot of approximately 50 meters by 100 meters.

I am just waiting for the mortgage (mutuo) to be approved by the bank, and then we go to settlement (I believe in Italian it's called 'lo strumento'). The house costs $18,300, a very large sum, but I am not worried.

To be honest, at first I was scared to assume a debt so large, and I had considered renting a house instead of buying one. But then I found out that the monthly mortgage payments would be only about twenty dollars a month more than what I would pay in rent, so I decided to go ahead and buy the house.

Furthermore, I turned 27 this past September and within two or three years I expect to be married, that is, if I can find someone who will want me.

I expect to be moving inside my house within about three or four weeks, and certainly before spring starts.

Everybody in my brother's family, especially my nephews, are very upset because "zio Lillo" is going away. Even Angelina, my sister in law, was very upset, but I told her I would be visiting them very frequently because I do not know how to cook, and she is a goddess in the kitchen.

Anyhow, it is something I have been thinking about doing for a while, and the time is now. Wish me luck!

I take this opportunity to wish you and your family also the very best for1963. Give my best regards to your parents and affectionate greetings to you also.

Lillo

Seven days, this time! That's how long it took for her next letter to arrive. And, I must say, I had been looking forward to receiving it.

Dear Lillo,

I was so happy to read that you are buying a house.

It must be a very excited time for you. I have always lived in the house of my father and mother, and I do not know what it means to change locations.

I am sure that in the beginning it will (shall?) be confusing – I have not made improvements in the question between shall and will – but you will (shall) be used to it.

I understand the why your brother and your sister in law and your nephews were upset when you said you were leaving them. They love you very much; I saw how they respect you when you was here last year.

I believe you have done the correct decision when you decided to buy instead of rental, especially because the monthly payments are not much more.

Also, as you said, if you will be married soon, and you are going to have a family, you will be in need of a house with more bedrooms.

I am certain you will not have any trouble finding a woman who will marry you because you are a very nice person.

I think it will be a good idea for you to take some lessons in cooking because you have to eat every day, and you cannot go to the house of Angelina every day to eat. And I hope the woman you will marry will know how to cook for you.

Please send me a picture of the house you are buying. I am curious to know what it is like and if the houses there are like in Italy.

Please say hello for me to your brother's family and to the Ravellos.

Best greetings from me and my parents, and also tanti e tanti auguri di felicità e buona salute nella tua nuova casa (*lots and lots of best wishes of happiness and good health in your new house*).

Rosa

My reply took longer than usual – about one month, but I had a good excuse. My mortgage had been approved sooner than expected – as a result, I had already gone to settlement and had moved in my new house.

Moving had been a traumatic experience – never in my wildest dreams would I have imagined that a simple relocation was going to cause so much turmoil, so much angst. And I had practically nothing to move!

My brother insisted that I take the bedroom set I had been using while living with him, and Ange gave me some pots and pans (as if I knew how to use them...), dishes and eating utensils. Plus my clothes, records and some other personal stuff, and that was all. Still, it was a trauma.

But that wasn't my only excuse for not writing sooner. Other matters were on my mind, significant matters, serious matters that I wasn't quite sure how to resolve on my own.

More specifically, just one important matter was on my mind, a matter that required considerable thought and a critical decision, a decision needing more than a simple "yes or no" or a "right or wrong" for an answer.

Relevant considerations were involved, matters like private feelings, individual perceptions, personal relationships and other intangible factors, the kind of stuff I'd never had to deal with before and – I had to admit – didn't feel confident enough to resolve on my own.

Mimmo knew Rosa and I had been corresponding. While I lived with him, all her letters – though addressed to me – went to his post office box number. He kept kidding me about our regular correspondence.

"You'll see, you'll wind up marrying her." – He would tease me good-naturedly, and I kept telling him not to hold his breath.

But since deciding to go on my own I **had** been thinking that living alone in a three-bedroom house didn't make much sense. Marriage was seriously on my mind and – yes, I couldn't deny it! – Rosa was the only candidate I had in mind for a wife.

Corresponding with her had not only been a pleasure, but had also validated what I had already surmised about her. Her letters confirmed she was a sensible and smart young lady, one definitely worth pursuing. Additionally, she was a knockout babe, one **most definitely** worth pursuing. So, what was the problem? Just go for it, right?

Yes! But... There is always some goddamned but, isn't there? Silly as it may sound, my 'but' was a feeling of annoyance, an undercurrent of resentment I felt about the perception, or just the notion that many people – relatives, friends, plus myself of course – would always think of our eventual union as an arranged marriage.

I could not stomach the idea of anyone thinking – even in passing – that I had been unable to find a wife on my own. And I had a feeling Rosa felt the same way, assuming she knew or was at the very least aware that an arranged marriage was in the works. And if she felt the way I did about arranged marriages, she might very well turn me down; and deservedly so. And then, how would I look?

And yet another matter was on my mind – a not exactly insignificant matter. It dealt with a little thing called love.

While I certainly did like Rosa very much as a person and as a personal friend, I just couldn't quite determine what my real feelings for her were, sentimental feelings that is.

Did I love her? All I knew about love had its roots in bad Hollywood movies and even worse pulp fiction. I had never previously experienced a sentimental attachment to any girl, never even had a crush on a girl as a teenager. And crushes – fleeting as they may be – are a stronger emotional attachment than love. Or so they tell me.

Did I love her? I didn't know; I was at a total loss. The only thing I knew for sure was that I did like her, I did like her very much, I enjoyed having her as a friend, I knew she was someone I could talk to or write to in confidence. We had a lot in common, that much I knew. And I knew of course that there was strong physical attraction – on my part, at least. But love? That I just didn't know, I was not sure of.

I believed – or hoped, anyway – that our friendship and the mutual regard we had for each other would eventually blossom into love. But what if it didn't? Then what?

And there was yet another important matter, a substantial concern that bothered me – we were friends, for sure, and I wanted that friendship to remain. But would our friendship continue if she turned me down? Could it continue? Would she feel uneasy with the knowledge I had tried to alter our relationship into a personal and more intimate one? Could she ignore it? Could I ignore it?

As usual, my ridiculous 'superiority complex' kept me from asking for advice from others – why ask for advice when you know it all?

All the nuances, the implications, the what ifs, the obstacles, the roadblocks had little, if any, substance in reality. That's what I kept telling myself, and yet I was unable to entirely dismiss them from my mind.

I finally had to admit to myself I couldn't resolve all my concerns on my own. My best bet – I decided – was to get some advice from my brother.

One Friday afternoon I called Mimmo and asked him if he could please stop by the next day with his pick-up truck. A couple of days earlier I had bought a practically brand-new console radio and hi-fi at an auction sale at a fraction of its actual cost. Yes, that same one that is now resting in my basement. It weighed a ton and I needed help to schlep it home. That was my pretext.

Mimmo came over with his pick-up, we managed to lift the console on the bed of the truck and, finally, in my new house. When we finished, I got a couple of beers from the fridge and we sat on the steps outside the back of the house.

It was a mild early March day and spring was in the air. The builder had seeded the lawn and the first tentative blades of grass were beginning to sprout here and there. The weeds would follow later.

As we sipped our beers, we just chitchatted about this and that for a while.

I have always felt in awe of my brother, both mentally and physically. The mental part is easy enough to understand – I'm no dummy, but next to him I've always felt borderline retarded. Unlike me, Mimmo has always had an insatiable curiosity about most everything – religion, politics, literature, mechanics, marine life, agriculture, aviation – you name it, and he's not only familiar with it but will also talk knowingly about it.

The physical part, on the other hand, is a bit hard to explain. I am 3 inches taller than he is and outweigh him by at least 30 pounds – yet, I still see him the way a child sees an adult. I mean I always feel like I need to look UP to talk to him. I am his kid brother, I know that, but to this day I still literally feel like a kid when I'm with him.

And like a kid brother, I can always talk to my older brother about anything. And that's because we are brothers, of course, but we are really more than that. I have always opened up to him, even with private matters, knowing full well he would just give advice without judging.

On that occasion, however, I felt uncomfortable in discussing this particular private matter, and I kept hemming and hawing and prattling on, not quite knowing how to broach the subject.

Mimmo knew how I felt about arranged marriages, and I was painfully aware that what I was thinking of doing went against the grain of what I had always believed in. And that bothered me.

If one looked at it rationally, this reticence of mine was ludicrous. Embarrassment, private matters, personal feelings, perceptions, those were precisely the reasons why I had decided to ask my brother for some advice. Now, there he was sitting next to me and those were precisely the reasons why I could not open my mouth.

Finally, in the middle of a conversation that had nothing to do with my dilemma, I took the bull by the horns, to coin a cliché.

"Mimmo... please don't make fun of me..." – I just blurted out, unable to even look at him – "but I am seriously thinking about asking Rosa to marry me."

"I knew you would and I told you so many times. You always thought I was kidding, but I was serious. I knew you would." – He said in a matter-of-fact voice, as if that was what we had been talking about all along.

Startled, I turned to look at him.

"You knew I would? You seriously knew I would?" – I asked surprised – "How in hell could you have known? I didn't even know myself until maybe three or four weeks ago."

"I knew you would think about it sooner or later," – He replied quietly – "and I knew you would because I know you are not stupid."

"What's being smart got to do with it?" – I asked.

"Now, that is a stupid question." – He said with a grin. Then, with a shrug: "Look, any smart person would at the very least consider marrying someone like Rosa."

Then, ticking off his extended fingers, he started listing all her attributes.

"One, she is a beauty; two, she is very intelligent and well educated; three, she has an exemplary character and a spotless reputation; four, she comes from an excellent family. Now, you tell me, what else would a man want in a wife?"

I tried a lame joke: "What about money? Has she got any?"

"Five, she's not an heiress, but she is not destitute either." – He said seriously, ticking his little finger – "She's an only child, so she'll inherit everything."

"Come on, Mimmo!" – I remarked, somewhat annoyed – "You know I was just kidding."

"I know you well enough to know you were kidding, Lillo." – He replied calmly – "But let's make it five and put that on the scale also."

"OK, I agree, she is definitely worth considering, and I am considering it." – I said – "But my problem is, or rather, my problems are that... Well, you know how I feel about arranged marriages. And this one definitely started that way."

"I feel exactly the way you do." – He pointed out – "But I also know – and you know it as well – that just because a marriage has been arranged doesn't mean it can't be as happy as a conventional one."

"I know that, I'm not disputing that... But my point is, I'm in an awkward position here." – I tried to explain, fumbling for words. – "I've developed a good relationship with her, a pleasant relationship, a friendly relationship, strictly friendly so far, as platonic as you can get; absolutely nothing else, really. You know we've been writing to each other, and that's all it has been so far."

I hesitated a while, not knowing exactly how to phrase it.

"Well, I just don't know how to approach the subject of – well, you know – asking her if she would consider marrying me." – I blurted out – "I mean, do I just ask her point blank? Do I fiddle around the subject, test the waters, or what?"

We were silent for a while. I got up to get a couple more beers from the fridge, popped them open and sat down again.

After taking a few sips, I then plunged on.

"My gut feeling is that she suspects mom and, who knows, maybe her parents too were trying to match us together. Hell, probably everyone in Torre Faro knows." – I said with a shrug.

Mimmo smiled amusedly and shook his head but he let me go on without interrupting.

And I went on: "And, anyway, that same gut feeling tells me she feels the same way I do about arranged marriages. From what I know about her, I get the feeling she is the type of woman who doesn't like the idea of being treated like a piece of goods to be traded, or sold, or married off. You know what I mean..."

"Are you saying you're worried she may say no?" – He inquired.

"Well, yes!... And no too!" – I exclaimed – "Oh! Hell! I don't know what I'm trying to say! It's not like I'm scared of rejection. I mean, I could deal with that. Hell, I know I'm not Marlon Brando! But I would hate to lose her friendship because of that. And I do like her a lot, I really do, but if I ask her outright and she turns me down, that's what would probably happen. And not because of any animosity... any ill feelings, or whatever. But, you know, it would be... I mean, probably it might be uncomfortable to continue being friends. Uncomfortable for both of us, that is… for her more than for me, actually… knowing I suggested marriage, an intimate relationship."

"I see what you're getting at, Lillo. And you may be right." – He said – "If you propose marriage and she turns you down, there definitely is a chance your correspondence **AND** your friendship could come to an end."

He hesitated a moment, seemingly debating the matter.

"But I think it's well worth the risk." – He then said firmly.

"You are probably right. In fact, I am sure you are right, I agree, it's worth the risk." – I said earnestly – "But what would you do? I mean… How would you handle it?"

"I don't know, I've never been in a situation like that." – He observed. "It's something you have to play by ear. Look, you've been writing to her for some months now, you should have some sort of feeling of where she stands, how she feels."

We both were silent for a while. He seemed to be re-evaluating the whole matter, but then he just shrugged his shoulders.

"You want my advice?" – He finally told me – "I'll give it to you, plain and simple. Go for it! I mean, don't just write and tell her 'Dear Rosa, we are OK, hope you are OK, the weather is fine and… oh, by the way, will you marry me'. You can drop a few hints here and there and see how she reacts. My feelings are that she likes you very much also and she'll say yes."

"And if she turns me down?" – I inquired.

"I don't think she will, but if that happens… well, just be honest with her." – He said – "If that happens, just write to her again and tell her you are sorry if you have placed her in an uncomfortable position. You can tell her – in fact, she should already know – that your intentions were honorable. Tell her that if she is uncomfortable continuing her correspondence, you will understand if she doesn't want to write anymore. Then the ball is in her court, and it's up to her if she wants to continue the friendship or not."

Dear Rosa,

I am so sorry I didn't write sooner, but I do have a good excuse: two weeks ago I moved in my new house.

The mortgage was approved sooner than I expected, we went to settlement, and I am now a 'bona fide' homeowner (well, actually the bank owns most of the house....).

You have no idea what a madhouse (che manicomio) it was to move! And, thank God, I had very little to move! Still, I had to pack all my stuff from my brother's house, and then unpack in my new house.

I had about 12 very large boxes all filled up, plus Angelina gave me some pots and pans, dishes, forks, etc. My brother let me take from his house the bedroom set where I slept, and I bought a small kitchen set consisting of a table and four chairs.

Little by little (un po' alla volta), I will fill the house with furniture. I still need two bedroom sets, a living room set, and a dining room set. Plus I will need to buy a lawn mower (un taglia erba) to cut the grass, plus assorted pictures and other stuff to decorate the house. As you requested, I enclose two pictures of the house, one seen from the front and one from the back.

As for my prospects about marriage, I confess I am in an unusual situation, and maybe you can give me some good advice on how to handle it.

Over the past few months I got to know pretty well a very beautiful young lady, and I am seriously thinking about asking her if she would consider becoming my wife. The problem is that I have never even gone out on a date with her.

A 'date' is an "appuntamento". I don't remember if I have ever discussed this with you, but here in America boys and girls date all the time, that is, they go out together to the cinema, to a dance, to a picnic, mostly without supervision.

I just like this young lady very much, and I think she likes me also, or at least I hope she does. To be honest, I am even embarrassed to ask her, because we do have a very nice relationship as friends, and I do not want her to feel guilty for refusing me, if she does not want to even consider my offer of marriage.

I would understand and accept her refusal, of course, but I fear she may feel uneasy continuing the friendly relationship we currently have, and may *want to break it off. It's a pretty awkward situation, and I would appreciate any advice you can give me.*

I hope to receive your reply soon. Please give my best regards to your parents.

Lillo

P. S.

My new address is 2616 Millcreek Road, Crossgates, Wilmington, DE (USA)

Her reply came exactly seven days later. It was a very short letter.

Dear Lillo,

I am so glad you moved in your new house – it looks very beautiful, and I wish you all the luck in the world.

Regarding your prospects of marriage, I am happy you are considering getting married, and I am sure you will make any woman happy. As for the advice you are asking me to give you, I believe you should simply ask the girl in question. If she has any brain – and I am sure she does, otherwise you would not have considered her as your mate for life – she will say yes to you.

Give my regards to your brother and his family and to the Ravello family. Let me know how things turn out. Affectionate regards,

Rosa

Absolutely perfect English, I noticed.

My reply was penned exactly two minutes after I received her letter, and it took less than thirty seconds to write.

Dear Rosa,

Thank you for your advice. Your suggestion is excellent and I have decided to take it.

Rosa, would you consider marrying me?

Lillo

Seven days again. And an even briefer letter than mine.

Dear Lillo,

I think you should ask my father first.

Rosa

One minute delay this time, and maybe ten seconds to write it.

Dear Rosa,

Of course I will, but is that a "Yes"?

Lillo

Eight days this time – still within regular mail time.

Dear Lillo,

YES!!! YES!!! YES!!! YES!!!

LOVE, ROSA

It was now time for a very formal letter addressed to Sig. Filippo Donato.

Dear Mr. Donato,

As you know, I have been corresponding with your daughter Rosa ever since my return from Italy.

While her beauty fascinated me since the moment when I first saw her, through our correspondence I have also learned to admire her for her intelligence, good sense, pleasantness, sense of humor, and many other virtues.

I have come to appreciate her and her attributes so much that I want to have her as my companion for life to ensure my future happiness. I am writing to obtain your consent to marry her, and to have the honor of calling you "papà" and calling Mrs. Donato "mamma."

I believe your daughter Rosa looks favorably on me, and you have my promise that I shall always treat her with the respect she deserves, and I will devote my life to making her happy.

I know that giving your consent will cause you and Mrs. Donato considerable sadness because, when Rosa becomes my wife, she will have to come to live with me in America, and you would not enjoy the presence of the daughter you adore as you do now. At the same time, I know you understand and will agree that her happiness comes first. I hope you will make her and me happy.

With the utmost respect for you and your wife.
Lillo

Eight days later.

Dear Lillo,

It will be an honor for us also to call you son, the son we never had.

Both my wife and I know you are a good person, of excellent character, and from one of the best families in Torre Faro. Furthermore, I know my daughter loves you very much. It is true we will miss Rosa very much, but I am sure you will come to visit us once in a while, and we hope it will be soon and accompanied by one or more children.

On more practical matters, we will need to discuss when and where the two of you want to get married.

As for the where, I am sure you will agree it will have to be here in Torre Faro because all our relatives, yours as well as ours, are here (except for your brother).

I can make all the arrangements for the marriage, both for the ceremony and the reception, but you will have to make the arrangements for Rosa to accompany you to America, as I do not know what the procedures or the requirements are.

As for when, it is entirely up to you and Rosa. Whenever the two of you feel ready to be married will also be fine with my wife and me.

I am sure, however, that I will need at least two, maybe three months' time to make the necessary arrangement both for the ceremony and the reception.

Just let me know when is the most convenient time for both of you.

Once again, son, welcome to my family. We are happy for both of you.

Dad Filippo

CHAPTER 15

Long engagements don't make much sense – barring major obstacles – when two people are engaged, they should marry as quickly as possible. That's how I feel.

Accordingly, in my reply to my future father-in-law I thanked him for his consent and for welcoming me in his family. I then added I could take a six-week vacation and return to Italy in late May or early June. If that time frame suited him, the wedding could be held about one week after my arrival.

I was planning on a four-week honeymoon in Italy, then spend the last few days in Torre Faro to allow Rosa to pack up and say goodbye to family and friends before we left.

Painfully aware that Italian bureaucracy proceeded at a snail pace, I also advised him to start making arrangements for his daughter to get a passport as quickly as possible. Getting a visa for Rosa to enter the United States would be my responsibility.

And it's now time to say it again, **God bless America**… again, and again, and again. And it won't be the last time.

Wherever I went to get the necessary documentation needed for Rosa's entry in the United States, I just had to explain that I was marrying an Italian girl and I wanted to bring her to this country immediately.

No questions asked, no ifs, ands, or buts, no silly requirements, just a few forms to fill, and a reasonable list of identification documents.

And everywhere I went, in every office I visited, people smiled and congratulated me, gushing how wonderful, how romantic, he is marrying a hometown girl and wants to bring her to the United States.

Try that in Italy, and I guarantee you will understand why some people go postal. In fact, experience just a brief sample of the apathy you will encounter in the cobwebs of Italian bureaucracy, suffer the infuriating feeling of being treated as a nuisance, experience the run-around from office to office to office you will have to endure, and I guarantee you will not only fully sympathize with the mass murderer, but you will actually root for him. Or her.

Yes! God bless America, again, and again, and again! There, I've said it again!

I also wrote a very long letter to Rosa.

Dearest Rosa,

I am a happy man – your dad (I can call him dad also, I am not used to it yet, but I will....) gave us his blessings to get married, but you already know that.

I want you to be my wife as quickly as possible. I informed your father that, if at all possible, I would like for us to be married in early June, which is only a little over three months from now.

There are many things to be done, on both sides of the Atlantic, and not much time to do it, but I am sure we will do it.

Before I forget, there is one thing I would like to discuss with your father, but I am a bit embarrassed to mention it.

I do not know him well yet – I only got to talk to him on a few social occasions while I was there last year, but from what little I have seen and from what everybody tells me about him, he is a gentleman and a truly honorable man, and I could not ask for a better father-in-law. And the same goes for your mom, of course.

Still, I am embarrassed to discuss this matter with him and, if you don't mind, I would like to ask you to please bring it up with him. And when you do, please make absolutely sure you make it clear I mean no offense in any way at all.

I am referring to the wedding related costs – the wedding ceremony itself and the cost of the reception.

I do not know, and I do not care to know what your family's financial status is. If you are rich it's OK, if you are middle class it's OK, if you are poor... I'll break off the engagement immediately (just kidding, ah! ah!). If you know me just a little bit, you should know that I am not materialistic at all. I just want you as my wife, regardless of your financial status.

Anyhow, I am embarrassed to approach this subject with your (our) dad, and I hope you do not mind if I ask you to do it for me.

As my future wife you have every right to know my financial status. I have a very secure job that pays fairly well – I am the assistant manager in a branch of a savings bank, and I fully expect to become the manager sometime this year, maybe even before we get married. When I do, my salary will increase accordingly, and I am quite sure I will be able to support you and any children we will have.

Presently, I do not have too much in my savings account for several reasons.

I will not hide anything from you, and I must confess that the main reason for my anemic bank account is that before coming to Italy I used to foolishly spend money as fast as it came in, just to enjoy myself and to live 'la dolce vita'.

Just to give you an example, speaking of 'la dolce vita', when that movie came out it was first shown in New York. Well, I went to New York two different times in one month to see it – that is a trip of about 160 kilometers one way. And then I went to see it again when the movie was shown here in Delaware a few months later, and that was very foolish. Actually, that movie could have been about me because until before I came to Italy I lived a totally carefree life.

I spent practically everything I made, and it's even worse when you think I didn't have to pay for room and board, since I lived with my brother.

That's how foolish and improvident I was. But that is all in the past, I have changed now, and I have changed because of you, and I know that I am now and will continue to be a responsible and dependable person. Once again, all because of you.

The trip to Italy also took quite a bit of my savings, and finally and most importantly, I just purchased my new home.

My new home, of course, will be <u>our</u> new home, and your name will go on the deed as soon as we are married.

Anyway, my savings are not very substantial right now, but still please tell your.... our dad (I'll get used to it, I'm sure), very tactfully, that I am prepared to pay part or even all of the wedding related costs, even if I have to borrow money to do it.

I have already asked him to make arrangements for you to obtain a passport. If everything works out fine, in a little over three months we will be husband and wife. Usually, most couples plan to get married at least twelve months after the official engagement, and frequently even longer.

We could have done the same thing, but a long distance engagement calls for a quick wedding – or at least I think so – and we will have to celebrate our marriage a little over three months from now.

I have just re-read this last paragraph, and I realize it was wrong for me to make that decision. It just hit me that I have made all these important plans without even consulting you, and this is not the way to start a partnership. And I want our union to be a partnership.

I am so sorry, Rosa! Please forgive me. Maybe I am rushing you into marriage. My only excuse is that when you answered YES, YES, YES, YES four times I assumed you were as anxious as I am to get married. But even if my assumption was correct – and I hope it was – still I had no right to make plans unilaterally, it was my duty and obligation to get your opinion and approval before making any plans. Again, please forgive me.

I can still make amends. Yes! I would like to get married this coming June, but if you believe it is too soon for whatever reason, we can certainly postpone it to a more convenient time for you.

I can schedule my vacation any time I want, so it would not be a problem as far as I am concerned. If you prefer to get married at a later date, please tell your dad (our dad) about it, and we certainly can reschedule it. Please let me know how you feel about it. In June, July or later, I promise I will make you happy.

Yours forever,
Lillo

Her reply came fast and was to the point.

My dearest Lillo,

Do you think it would be possible to marry in May? Or maybe in April? I know, I'm just dreaming, but, as the song says, "I sogni son desideri" (A dream is a wish your heart makes), and that would be my dream.

I swear that if you were in Italy I would elope with you. Well, maybe not, because it would hurt my mom and dad (our mom and dad), but I certainly would think about it.

June will be absolutely fine with me, and I hope and pray we will be able to do it because there are many details to take care of and, as you say, we have just a little over three months to take care of all of them.

I talked to dad about your concerns. He is definitely not offended – in fact, he appreciates your thinking about sharing or even assuming the expenses for the wedding. But he says I am his only daughter, and marrying me off in style is the least he can do for me. He would like to have the reception at the "Due Mari" restaurant, you may remember the place, it's a fairly new place right near the lighthouse, on the beach. It's very beautiful and can accommodate over 300 guests. The owners are relatives of my father and they will give him a good deal.

Since you mentioned finances, I can tell you that we are not the Agnellis, but we are not on welfare either.

Dad is the chief of the railroad station in Messina and has a very secure job as well as a very good income. Additionally, he has inherited some very valuable farmland in and around Torre Faro.

We are doing OK but, like you, I do not care about wealth. I am just happy with the idea of becoming your wife.

Please do not worry about anything here – we will make all the necessary arrangements. One thing we have to decide is where we will go for our honeymoon, and I would like to be included in this decision.

Actually, my only request is that we include Genoa in our trip. The only reason I want to go there is because I want to see where you grew up, where you went to school, where you used to play. I want to know all that was a part of you, even when I did not know you. Please do not think I am being foolish or overly sentimental, but it is important to me, and I hope we can arrange it.

I am already counting the days, and even the hours.

All my love.
Rosa

Does she love me that much? Why?

Dearest Rosa,

April or May? How about yesterday?

I wish we could do it, but realistically I believe June is the earliest time we can be together. Genoa will definitely be one of our stops, and no, I don't think you are overly romantic. In fact, I am rather touched by your reason for wanting to see my hometown.

I promise to take you to the places where I lived – my parents still live there, and we can stay a few days at their apartment. They rent a huge apartment; I lived there for about ten years, and it will be all ours because they will still be in Torre Faro.

We will go to Venice first, then Genoa, then come down to Florence, then Rome, and stops in between; we can stay a few days in those cities and then we can head back to Torre Faro.

I'll take a six-week vacation, three weeks without pay, but it will be worth it. The first few days in Torre Faro will be for last minute arrangements; then we will get married and go on our honeymoon, and that should last about four weeks.

We can then return to your town for a few days. I'm sure you'll have a lot of packing to do – well, you can do some of the packing even now. I am sure we will be getting a lot of wedding gifts, and all of them also will have to be packed. Most of your stuff, plus the wedding gifts, will have to be packed in a trunk and shipped by boat.

We will return by plane, of course, and you can take with you enough clothes and stuff to last you until we get the bulk of your stuff.

By the way, have you ever flown before? I hope you are not terrified of flying; I assure you it's a lot of fun.

Mannaggia! (Darn it!) Here I go again making all kinds of arrangements assuming you will think it's OK. I am really incorrigible. Please forgive me.

Let's do this – every time I write about something I want to do, please do not interpret it as something I have unilaterally decided to do, but as a suggestion and as a request for your input and approval, OK?

Come to think of it, I believe now is the time to talk about this matter because it is very important. As I told you before, I want our union to be a partnership.

I mean what I say, and to me a partnership means I will never be the kind of husband who expects to be the absolute boss of the house.

By nature I am not that kind of person, but mainly I do not believe it is very respectful toward a woman, any woman, to behave in that fashion. In other words, all the important decisions that will be made in our family will be fully discussed and analyzed between us before being implemented.

I am certain that 99.9% of the times we will be in total agreement or we will be able to reach some kind of compromise. The only time I expect you to accept my final decision without discussions is on that 0.01% of the times when we will be in irreconcilable disagreement.

And, please believe me, the only reason why I expect that is only because traditionally the man has been recognized as the head of the house. I hope you will agree with me on that.

To show you I really mean that I want your input, I was going to buy some furniture and some decorative stuff for my (our) new house. Well, I have just decided to wait until you are here because you should have some input on what goes in the house (well, I confess there is another reason – I know less than zero about decorating, and from what I have seen about your house, you have very good taste, certainly much better than me).

You say you are counting the days? I haven't had a good meal since the last time I went to Mimmo's house. Not to mention the fact that I haven't been out with anybody since before going to Italy.

Please sharpen up your culinary skills and be prepared to shower me with lots of love. Yours forever.

Lillo

Several packs of American cigarettes greased the way for the release of all the required documentation – in Italy, of course. With the red tape out of the way, we scheduled the wedding for Sunday, June 23rd.

We had previously scheduled the date for Sunday, June 9th, but in early May a minor, but pleasant, contretemps occurred – my promotion to branch manager came through. The operations connected with the changing of the guard required me to stay at the branch an extra couple of weeks.

I immediately informed Rosa and my future father-in-law, and the earliest available date for the reception was June 23rd. And June 23rd it was.

My brother, whom I had selected to be my best man, left for Italy with his family in early June making arrangements to return to the States about a week after the wedding.

On Friday, June 14, right after closing the branch, I left Wilmington carrying just one suitcase and headed straight to New York to see the Ravello brothers, just like in the good old days.

The good old days were now over. In fact, New York had been more or less intentionally off-limits for me since my return from Italy the year before, and quite honestly I hadn't missed it at all.

The Ravello brothers greeted me with open arms and asked me teasingly if I wanted to have one last wild night out. They could have and would have arranged a mini bachelor party *cum* orgy at a moment's notice.

I hadn't had any serious dates since before going to Italy the previous year. They didn't know that, of course, and they probably wouldn't have believed me if I had told them, but it was true. I did consider the offer, but I told them thanks but no thanks.

I spent an uneventful night at their apartment. The next day Tony took me to Idlewild airport and kept my car with instructions to pick me up six weeks later.

CHAPTER 16

Rome – Sunday, June 16, 1963.

A taxi took me from the Fiumicino airport to the Termini railroad station. And that's where the real fun began – a wildcat strike of railroad workers had stopped all trains until the next day.

Great way to start a trip! That presented a major problem – neither my parents nor the Donatos had a telephone. They expected me in Torre Faro that same evening, so how the hell do I inform them? What do I do now?

I explained my predicament to a policeman who wisely suggested I call the Torre Faro station of the '*carabinieri*' – the local police – and ask them to inform my in-laws or my parents.

Good idea! Except that, what with the antiquated phone system they had in Italy, it was like running a high hurdles race on crutches. Public phones in Italy worked only with tokens you could purchase in selected stores. And where the hell do I find a Messina telephone directory for the phone number?

I never did find a directory but I finally managed to get a number for the Messina *carabinieri* station through the Rome *carabinieri* station. After I got it, I lost God knows how many tokens before learning how to operate the damn phone. With the help of some kind stranger I finally managed to figure out how to put a call through.

The Messina's *carabinieri* number rang easily more than a dozen times but nobody would answer, and already I was cursing a blue streak.

Finally, somebody at the station deigned to pick up the phone only to inform me that Torre Faro did not have a formal 'carabinieri' station. He did, however, give me the phone number of someone who did police patrol work there.

"But there is a good chance nobody will answer," – Was his not very encouraging comment – "because he is the entire police force in Torre Faro, and he is probably out on patrol."

Then, dismissively: "Or God knows where..."

And the guy knew what he was talking about. I tried that number about a dozen times, and nobody indeed ever answered.

Now I was very concerned. Being late wasn't a major problem as such – I just didn't want them to worry about me, thinking that perhaps I had incurred in some accident.

There I was, racking my brain, thinking of what I could do or who I could call to let them know I was delayed, when it finally hit me.

"You stupid asshole jerk!" – I told myself, actually punching myself on the head – "Mr. Donato is the railroad chief in Messina! He should know about the strike... Hell! He is probably on strike also!"

I spent the night in a cheap hotel close by the Termini railroad station. Figuring there would be a big crowd at the railroad station, I left instructions with the desk clerk to wake me up at six in the morning just to make sure I would be there before the rush was on.

It wasn't early enough.

Jesus, Joseph, and Immaculate Mary! I arrived at the station just before 7 AM, and the sight that greeted me left me speechless. Well over five hundred people were already massed in front of just two open ticket windows, and many more kept arriving by the minute.

It wouldn't have been too bad if that human tide had been lined up in an orderly fashion like you would see in America, or in any other civilized country. No, sir! It wasn't!

I said it was "massed", that is, herded, crushed together, jammed, mobbed, and squeezed, with everyone pushing and shoving, and trying to get ahead of everybody else. A hair-raising sight!

It was a funny scene, in a way, and a depressing one at the same time – funny if you were just an uninterested spectator observing that typically Italian scene, depressing if you were part of the scene. And I was part of the scene.

Just for the record, I got to the station shortly before 7 AM and I finally managed to buy a goddamned ticket at noon.

I am the most peaceful human being you will ever want to meet, but I swear I nearly came to blows a couple of times, once even with a lady, some fat bitch who called me *"Maleducato!"* (Rude!) just because I had told her – somewhat testily but politely – to wait for her turn.

On my word of honor, had I come to Italy just for a vacation, or for any reason other than to get married, I know I would have hopped on the first passing taxi and headed back to the airport to return to the States on the first departing plane.

Unbelievable! And to think I had so eagerly anticipated returning to Italy! To get married of course, but also just looking forward to being in the romantic Italy I remembered, that gorgeous, passionate peninsula I had grown to adore only ten months before. But now, this incredible scene of mass confusion, hysteria, chaos, you name it, short-circuited all that love and longing and turned it into plain disgust.

My love for Italy has always been deep, strong, and unlimited, and I will defend anything Italian till my dying breath, but there is no way one can sugarcoat that type of behavior.

There is only one accurate name for it – lack of civility. And what made it even more appalling was that it was happening in Italy, my country, the nation that practically invented civilization!

I know, I know, civility and civilization are different things, but surely there is a connecting thread between the two. Let's just say I had never witnessed this ugly side of the Italian character, and I didn't like it one bit.

I finally managed to purchase a second-class coach ticket and rushed to the platform where the next train to Sicily was scheduled to leave.

Ah! Finally a lucky break! Or so I thought when I found out the train would depart only fifteen minutes after I got my ticket.

A lucky break, my ass! Another miserable, rotten experience, that's what it was, even worse than the ticket-buying nightmare.

By the time I boarded the train, all the available seats had already been taken. And not just all the available seats, but all the available space also – every square inch of space on that train was crammed with passengers standing up. And I was one of them, of course.

A few lucky passengers – loosely speaking, that is – had managed to park their ass on their suitcases placed in the aisles, but I wasn't one of them. My suitcase was dumped in some corner on top of about five or six other suitcases.

And naturally it was June, and hot as hell! And there was no air conditioning, of course! And the only available place where I could stand was right next to the toilet. Of course! And whenever someone opened the toilet door – which was every two minutes – a fetid stench of urine and shit would waft all over the goddamned compartment. Of course!

Picture this – a ten hour trip, standing up, with people pressed all around me, all of them sweating profusely (including me), the smell of shit and piss all over, and with the only relief from the heat coming from an open window. I repeat, ten hours! Compared to that, even goddamned Korea looked good.

The train stopped in Naples and in a couple of other places, and finally got to Villa San Giovanni – a small burg on the Strait of Messina directly across from Sicily – at about 10 in the evening. It then entered a ferryboat that carried it to Messina.

Another wild scene developed in the ferryboat. A famished and parched mob of train passengers disgorged from the train wagons and rushed to the ferryboat bar to buy some refreshments.

Same, identical scene as at the ticket counter in Rome – only two bartenders and about five hundred irate customers demanding immediate service. By the time I managed to have my order taken, the ferryboat had already docked in Messina, and not a minute too soon because I was ready to pass out.

I hobbled off the train and – small miracle! – I managed to find a taxi. Shortly before midnight I was in my parents' home, dead on my feet and swearing to God Almighty I would never get on a train in Italy again.

The next morning I went to see the Donatos. My in-laws greeted me with unrestrained joy and embraced me like a son, *papà* Filippo beaming broadly and *mamma* Lucia crying and gushing all over me.

When I walked in, Rosa was out in the garden picking vegetables. When she heard my voice, she dropped the basket with the veggies on the ground and rushed in but stopped abruptly at the entrance, holding on to both doorjambs. Her gait, her slenderness, the excited as well as timorous look in her eyes evoked the image of a startled fawn coming to a sudden stop in a meadow.

She gave me a quick, almost stealthy glance, a light of pure joy dancing in her eyes. Though she stood there perfectly still, I could sense her intense, electric desire to rush to me. But she just kept waiting there, firmly holding on to the doorjambs, alternating quick glances at me and at the floor, obviously flustered, not quite sure of how to act or what to do.

To hide my own embarrassment, I approached her smiling an ersatz smile, unsure myself of what to do or how to act. Since her parents were present, I just gave her a gentle hug and told her softly: *"Grazie, Rosa, mi hai fatto tanto felice."* (Thank you, Rosa, you made me very happy.).

Blushing and unable to look at each other for more than a second or two, we just stood there, both of us flustered, not knowing what to do next.

Trying to smooth over that brief moment of awkward and yet pleasant discomfort, I then gave her just a slight peck on the side of her face. We finally managed to overcome our embarrassment and walked hand in hand to the living room where we all sat down on two leather sofas facing each other around a coffee table.

While *mamma* Lucia brewed a pot of coffee, I excused myself for not coming to see them as soon as I had arrived, explaining the reason for my delay and the late hour of my arrival. Just like I thought, they knew about the wildcat strike and were not worried at all.

I told them about the nightmarish train ride I had had, and my father-in-law ruefully explained that it was par for the course in Italy.

Throughout the rest of the day, we went over the wedding plans and the reception, and there really wasn't all that much I could contribute since *papà* Filippo had taken care of everything.

One welcome piece of news was that, knowing our honeymoon plans, my father-in-law had managed to get us first-class accommodations with reservations in sleeping coaches for all our train trips – and he got them for free. As a railroad worker he was entitled to an annual free trip for himself and his family. As he rarely used this perk, he had transferred the accumulated benefits to us.

Discussing a small but important topic was the unwitting cause of some mild embarrassment. Uninformed about the local hospitality scene, I hadn't made any plans on where we would spend our wedding night. I therefore asked Rosa in front of her father if she had any preferences as to where we should spend our first night together, but just as I mentioned the words "first night', I saw her blush deeply.

Realizing I had made her uncomfortable, I awkwardly attempted to smooth over her embarrassment by redirecting the question to my father-in-law, asking him if he could suggest a hotel in Messina or maybe even in nearby Taormina.

Papà Filippo smiled a smile of pleased approval at his daughter's obvious embarrassment and innocent discomfort. He then assured me he had already taken care of everything. Figuring I would have no way of knowing about hotels in Messina or anywhere near, he had taken the liberty of booking a room for our first night together in a luxury hotel right on the Straight of Messina. And, of course, he had already paid for it.

I wanted to reimburse him, but he wouldn't even let me open my mouth – he just waved off any attempts to even approach the subject. So I just said thank you.

As for the wedding rings, my dad had insisted that I take his own wedding ring as a keepsake – he would get another one for himself.

Tradition dictated that my brother, being the first born, should have gotten that ring. But Mimmo had married in America and dad couldn't deliver the ring to him. My brother bought his own ring and I got my father's wedding ring, a ring that I wear to this day.

I hadn't given Rosa any engagement ring, but in one of my letters I had insisted that buying her wedding ring was going to be my gift to her. I had then commissioned my mother to take Rosa to a jeweler with instructions to let her select whatever she wanted, sparing no expenses – a shrewd, well-calculated move on my part, of course. Knowing my mom, I knew she would surely get the ring at a deep discount – as a matter of fact, I even felt a bit sorry for the jeweler.

Another minor wedding related problem was quickly resolved. I had no tuxedo for the wedding ceremony but I figured I would rent one in Messina. To my dismay, there were no tuxedo rental shops in that town. Luckily, it turned out to be no problem at all – Rosa and *mamma* Lucia assured me that in Italy it's a very common practice for bridegrooms to wear just a good business suit for the wedding ceremony.

A couple of weeks before leaving the States, I had bought on sale a good double-breasted dark gray suit, expecting to wear it during our honeymoon. Rosa and *mamma* Lucia said it was perfect, needing only a good ironing, and Rosa did that for me.

My brother had brought his own tuxedo from America. Not wanting to outshine the bridegroom, however, he chose not to wear it and switched to a regular suit also.

We spent the last few days before the wedding just hanging around.

I never got to go out with Rosa – just the two of us alone, that is. Wherever we went – to my parents' house, to the beach, visiting relatives, shopping, or just for a walk – there was always a chaperone with us – her mom, a cousin, a friend. And I was OK with that.

Knowing what Sicilians are like, I expected that and never even showed or felt any annoyance at the presence of a chaperone. I did view Sicilian customs and traditions charming but old-fashioned, but I respected them and, to some extent, I even admired them. Surely, I would do nothing to thwart them.

Everywhere we went, Rosa and I just held hands, a practice I absolutely adore anyway. Next to love making and kissing, I consider hand holding the most intimate physical action between a man and a woman.

I am a charter member of the Incurably Romantic Club. Just seeing a young couple holding hands always touches me. And the sight of an old couple walking along holding hands literally brings a lump to my throat – to me it's clear evidence of a good, rock solid, happy marriage. To this day, after forty-five years of marriage, I still hold hands with my wife whenever and wherever we walk together.

At the end of each day, before taking her back to her parents' house I would just give Rosa a little hug, I would ruffle her hair a bit, and slightly buss her near her temple. We would then squeeze each other's hands, and we would whisper a few endearments, before saying: "I'll see you tomorrow, honey."

In the five full days before our wedding, I did not kiss Rosa on the lips one single time. This may sound unbelievable by American standards, but it definitely is – or was – par for the course by Sicilian standards.

In a traditional engagement – say, one lasting six months or longer – I'm sure even Sicilian lovers will find a way of sharing some pre-marital intimacy; maybe not actual sex (and then again, maybe yes), but certainly some kissing and maybe even some heavy petting. As a sign of respect for her and her parents, however, I knew I could wait. And so could she.

The most wonderful development of those five days was getting to know my in-laws well. And them getting to know me well, of course.

To my joyous surprise, we got along marvelously and our relationship became increasingly familiar and pleasantly intimate by the hour. And I emphasize 'joyous' not because it was unexpected, but because we managed to accomplish it in such a short period of time.

But it was more than just getting along – I grew to actually love them. Yes! Love them! I enjoyed and loved being with them, I looked forward being with them, I felt comfortable with them, I felt home with them, I felt like I belonged there. I never had to put up a front, the way we do in most social circumstances, it was like they had become my own family, the Donatos had become just like my mom and dad.

This in just five days!

Just as important, I could sense they felt the same way about me, I could sense they had accepted me as one of their own, as if they had raised me. Calling them *mamma* and *papà* didn't seem an affectation or a conventional way of calling your in-laws – it came totally natural and spontaneous to me.

Mamma Lucia especially was an absolute joy. She would rejoice in preparing for me little delicacies, she constantly worried about my welfare, and she took special delight in showing me pictures of Rosa as a baby.

We had become so close that I would openly tease her by saying Rosa was very beautiful indeed, but not as beautiful as her mom. And I would jokingly voice my hope that, as she grew older, Rosa would never become as beautiful as her mom, or I would always have to worry about somebody trying to steal her away from me.

Mamma Lucia would blush whenever I insisted Rosa's beauty came from her. Shaking her head in denial, she would say with a shy smile: "No, no, no... Rosa has her own beauty". But I believe she was also pleased.

Papà Filippo was very interested in international politics and was fond of inquiring about anything American. He was surprisingly well informed about a variety of subjects, and I say 'surprisingly' because Rosa had told me he had only had an 8th grade education, just like her mother.

During the course of our conversations, we did not always agree on everything – politically he stood right of center while I was more liberal. Despite our differences, or possibly because of them, we always managed to gain a new understanding of each other's positions and maintain deep respect for them.

We spontaneously dropped the façade of cordial politeness we had adopted when they had invited me for dinner that first time the year before. Our relationship changed quickly and quite naturally into one of absolute familiarity, aided by the joyous discovery that we liked and felt natural warmth for each other.

Except for the night hours, all my time was spent with Rosa and her parents, and we used it to catch up on family matters, and we had a lot to catch up on because, literally, we hardly knew each other.

Rosa told me about her childhood, the schools she had attended, her dreams, her ambitions, her likes and dislikes, and other aspects of her life that she had only briefly touched on in her letters. *Papà* Filippo and *mamma* Lucia told me how they met, how they fell in love, the many ruses they resorted to in order to communicate with each other, how they finally managed to convince her parents he was a worthy match despite his lack of resources, how they struggled to make ends meet in the first few years after their marriage and how he finally managed to get a job with the railroad.

Rosa was born soon after he landed that job. In unassuming terms, he told me of his determination to rise up in rank until he achieved his dream of becoming the stationmaster in Messina.

On my part, I told them about my misspent childhood in Genoa, my lackadaisical scholastic achievements in Italy and of my foolish dreams of finding instant wealth in America. I also went over my Army experiences, detailing the appalling conditions I had found in Korea.

Poking some fun at myself, I also entertained them with my misadventure with the Korean hustler and how he had relieved me of my camera. We all got a good laugh out of that. Rosa, especially, look-ed at me fondly, ruffled my hair and smiled, shaking her head in amu-sed appreciation.

The only difference between my interpersonal relationships with them and with my own parents was that I always addressed the Donatos with the respectful "*voi*" (you) while with my parents I used the familiar "*tu*" (you). Other than that, everything was the same – I could and did barge in their house at will and I had no qualms about opening their fridge to get me a drink. Quite simply, I behaved as if I belonged there.

And that's because I did in fact belong there, and I know they were overjoyed I felt and behaved that way with them.

Sunday, June 23, 1963! A glorious day! A splendid day! A clear day! A sunny day! A happy day!

A shower, breakfast and then, for at least an hour, the pure delight of listening to my mom imparting last minute recommendations and instructions on how to behave **THAT FIRST TIME.**

Yes! Because – you see… – mom still thought of me as her *picciriddu* (her little one). I was the last of the brood, and to her I was still *'nnuccinteddu* (a little innocent one).

And it was wildly hilarious listening to her nimbly waltzing around certain risqué subjects while using "clean" terminology so as not to shock me, because I – a young *'nnuccinteddu* – couldn't possibly have been exposed to such adult matters. I mean, after all, I was **only** 28 years of age.

About an hour of that, and I then put on my good suit and a tie Rosa had selected for me. In between recommendations and right through the very last second before leaving to go to the church, mom kept straightening my tie and continuously brushed off real or imagined pieces of lint from my jacket and pants.

Only after she was absolutely sure I looked perfect, we left to walk to the nearby church where my brother and father were already waiting.

We got there about fifteen minutes before the appointed time. As we waited for the bride's arrival, the church began filling up with relatives, friends and assorted guests.

I didn't feel particularly nervous but I did feel somewhat uncomfortable – my new suit was just a bit heavy for that time of the year and it was getting quite warm.

The priest had placed a couple of large fans by the main altar's balustrade, but they provided little relief unless you stood right next to them, as they just moved warm air from one place to another.

Precisely at 10 AM, Rosa walked in escorted by her father. *Mamma* Lucia and Mariangela Rando – Rosa's cousin and best friend whom she had named as *"testimone di nozze"* (maid of honor) – walked behind her making small adjustments to her bridal train.

When I saw her I damn near swooned. And no, it wasn't an attack of nerves – it was more like incredulity, plus shock. Yes, shock!

God! I know this will sound trivial or even mawkish, but I was in a state of disbelief, in a trance like, because... because – damn! – she looked simply ravishing!

What it is about wedding dresses, anyhow? Invariably, they seem to have a way of bringing out or enhancing a woman's beauty. Even plain looking girls look quite attractive with a wedding gown. Rosa was a knockout while wearing an ordinary housedress – wearing a wedding gown she looked mesmerizing, breathtakingly beautiful.

She had her hair done dramatically different, an upswept hairstyle that held up a tiara of white pearls matching a simple necklace. An elaborate silver brooch rested on her breasts holding the folds of her wedding dress at the neck.

She approached the altar walking slowly down the aisle next to her father. And as she passed, you could see a spellbound expression in everyone's eyes, and you could hear a rustle of guests voicing their amazement for her beauty.

I literally gasped, and even my brother couldn't help exclaiming: *"Madonna mia, quant'è bella!"* (Mother of God, how beautiful she is!).

But it wasn't just a question of beauty. What really knocked me out was her visible joy – she looked happy, incredibly happy, and her happiness was so real, so palpable, so obvious, that everyone could see it.

Like everyone else, I saw it, and knowing she was so happy because she was marrying me filled me with a rush of pure joy. And pride also – lots of pride.

Papà Filippo brought her to the altar. I shook his hand and embraced him and *mamma* Lucia. When he handed Rosa to me I assured them I would always take good care of their daughter.

He just told me: "I know you will!"

When the priest pronounced us man and wife, Rosa cried unrestrained tears. Of course, being a sucker for emotional scenes, I started crying also.

And right there at the altar, we alternated crying and smiling, drying each other's tears with the handkerchief mom had thrust in my jacket's breast pocket. And, sheepishly, we kept turning away trying to hide our embarrassment from the guest who were nonetheless applauding.

When the priest smilingly motioned for me to kiss the bride, I turned to embrace her and held her in my arms.

The kiss we exchanged was still a chaste kiss but, for the very first time, she gently brushed my lips with her tongue – just a very soft, a very gentle but totally unexpected brush, so unexpected that it gave me an incredibly sensual jolt – sensual enough to give me an instant erection right there at the altar.

A photographer had taken dozens of pictures of the salient moments of the nuptial Mass, and immediately after the ceremony the wedding party stopped by his studio to take formal pictures with our parents and assorted relatives.

We then headed for the reception at the *"Due Mari"* restaurant and... *Mamma mia!* What a reception that was, really the mother of all receptions!

It was the first wedding reception I had ever attended in Italy, and it happened to be my own. I had been at dozens of wedding receptions in the States but – trust me on this! – they all paled in comparison with this reception. I'm talking about the quantity and quality of food, of course.

Our reception had eight – count them! – eight entrées. And I don't mean you had a choice among those entrées – I mean you got all eight of them! That's no lie, eight! Four of the entrées were meat based ones, including a couple of pasta dishes. After the meat-based entrée's, they served the guests some sherbet to 'cleanse' the palate and prepare it for the other four seafood-based entrées.

Italians are blessed in many ways, and one of their blessings is the incredible variety, quality and quantity of food they have. It's not by mere chance that every nation on this planet has more Italian restaurants than of any other ethnic extraction.

Every Italian dish – well cooked, of course – **DEMANDS** to be eaten.

At our reception every entrée had been prepared with loving care and skill and **begged** to be eaten. But not even an inmate in a German concentration camp could have consumed all that food.

I have been known to display a good appetite now and then, but there was no way I could finish all eight entrées. It was simply impossible.

I had told Rosa I had never been to an Italian wedding reception before, and she had forewarned me about the incredible abundance of food they usually serve. She had wisely suggested I just taste a bit of each, if I liked it. And that's exactly what I did, and with some reluctance I may add because all the entrées were delicious.

And yes! There was also an array of antipastos that would have been enough to feed an army of homeless people, and of course they did have the pastries, an endless variety of Sicilian specialties, *cannoli, cassata, paste di mandorle, ossa di morti*, you name it. And wines, good robust Sicilian wines, and liqueurs, and coffee, plus the wedding cake, of course!

My father-in-law had hired a band, of course, and Rosa and I did some good dancing. To my delight, Rosa could really move, even wearing a wedding gown. I had visions of many good times at dinner dances in the United States.

I had asked – **ordered!** – my brother not to ask me to sing, and he didn't. But Rosa begged me to sing. And how could I refuse my bride on our wedding day?

I asked the band if they knew *"Roll out the barrel"*, which is called *"Rosamunda"* in Italian, and I sang it for her changing the words to "Rosa *bella*" (Beautiful Rosa) and "Rosa *mia*" (My Rosa). It was a big hit, with everybody asking for encores.

I then sang "*Scrivimi*", the song I had sung for her the previous year, because it was the song that had been indirectly responsible for bringing us together, and finished with "*Mamma*", everyone's eternal favorite, expressing my hope that in the near future Rosa would become one herself.

To everyone's laughter, I mischievously added: "*E io farò del mio meglio per farla diventare mamma al più presto possibile.*" (And I'll do my best to make her become a mom as soon as possible).

The reception went on to all hours, but we left at about 8 in the evening. We returned to her house and, after a quick shower – still separately because her parents as well as mine were there – we then changed our clothes and spent about an hour looking at the wedding gifts and counting money.

The size of the money gifts we received was astounding, by American standards. In the 60s, the average money gift for a middle-class wedding in America was about 30 or 35 bucks. In Italy, the smallest gift we got was the equivalent of a hundred bucks.

Rosa told me that in Italy people go crazy for a wedding – usually the newlyweds get TV sets, furniture, washing machines and all kinds of stuff to furnish their house or apartment. Knowing we would be moving back to the United States, most of the guests at our wedding had sensibly given us money. Still, we got several gorgeous porcelain and crystal sets that we would have to pack and send to the USA in a steam trunk.

We counted more than enough money to finance our honeymoon as well as our trip back to the United States. Finally, we picked up our suitcases and, amid a chorus of "*Auguri!* (Best wishes!), we said our goodbyes.

Mimmo and Ange took us to our hotel in Messina in his rental car. As they were scheduled to go back to the USA before our return from our honeymoon, we said goodbye to them when they left.

I had privately asked Ange to prepare some kind of surprise for Rosa when we arrived in the United States after our honeymoon. My suggestion was to place a flower arrangements spelling "Welcome home Rosa" around the top of my house's front door. Surely Rosa would be sad about leaving her parents and would also feel out of place in a strange land, and I figured a little surprise would cheer her up.

Ange assured me she would take care of everything, including preparing some light food for our arrival and stocking my refrigerator.

And finally we were alone.

CHAPTER 17

"Oh! What a night!" – Frankie Valli used to sing.

Talk about a night to remember! Talk about an unforgettable night! Definitely, our wedding night was one for the history books! For both of us! But mostly for Rosa!

The hotel management had been informed it was our wedding night and had thoughtfully provided for us in the bridal suite a lovely bouquet of red roses, a tray with fruits and pastries plus a bottle of *spumante* in an ice bucket along with two fluted glasses.

Having just come from the reception to end all receptions, we didn't even touch the fruit and pastries, but I did pour two glasses of cold *spumante*. The occasion did call for a special toast and the toast called for an appropriate setting. The best scenario was only a few feet away. I opened the glass door leading to the balcony overlooking the Strait of Messina and Rosa followed me there.

Leaning on the balcony railing, we just stood there side by side for a few moments contemplating the marvelous vista of glittering lights and shimmering waves under an indigo sky decorated with a quarter moon and a million stars. And then – our arms folded around each other – we toasted our happiness, sipping some *spumante*.

"Are you happy, baby?" – I asked her.

She looked at me smiling an adoring smile.

"*Amore mio* (My love), you can't even imagine how long I

have been waiting for this moment." – She said, and came even closer to me.

Our arms still intertwined, we looked at each other and sipped some *spumante*. I then placed my glass on the balcony floor, took her glass from her hand and placed it on the balcony floor next to mine and pulled her to me. I embraced her, she pressed her body close to mine and we kissed – finally, for the very first time, a real kiss! And we kept on kissing even as we reentered the room, even as I closed the glass door, even as I pulled the curtain shut.

We fell on the bed still embraced. I kept covering her face and body with kisses, caresses and little nibbles on her neck, and she returned every one of them. And I was getting all steamed up in the process. And so was she.

"Let's go to bed…" – I managed to pant in between kisses.

We untangled from each other without another word. She opened a small suitcase, took out a nightgown and went to the bathroom to change.

I undressed in less than a minute and laid down in bed under the sheets waiting for her. She came out of the bathroom a few minutes later wearing a sheer white negligee and nothing else and eased herself in bed next to me. I turned to embrace her, and we remained tightly embraced for maybe a minute, just breathing in each other's scent.

She had sprayed on just the hint of some perfume that seemed to bring out, or enhance, the natural scent of her body.

It wasn't her natural scent – it couldn't have been her natural scent, because no human body could possibly have such a heavenly scent. It had a faint flowery aroma, barely perceptible, but enough to make an indelible imprint in the olfactory part of my brain. I knew I would recognize that fragrance, that intoxicating bouquet, anywhere, anytime, even blindfolded.

It was a delicate fragrance, yet distinctive enough to overpower all other scents, and I literally began to sniff her, her face, her neck, her breasts. I wanted to become inebriated with that heavenly essence. I just couldn't get enough of it.

Trembling and panting with desire and excitement, I raised her negligee and then climbed on top of her.

I hadn't been with a woman in quite a while. And I was now with an incredibly beautiful woman who loved me deeply and was my wife.

I couldn't control myself. I just felt this sheer animal urge to possess her, a need to release the pent-up lust, a need to please myself and to please her, a need to make her mine, a need to be a part of her. I wanted her to want me as much, or even more, than I wanted her. I wanted this night to be so filled with pleasure for both of us that we would want more and more and more. And then some more.

Wanting, craving to be one with her, I thrust myself into her with a frenzy I had never felt before. But just as I did, Rosa cried out an intense cry of pain that shocked me.

Startled, I stopped. "What's the matter, baby?" – I asked her.

"*Mi hai fatto male.* (You hurt me.) – She whimpered softly, almost apologetically.

"I am so sorry, baby," – I murmured – "I'll try to be gentler."

"No, *amore mio… Mi hai fatto proprio male* (You really hurt me)" – She moaned, and there were tears in her eyes.

I dismounted immediately. "I'm so sorry, baby." – I apologized. "You just excite me so much I can't hold myself. You drive me crazy."

Only then I realized that she was bleeding, and bleeding profusely.

Holy Mother of God! My mind boggled. I can't even try to articulate what I felt. I don't know, I honestly can't tell; a mess of conflicting yet closely related emotions cluttered my mind – bewilderment, shock, fear, dismay, shame, sorrow. I couldn't concentrate, I just couldn't think straight.

Jesus Christ! What have I done? What do I do now?

Unable and even embarrassed to look at Rosa in the eyes, I just kept mouthing a rambling series of unintelligible groans mixed with pathetic apologies. And when I finally managed to regain some semblance of composure, I still had no idea of what to do next.

There was worry, of course, I felt very worried, yes, worried and foolish, very foolish, incredibly foolish. But mainly guilty; yes, very guilty because I should have known or imagined she was a virgin.

It's not like I am over endowed – hell, I wish!… Over excited, yes! Over eager, yes! And over stupid, definitely! Not to mention inexperienced in these matters!

This last excuse was surely the most valid one because all my previous adventures, all my previous sexual encounters had been with women who had been around the block, ladies who had been tried and tested before. And I never had any problem with that.

You know how it is. When a young man is looking for a piece – which is always… – he'll go after anything that turns him on, young, old, heavy, slim, anyone who is available and willing. And when he finds one and she's a swinger, he'll just take her and be damn grateful he got lucky.

I had never given any thought to the concept of virginity. I mean, I knew about it, but I'd never been with a woman who still possessed that precious commodity, and I had no way of knowing what difficulty it might present.

In the Army, during our raucous Saturday nights barrack banter, soldiers frequently boasted about having "popped her cherry".

I knew perfectly well what they were talking about, but I just figured it was a figure of speech, or youthful bragging. In my rush, in my animal urge to possess her, and mostly in my stupidity, I had actually popped or torn her hymen and, in the process, I had physically hurt her.

I felt like a piece of shit. Bumbling awkwardly, I kept begging for her forgiveness. Seeing how miserable and how remorseful I felt, Rosa tried to smile and make light of it, even going so far as telling me it wasn't my fault.

The bleeding, however, continued and a large area of the sheet was now red with blood. Sex now was out of the question, of course. I put on my pajamas and went to look for some tissues in the bathroom to see if we could stop the bleeding, but there were none.

I thought about calling the desk downstairs to see if they had any kind of medical help, but she begged me not to. She was too embarrassed to summon help for that particular reason and, to tell the truth, so was I. But when Rosa told me she was feeling a bit light-headed, I told myself:

"Screw the embarrassment!" and went downstairs to summon help.

I explained the situation to the night clerk who, to his credit, did not make any comments. With my agreement, he suggested we call for an ambulance. Half an hour later we were in the hospital.

"I am so sorry, honey." – Rosa kept apologizing. "This is not the kind of first night I wanted to give you."

And she said that as if it had been her fault.

"Baby, **you** are sorry?" – Was my dejected response – "I deserve to be horse whipped, that's the least I deserve. I really do not deserve to have you as a wife."

At the emergency section of the *"Piemonte"* hospital, a mannish looking *dottoressa* – a female doctor – visited her and asked for details. She looked at me sternly and I got the impression she thought perhaps Rosa might have been the victim of a sexual assault. I identified myself as the husband and awkwardly tried to put into words exactly what had happened. Of course, I couldn't look the *dottoressa* in the eyes as I explained to her what had led to that state of affairs. And even less when she explained to me what damage I had done.

In my eagerness, in my vehemence, in my animal frenzy, I had torn her hymen and caused a tear in the vaginal muscle. The heavy bleeding came from the torn muscle, she said, and they were now going to do some repair work to stop it.

"I understand it's your honeymoon," – She warned me – "but you will do nothing, and I do mean nothing for at least the next three, maybe even four days."

She left, took a couple of steps and then turned around – she had forgotten something: "Or nights!" – She added.

"Of course, of course..." – I just managed to mumble as she left.

One minute later she returned; she had forgotten something else.

"And when you try again," – she said pointedly – "be gentle, and use this, and plenty of it." And she handed me a small jar of Vaseline.

I don't know how many shades of red there are in the spectrum, but I'm sure I covered them all, from pale pink to deep purple, as I blushed furiously.

Seeing my obvious embarrassment, she tried to make light of it.

"Look, this happens more frequently than you can imagine." – She comforted me – "Especially here in Sicily."

After they treated her, they stuck a hypodermic needle in her arm to drip plasma, or whatever, in her bloodstream and then placed her in a hospital bed in a dingy room with three other patients. They assured me she would be fine and out of the hospital by the end of the day or the next morning at the latest.

I looked at my watch – it was about three in the morning. Rosa was now asleep and resting comfortably. With nothing else to do, I just stayed in the same room next to her, sitting and fidgeting on a very uncomfortable chair.

"Is this a great wedding night or what?" – I thought with some chagrin, but then I thought about Rosa and felt ashamed of myself for even thinking about that.

I also thought about the many recommendations my mom had given me before going to church. Without a doubt, she had mentioned the possibility, maybe even the probability of this happening, but I was too busy laughing at her selection of words to pay any attention.

About four hours later, while Rosa was still asleep, I asked a rather churlish female nurse to tell Rosa when she woke up that I had gone to inform her parents. I then left the hospital and took a taxi to Torre Faro.

Mamma mia! That was another tough one! Even inside the taxi I was already blushing just thinking about what I had to report and how I could phrase what had happened. Once again words fail me – embarrassment is not an adequate word to describe what I felt. It went way, way beyond that.

When I walked in my in-laws' house, *mamma* Lucia was brewing coffee and preparing breakfast for her husband. Hearing the front door open, she turned around and, seeing me, a worried look came on her face.

"Lillo! What are you doing here?" – She exclaimed alarmed. "Where's Rosa? What happened?"

"Good morning *mamma*... No! No! Don't worry, *mamma*, nothing happened, everything is all right, don't worry." – I replied, feigning casualness. "I just need to talk to *papà*. Where is he?"

"He's in the bathroom, shaving." – She said, and she sounded unconvinced – "Did you forget something?"

"No, no, I just have to talk to him about something." – I said, still trying to be casual, even as I was desperately trying to figure out how to articulate the reason Rosa was in the hospital.

Hearing my voice, my father-in-law came out of the bathroom, a razor in his hands and his face still covered with shaving cream.

"Lillo! What's the matter?" – He asked with a worried tone – "Are you OK? Where is Rosa? Is she OK?"

I couldn't look at either one in the eyes. Casting my eyes all over the room, I began to mumble unintelligibly. They both stared at me perplexed, waiting for some explanation.

Flustered as I was, I kept telling myself over and over: "Come on, Lillo. The hell with embarrassment, you just got to tell them!"

Staring at the floor, I finally managed to plow ahead.

"Rosa is fine but…" – I mumbled in a barely audible voice. – "But… well, she is in the *"Piemonte"* hospital right now."

Mamma Lucia gasped and brought her hand to her mouth to stifle a scream.

"No! No! *Mamma,* don't worry, she's OK." – I hastened to explain – "We just had some problem… well, you know…"

Profoundly embarrassed again, I lowered my eyes and tried to explain, still without specifically mentioning what the problem was.

"And… anyhow, she was bleeding pretty badly," – I went on – "and I had to take her to the hospital."

I was pretty sure they understood what I was talking about. My mother-in-law, now reassured, looked at her husband with a look between shocked amazement and mild amusement. He returned her look and faintly smiled also.

Seeing my puzzled face, my father-in-law quickly explained: "The same thing happened to us when we got married. Only, fortunately, my wife didn't have to go to the hospital."

I felt a bit relieved, and part of my embarrassment disappeared.

Mamma Lucia quickly provided some coffee and a bit of breakfast, and we then got ready to visit Rosa. Before going to the hospital, however, the three of us went to inform my parents.

Same scene, same looks, same questions, same explanations and same reactions.

Here – if I haven't done it before – I must explain that my mom was, without a doubt, the funniest woman God had ever created, bar none. And I state this even though, to be absolutely honest, she really was not an exceptionally witty woman, never told a joke in her life, and never even fully realized how funny she was.

"What the hell are you talking about then?" – One could right-ly ask.

It's a bit hard to explain my mom's funny bone. She just had a ge-nial way, a masterful way of phrasing things, of using wildly hysterical similes, of coining new expressions – especially when dealing with sub-jects with sexual allusions – that simply left people in stitches, literally running to the bathroom before they peed in their pants.

I must emphasize that her comic vein came alive only when she spoke the Sicilian dialect. Whatever comic line she delivered wouldn't sound very funny if translated in English, or even in Italian, but in the Sicilian dialect it was a riot.

Her reputation for bust-out-laughing expressions was so known and renowned that whenever she came from Genoa to spend the sum-mer in Torre Faro, word of her arrival would spread quickly. And every evening her house was always full of lady friends who came for a visit just to listen to her talk. They knew that sooner or later she would come up with some gems that would floor them.

With some embarrassment, I tried to explain to my parents what had happened the previous night. As soon as she heard the vague details I provided, my mother immediately frowned and planted her hands on her hips, resembling an oversized amphora.

She first gave a look at my father, and then at me, a look that I can only describe as filled with both awe and contempt.

"**The Vadalas!**"– She literally spat out – "They are all like donkeys, on top and on the bottom, in the head and you can figure out for yourselves where else!"

Then, addressing me with a disdainful look, she sneered sarcastically: "**YOU!** All I told you yesterday morning. In one ear and out of your ass, right? You weren't even listening, were you? *L'uomo di mondo!* (Man of the world!), *l'uomo di mondo* knew it all, right?"

My in-laws were already laughing and I couldn't help giggling softly also. Pointing to my father, mom then pressed on.

"**THIS ONE!**"– And again that look of contempt, only more glaring now – "**THIS ONE!** When we got married, he was like a stallion smelling a mare in heat."

And at this point she made a devastatingly funny imitation of a mating, moving the lower part of her hefty body back and forth and accompanying each forward movement with a gruff grunt.

Mamma Lucia was already laughing so hard she was holding her sides. *Papà* Filippo also was in stitches. Mom was now in high gear.

"When we got married, he was already groping me in the *carrozza* (horse-drawn carriage) that took us to the hotel." – She recounted – "And when we got to our room and we went to bed, he was wild. I was cowering in a corner of the bed *comu n'agnidduzzu* (like a little lamb), and he kept butting and butting and getting nowhere. Oh! And he wouldn't stop..."

Even my father, always a very serious man, was now laughing.

"And when we returned from my honeymoon," – She then concluded – "I still was more whole and tighter than when I left."

Mamma Lucia was now laughing non-stop but urged her to go on, even teasing her a bit: "And then, and then what happened, Nella?"

And that's when my mom went into overdrive. Shrugging her shoulders, she just winked at my mother-in-law.

"Well, eventually he did manage to drop anchor." – She commented with a mischievous smile. – "And when he did, of course, I made sure he stayed put for a while."

That may not read or sound exceptionally funny, but the way my mom delivered it had us all laughing hysterically.

Mamma Lucia was laughing so hard she had problems breathing. With tears in her eyes, she excused herself and made a beeline for the bathroom. When she came out she was still holding her sides, unable to stop laughing.

Thanks, mom! In her own inimitable way she had managed to transform what I thought would be a mission of pure embarrassment into an uproariously funny event!

The five of us then went to the hospital and we all entered Rosa's room, ignoring a well-posted rule stating that no more than two visitors at a time were allowed.

My in-laws embraced and kissed their daughter. *Papà* Filippo, holding her tightly, whispered something in her ear. Rosa later confided that he had told her: "Thank you for being a good daughter and bringing honor to me and our family. I want you to know mom and I never had any doubts you would make us proud of you."

They were all concerned, of course, but mixed with their concern there was also great pride and satisfaction. And you know what? That was exactly the way I felt.

That same evening Rosa was discharged from the hospital. Pulling rank, my father-in-law got our first class reservations in the sleeping car changed to the next day, when we finally began our honeymoon.

A long but comfortable 18-hour train ride took us to Venice where we spent our first three days together.

In that splendid city, appropriately called the Queen of the Adriatic, we performed the predictable touristy bit – the obligatory picture with the pigeons in St. Mark's Square, a boat ride on a *vaporetto* in the Grand Canal and a moonlight ride in a gondola under the Bridge of Sighs; all very beautiful, very romantic, and very memorable, but very chaste also.

On the third day, however, Rosa told me bashfully that she was feeling well – exactly what I had been waiting to hear since she had left the hospital.

We immediately returned to the hotel where we spent the entire day and night in bed, getting up only to get something to eat. And we got room service of course.

And yes, I did use that Vaseline jar! And yes, it was a day and a night to remember, for both of us. And for the right reasons this time!

Our next stop was Genoa. Anxious to see where I was born, Rosa wanted to see where I went to school and where I used to play. She wanted to meet my friends, go to the movie house I used to go to, live and breathe the life of my youth, immerse herself into the world I'd lived in, absorb and experience what it was like to be me, a young boy growing up in a big city. She just had to feel, to know everything she didn't yet know about me, she had to really, totally **KNOW** me. Body and soul.

Wandering aimlessly in the old quarters of Genoa, we drifted in the maze of narrow *"carrugi"* (alleys) and wound up in *Via Prè*, the street where I was born.

Via Prè is the most notorious and disreputable street – a long alley, really – in Genoa. It's known to all the sailors in the world for one reason and one reason only – in and around *Via Prè* is where the most famous *casinos*, or whorehouses, of Genoa used to be.

Despite the *casinos* legally mandated shutdown, the flesh trade hadn't disappeared or even decreased. What had once been an indoor commerce had simply been transferred outdoors.

Via Prè was – and still is – a surreal and extraordinary scenario of various activities, legitimate and clandestine. Some of the most prominent performers are dealers in contraband cigarettes, peddlers of all types of goods ranging from cheap necklaces to hand-embroidered tablecloths. And then there are the hookers, of course – hookers of all ages, sizes and colors leaning languidly on walls trying to entice interested johns.

Rosa was totally fascinated and enchanted by this particular street scene as well as by the street's overall bohemian ambiance.

Attracted by the enticing odors, we went for dinner at hole-in-the-wall *trattorias*. Daily menus handwritten on oil-stained sheets of paper, minimal décor, small alcoves reeking with the smell of cooked garlic and onion, gruff but adequate service, few but uniformly excellent entrée's and dirt cheap prices – Rosa was bewitched!

She begged me to please stay an extra day in Genoa so she could explore even more of the world I had almost forgotten. I agreed heartily.

We met some of my friends, and all of them, upon seeing her, told me unabashedly: *"Che culo! Dove l'hai trovata un pezzo di ragazza così bella?"* (You lucky dog! Where did you find such a beautiful girl?).

And I know they all meant it, because Rosa was indeed a real find!

We spent an evening in that same *'balera'* where my friend Luigi had taken me the year before, and we danced till all hours. I had told her about my first visit there, how it had affected me, and how it had been instrumental in making me fall in love with Italy.

"Before we leave I have to thank Luigi for bringing you here." – She said very seriously. – "If he hadn't, maybe you wouldn't have returned to Italy, and maybe you wouldn't be mine now."

Quite possible, I thought.

Our next stop was Florence. There, against her protests, I bought for her a pair of gold earrings in one of the many jewelry shops on the *Ponte Vecchio.*

"I don't know about you," – I explained, trying to justify that purchase – "but I expect this honeymoon to be the only one I'll ever have, and I want to make sure my wife will always remember it."

"I'll remember it all right..." – She said grinning and elbowing me on my forearm –"especially the first night."

"Oh God! You are not going to hold that against me for the rest of my life, are you?" – I asked with mock worry.

"No. Just for the first hundred years." – She said laughing.

Neither one of us had ever been in Florence. We walked miles and miles trying to see as many as possible of the art treasures that magical city holds. In the Uffizi Gallery we saw Botticelli's "The Birth of Venus" and – honest to God! – except for the long hair, Rosa could have been the model.

Most of our waking hours were spent in art galleries, roaming in alleyways past *Ponte Vecchio* and eating in cozy *trattorias* with no more than three or four tables. A couple of times we just bought some freshly baked bread, freshly sliced *"mortadella"*, a bottle of wine, and repaired to our room in a luxurious hotel near *Piazza della Signoria.*

Entering that splendid four-star hotel holding brown paper bags containing very pedestrian grub felt almost sacrilegious. We sneaked in furtively, almost scared they would kick us out if they discovered what we were doing. Once in our room, we would lock the door and, laughing like maniacs, we would hug each other and plop on the bed. A couple of times we even got to eat what we bought.

The next and final stop of our honeymoon was Rome.

Rome – a magical city! In a magical country! I had been in Rome twice before, the first time in 1950 when Nick Ravello took us from Torre Faro to Genoa, and then only about three weeks before, at the start of that miserable train adventure. But I really didn't know Rome at all, and Rosa had never been there.

And of course we did what all tourists do when in the Eternal City: a horse drawn carriage ride – a first for both of us – the obligatory coin toss in the Trevi Fountain, a visit to St. Peter Basilica, the Vatican Museums, the Colosseo and as many of the sites as we could. And we walked, and walked, and walked. We walked so much that, for the first and only time during our honeymoon, we spent one night without making love.

So many pleasant Roman memories... *Memories, misty, water colored memories...* Barbra Streisand used to warble.

One such misty memory comes to mind, a very misty one indeed, an unforgettable pastel watercolor still and always indelibly etched on my mind. The backdrop is the Spanish Steps and the main characters are two young hippies – a boy and a girl – sporting long hair, wearing ragged but somehow agreeable clothes and an innocent, carefree look. He is playing a guitar and she is singing Joan Baez folk songs, and they are both doing a remarkably good job, too.

They are seated at right center on the marble upright of the first ramp of the Steps. Around them huddle easily two hundred folks, flower children like them, and other youngsters. Rosa and I are among them – we are sitting further right on the Steps, right under the house where John Keats died.

Dog-tired from all the walking, we have plopped down on the Steps to rest our weary limbs in that always-festive ambience, and we are licking with gusto two luscious hazelnut ice cream cones.

It's well after midnight, but the Steps and the entire Piazza di Spagna are still jammed with colorful, carefree beatniks as well as hundreds of casual tourists.

Unexpectedly, a very fine, refreshing drizzle starts falling, but it doesn't seem to dampen anyone's spirit.

A few folks repair in nearby bars, but most others – including Rosa and I – choose to remain where we are, enjoying the music, the ice cream and the youthful spirit of friendship always present on those Steps; simply enjoying life.

We sit there under that steady drizzle for nearly an hour. Then, soaking wet, we skip hand in hand to our nearby hotel – "Hotel Margutta" – splashing on as many puddles as we can find.

"Memories... of the way we were..." – Barbra chirped, indeed the perfect segue for that canvas.

Aaaaaaah!... Life was good...

We finally returned to Torre Faro.

Lots to do in those last few days: preparing our suitcases, making arrangements to ship Rosa's dowry, personal stuff and the wedding gifts to America; and, mostly, saying goodbye to all her relatives and friends. And when that time arrived, it was a heartbreaker.

The day of our departure saw the Donatos' house practically mobbed by an endless procession of visitors – friends and relatives – who came to say good-bye and to wish us good luck.

Every visit followed the same pattern – it began with smiles and ended with tears. My self-appointed task was to try to cheer everyone up by assuring them we would be coming back within a year or two.

Our last farewells were for our immediate families. We first said goodbye to my parents. Despite her bust-out-laughing reputation, my mom could be very serious. Taking Rosa aside, she somberly talked to her.

"Rosa, not because he is my son," – she told her, near tears – "but Lillo is a good boy. America may have changed him a bit, but he is and will be a good man for you, I am sure of that."

Then she began to cry. "And I know you will be a good wife for him. I am sure you will make him happy." – She went on, still sobbing – "and he'll be good to you also, he'll be faithful to you, I am sure. But if he isn't…" – and here she stopped crying and turned very, very serious. Then, looking at me, she said firmly: "If he isn't, if he mistreats you, if he becomes frisky and starts looking around at other women, you have my permission to kick him in the nuts."

"*Mamma!*" – I screamed in mock protest – "If she listens to you, you won't have too many grandchildren from me!"

She just looked at me sternly and nodded her head in agreement.

"*Raggiuni hai!* (You are right!)." – She said in Sicilian.

Then, turning back to Rosa: "He is right, don't do that. Just massage his head with a rolling pin." – She instructed. – "And if you don't, I will."

And I knew she meant it.

My dad, always a man of few words, simply told us: "Love each other, care for each other, respect each other, and you'll be happy."

He then embraced both of us.

Saying goodbye to her parents was far more emotional, and not just for Rosa. In those few days, I had grown not just to respect my in-laws, but to love them also. It was a new love, a true love I didn't take for granted like the one I felt for my own parents, a new love I found hard to distance myself from.

Rosa and *mamma* Lucia secluded themselves in a bedroom for several minutes, surely to whisper encouragements and endearments to each other. When they came out they were both crying and kept embracing each other, an embrace that lasted several minutes. My father-in-law and I stoically tried to cheer them up while barely managing to hold back our own tears.

When I said goodbye to them I cried also, of course. Sobbing unashamedly, I assured both of them Rosa was in good hands. I thanked them for all they had done for me, promising we would be writing weekly; repeatedly, I pledged we would be back on vacation as frequently as possible.

A taxi took us to the train station in Messina. During that short 15-minute ride, Rosa kept turning around to catch one last glimpse of her hometown.

"Do you have any regrets, baby?" – I asked her.

"No, of course not, honey." – She assured me. – "I am sorry, I shouldn't be so sad because I have you, and we are going to be together in America, but it's a big change for me, and I can't help feeling some sadness. You understand, don't you?"

"Of course I do, baby." – I reassured her. – "I am sad myself; I love your parents just as much as my own. You know that, and I hate to leave them."

It was Friday, July 26. I was scheduled to return to work on the following Monday, July 29. And I wasn't a bit happy about it.

Conventional wisdom states that a vacation is supposed to recharge one's batteries, it's meant to make one more productive when he returns to work, indeed even eager to return to work!

Bullshit! My vacation had followed the script on just one count – for six full weeks I hadn't given any thoughts whatever to the bank or to my new job as manager. My vacation had now come to an end, however, and the prospect of having to return to work in just two days had me in the dumps. And if that wasn't enough, I was also deeply worried about Rosa and how she would cope in a new environment.

On the plus side, Rosa spoke passable English and I was certain she would be fluent within a few months. But would she miss her parents, her friends, and her hometown? Mainly, would she at any time regret marrying me?

She seemed to sense my anxiety. Taking hold of my hand, she looked at me and smiled.

"Don't worry, honey." – She told me reassuringly. "I'll be all right."

Easier said than done – I worried. And kept on worrying.

That same night we were in Rome. We still had quite a few *lire* left over from our wedding gifts and we splurged spending our last night in Italy in a luxurious hotel. The following morning a taxi took us to the airport.

It was Rosa's first plane ride. She was apprehensive at first but soon after the plane took off she loved it and was almost sorry when the plane landed.

"I can't wait to write mom and dad to tell them about it." – She exclaimed enthusiastically – "Maybe next year they could come visit us instead of us going to Italy."

"What a great idea!" – I agreed heartily. "I never even thought about that! There's plenty of room in my house... our house, I mean."

The Ravello brothers were at the airport with my car. Their reaction upon seeing Rosa was typically Sicilian.

"*Minchia! Che bella pupa!* (Damn! What a beautiful doll!)" – Was Tony's first immediate comment upon meeting Rosa.

"Now I understand why you stopped coming to New York for the past year." – He grinned, winking at me and nodding his head in appreciation – "You were saving yourself for her, you dog!"

Rosa laughed. "Did he really stop coming?" – She inquired jokingly – "I thought maybe he was lying to me."

Tony respectfully placed his right hand on his chest to indicate his truthfulness, then fervently declared in a very serious tone: "*Signora* Vadalà..."

"Please, call me Rosa," – she interrupted him.

Still holding his right hand on his chest, Tony stated earnestly: "Rosa, on my word of honor, he didn't come to New York once in the past year. In fact, even the night before he left to go to Italy, we were trying to lead him... well, astray. I mean... no offense to you... One last time as a bachelor... You understand, don't you? But he refused... *Parola d'onore! L'hai proprio affatturato!* (On my word of honor! You really put a spell on him!)".

"Of course, we don't know what he did in Wilmington." – Jack jokingly interjected. – "I'm sure there is no shortage of girls there also."

"Shhhh!" – I shushed him with a stage whisper. And we all laughed.

After placing our suitcases in the trunk of my car, we thanked the two brothers for their availability, said our goodbyes and headed home.

Coming out of the airport I took the wrong exit and quickly got lost. Driving around in heavy traffic, I looked for signs that pointed to familiar places. I finally saw one pointing toward Manhattan.

Oh, what the hell, no big deal! It was quite a detour but at least Manhattan was known territory. I took that ramp and soon found myself on 42nd Street, very familiar territory. Another brief detour took us to Times Square where I showed her the famous Camel advertisement and the skyscrapers. We then cruised by Radio City Music Hall, only a few blocks away, and I told her about the Rockettes and the famous Christmas Show they hold every year.

"I'll take you there in December." – I promised her – "It's a fabulous show, I saw it twice already, but I'll take you there in December. I know you'll love it."

Finally we left New York. The trip home was a *déjà vu* for me, mirroring my own when I first arrived in the United States.

Halfway into the Lincoln Tunnel, I told her casually we were under water, just to see her reaction. And what do you think her reaction was?

"Ma va! Davvero? (Are you kidding me?)" – The same exact words I had used 12 years before.

And just like me, she also marveled at the New Jersey Turnpike, at the wide expanse of green and the immense fields of mostly uncultivated grass that bordered the highway.

We made a brief stop at a Howard Johnson Restaurant to refuel and to get some refreshments. While sitting at the counter, Rosa read the Menu offerings and was able to identify most of them, but was stumped by the sign "Milk Shake".

She knew what milk was of course, but 'Shake' was not part of her vocabulary yet and I explained what it was.

"Oh! It's a *frappé*..." – She quickly interjected. "That's what they call it in Italy it. I've never had one."

I immediately ordered one for her – a strawberry milk shake – and she loved it. Since we still had about an hour to go before getting home, we also made a brief pit stop. Rosa came out of the ladies room literally stunned.

"My God!" – She exclaimed – "That was a restroom? It's bigger and cleaner than a ballroom!"

Before leaving the restaurant I called my brother from a payphone to let him know we were on our way and at approximately what time we would be home.

The next big attraction was the Delaware Memorial Bridge, just like it had been for me twelve years before.

"Wouldn't it be nice if they could build a bridge like this across the Strait of Messina?" –Was her awestruck comment as we passed over the graceful suspension span soaring over the Delaware River.

Yeah! Sure! They've been talking about connecting Sicily to the mainland practically since the days of Julius Caesar, but nothing has been done yet and probably never will.

Crossing through Wilmington I purposely went a couple of miles out of my way to drive by Union Street just to show her my branch office.

"See that white building? That's where I work, that's the branch I manage." – I told her nonchalantly, but brimming with pride.

My casual demeanor during the entire trip – all I did, all I said – was an act. The anxiety I felt as we left Torre Faro had been steadily escalating. In Rome, on the plane, in New York, driving home, I had been feeling jittery, tense, antsy.

Striving to appear normal, I purposely kept looking for things to do, or say or show, but I felt on edge, uneasy. Those same worrisome questions kept bouncing around inside my head. Will Rosa like it in America? Will she be happy? Will she miss her parents? Will she miss Torre Faro? Will she be crying? Will she resent me for bringing her here? And mainly, will she regret marrying me?

And those worries kept increasing as we approached home. On the Lancaster Pike – just a couple of miles from my house – my anxiety level was at the boiling point. Restlessly, I kept glancing at Rosa, fidgeting, still trying to act casual and hoping she wouldn't notice my uneasiness. It got to the point where I was unable to contain myself any longer. I thought it best to unburden myself and tell her about my anxieties.

Easing the car off the road, I stopped on the shoulder of the highway and turned the radio off. Then, glancing straight ahead, I began to speak softly.

"Rosa, honey, please listen." – I murmured – "We are almost home and… well, I don't know how to tell you this, and I hope you don't mind my telling you."

She quickly turned to look at me with a surprised, almost alarmed look on her face.

"What is it, honey?" – She asked. – "Are you OK?"

"I'm fine, I'm fine." – I hastened to tell her, still fidgeting and avoiding her glance. – "It's just… it's just that for quite a while, since we left Italy, in fact, I have been… and still am so very, very worried."

"Worried about what? " – She inquired, clearly surprised.

Shooting her quick glances, I tried to explain: "Well, I'm worried about all this, you in America, that is. It's all new stuff to you. I am worried because… well, I don't know if you're going to like it here. I mean, I hope you'll like it, but maybe you won't like it. I mean, if you like it, fine, but if you don't, then what? That's what worries me. The only thing I want is for you to be happy, baby. That's all I want."

She seemed to be on the verge of saying something, but I went on before she could speak: "No, no, listen, baby, please… please, let me finish. If you don't like it at first, just give it two or three months. That's all I'm asking, a few months… And then, I swear and I mean it… if you are unhappy here, if you don't like it here, just tell me and we will move back to Italy, I'll find a job there. I just want you to be happy, that's all. I mean it… That's what I'm worried about."

I shot another quick glance at her to gauge her reaction, hoping she would understand my concern.

Looking at me with an incredulous expression, she said: "Honey, is that it? Is that what you are worried about? You really scared me. Oh, come on, Lillo! Stop worrying. I told you before. Please, don't worry, I'll like it, I know I'll like it, I'm sure I'll like it, I'm sure I'll love it."

And then, oh so tenderly, she added: "I'll love living anywhere. I'll love living anywhere as long as you are there with me."

And as she said that, she reached with her left hand and softly caressed the back of my head and neck.

Smiling with relief, I turned my head to express my appreciation. And as I looked at her I saw a look in her eyes, a look that left me spellbound, literally breathless, a look that I can only describe as adoration, plain and simple worship.

One look, one simple look, that's all it was. But – oh God! – where do I find, where does one find words to explain how much, how much more than a simple look it really was? How infinitely more than a simple look it was? It was a look that opened up her soul to me, a look that revealed the depth of her feelings for me, a look that plainly stated she lived for me, a look that openly declared she cherished being my wife, a look that simply told me I was her reason for living, her only reason for living.

Just one look, one simple look. A plain and guileless look that instantly filled me with an emotion I had never felt before, a gushing sensation of pure rapture that I felt flooding my chest, my head, my everything, a feeling of unworthiness mixed with gratitude, an exquisitely sweet, overflowing feeling that lifted me to an emotional level I had never experienced before.

For the first time in my life I felt a desire – no, not a desire... a need – a primal need to be with and to belong to someone, and I had just realized that Rosa was the someone my empty life needed. At that very moment I knew that all I wanted in life, all I needed in life, all I had to have in life was to be with her forever, to worship her, to become worthy of her, to make her my only reason to live.

Looking deeply into her emerald eyes, I spoke out plain, simple words that came out on their own.

"I love you, Rosa, I love you so much." – I blurted – "You don't know how happy you have just made me."

Not exactly original words – I am well aware of that – and yet I felt like I had just invented them.

She looked at me with that same adoring gaze, but there was now also startled surprise on her face.

"Lillo!" – She said softly, covering her mouth with her hand. And she seemed to be near tears.

Taken aback, I just looked at her.

"What is it, baby?" – I asked.

"Lillo!" – She repeated, as tears welled up in her eyes and quickly slid down her cheeks –"That's the first time you have said you love me!"

I was dumbstruck – it seemed impossible, yet it was true, I knew it was true.

I again turned toward her, but was now unable to look her in the eyes. Staring at the car seat, I began to mumble.

"Baby... Baby, you are right... It's the first time... Probably... No, not probably. **IT IS** the first time."

Stealing a quick glance at her, I stammered: "But I do love you. **NOW**, I mean. Yes, I do love you now."

Still unable to look at her in the eyes, I mumbled: "Oh, God, Rosa! I don't know how to say this."

Blushing slightly but determined to follow through, I stumbled on.

"It's just that... it's just that when I asked you to marry me, I really didn't know you all that well." – I explained – "I just knew you through your letters. I did like you very much, that much I knew. You were beautiful... I mean, you **are** beautiful... and I knew it was time for me to get married. I'd just bought a new house, and the house was too big for just one person. I know, that's not a good reason to get married, but it counts for something. What I am trying to say, baby, is... Oh, God! I don't even know what I am trying to say."

Deeply embarrassed and totally at a loss for words, I sneaked another quick glance at her. She didn't seem angry or even resentful.

Still fumbling for words, I stumbled on awkwardly, but she never interrupted me. "You see, when I asked you to marry me, I really wasn't sure that I loved you. I did like you a lot, that's for sure. But love? No, I wasn't sure about that, I just wasn't sure that I loved you. Still, I asked you to marry me because of... what? Selfishness?... I don't know. Convenience?... I don't know. But please, honey, don't think for a second that I'm sorry I married you, or that I was sorry at any time. You and your parents.... I mean, mom and dad, are the best thing that ever happened to me. I feel so lucky that I got to know you and your family, and I wouldn't change one minute, one second of these last six weeks, these last three or four months, in fact, for all the gold in the whole world."

I sneaked another quick glance at her to see her reaction. She just listened silently – she just wanted me to go on, I supposed; and I did.

"You said it's the first time I told you I love you." – I tried to explain. – "And you are right, of course, it is the first time. But please, baby, believe me, there is a reason for it. Just let me explain, please."

Again I paused for a few seconds trying to find the right words, and then plunged on.

"I know this will sound conceited, or maybe even a poor excuse, but it's the truth, I swear to God it's the truth." – I explained. "It's just... I never said I loved you because... well, because I never wanted to lie to you. And no, I don't mean to sound like I am a saint because I am not, but I was trying to be as honest as possible. And definitely I wanted... I'd made up my mind, the minute I decided to ask you to marry me I made up my mind I was going to be honest with you, always. I will always want to be honest with you. And if I had told you I loved you before it would have been a lie. No, wait... maybe not a lie, but I just wasn't sure. Do you understand what I am trying to say, honey? I wasn't sure, I wasn't sure that I loved you, and that's why I never said it. That's why I never said 'I love you' before. But I am sure now, baby, and I'll say it over and over again, I love you, I love you, I love you, I love you, Rosa, I love you so much, honey."

With nothing else to add, I just sneaked another quick look at her and mumbled a pathetic: "Can you forgive me, baby?... Please, honey?"

I then stared straight ahead waiting for her reply. After what seemed like forever but were only a very few seconds, she reached with her hand and again caressed the back of my head and hair.

"Lillo, I knew that." – She said, startling me – "Yes, I always knew that, I knew that all along. I knew you were not sure about your feelings for me, but I was in love with you and I was happy just to have you. But I knew…" – and here she paused for a couple of seconds – "No, that sounds conceited also. I hoped… that's it, I hoped with all my heart you would come to love me the way I love you, and now I know you do and I am happy. But I have been happy since the day we started corresponding, since the day you asked me to marry you, since we have been married. Only I am happier now."

Heaving a huge, audible sigh of relief, I exclaimed: "Oh! Thank you, my love! Believe me, honey, I am as happy as you are; happy and relieved. God! That's a big load off my mind."

Leaning over, I gently brushed her cheek where a tear had rolled down and I then kissed her, just a simple kiss, a gentle kiss, our lips briefly touching. That's all it was, a simple, gentle kiss, yet infinitely more satisfying than the hundreds – thousands! – torrid kisses we had already exchanged over the past five weeks.

Easing into traffic again I then turned left on Hercules Road.

"We are almost home, honey." – I told her cheerfully – "My house is less than a mile from here. I'll tell you when we are almost there, and when we get close I want you to close your eyes."

"Why?" – She inquired, a bit surprised but good-naturedly.

Waving off her inquiry, I explained: "I know, I know. You have seen my house in pictures before, but it may seem different when you see the real thing, and I want it to be a surprise to you, OK?"

She snorted an odd, soft chuckle and quickly brought her hand up to her mouth as if trying not to laugh out loud. Her reaction puzzled me – it didn't seem to be quite in tune with my desire to surprise her. Did she like being surprised? Did she think it was a childish idea?

She kept on giggling and I couldn't understand why.

"What's so funny?" – I asked her.

She was grinning mischievously now.

"Well. It's just... it's just..." – She started saying.

"It's just what?" – I interrupted her, still mystified.

"It's just... It's just that I'm pretty sure I have a little surprise for you too." – She chortled, and she kept on grinning.

Startled, I sneaked a quick look at her and – yes! – she was now clearly giggling and purposely covering her mouth to keep from laughing.

I felt a tingling sensation from head to toe, my entire frame quivering. Again, I had to stop the car on the side of the road.

"Are you saying you think you are, by any chance?..." – I asked her, wide eyed, ready to explode with joy.

She stopped giggling. "Well, I am not one hundred percent sure, honey," – She said hesitantly – "but I have never been late before, not even a day, and I am ten days late now. I hope I am, but I am not one hundred per cent sure."

I just let out a massive whoop. **YEAAAHHH!!!!!... I WAS GOING TO BE A FATHER!!!...**

"But I am not one hundred per cent sure, honey." – She cautioned me again – "I may be late because of all the excitement, all that we've been through, you know..."

But I would have none of it.

"Rosa, baby," – I swaggered – "if you are not pregnant now, you will be before the night is over, I promise you."

Glowingly, I put the car in gear and just for the hell of it I turned the radio on – I wanted some music, the occasion clearly called for some music.

A Johnny Mathis song was playing, *"Wonderful, Wonderful!"* – I couldn't have picked a more appropriate background music. Wonderful, wonderful, that's exactly the way I felt, that's the way we both felt!

Man oh man! On top of the world! That's where I was! Pure, distilled happiness, that's what I felt!... Oh! Wait till I tell my parents, her parents, my brother, everyone, even strangers! Mom was sure to make some funny comment about the Vadalàs virility! Even the idea of returning to work the following Monday was now appealing – I couldn't wait to show off my wife – **my pregnant wife!** – to my co-workers.

"**And I say to myself... it's wonderful, wonderful... oh, so wonderful, my love!**" – I sang out loud along with Johnny Mathis.

We were now only a few hundred yards away from my house in the Crossgates development. At the intersection at the Newport Gap Pike where Hercules Road becomes Millcreek Road, I had to stop for a red light.

"OK, Rosa, we're almost there. My house is just past that curve after the traffic light." – I told her beaming.

God! Literally bouncing up and down on the car seat, I could hardly wait to get home, I could hardly wait to see Mimmo and Ange and surprise them with the fabulous news I had just heard.

"Guess what?" – Would be my first utterance, the very first thing I would shout out as soon as I saw them. Yes! Even as I was getting out of the car, even before saying "How are you?", even before the warm embraces, even before getting our luggage out of the trunk.

"**Guess what?!?**" – I would blurt out breathlessly. And then, without even waiting for an answer I would gloriously announce – "**ROSA IS PREGNANT!!!**"

Mimmo would flash a dazzling smile, and shout *Auguri!* (Congratulations!) and Ange would coo a heartfelt "Oooooh!...", embrace Rosa tenderly, and surely shed a few tears. How much better could it get?

I managed to calm down a bit.

"OK, now. I want you to close your eyes now," – I told her. – "And don't open them until I tell you. Promise you won't look, Rosa, OK? You can open them only when I'm parked in my driveway, OK? I'll tell you when we get there."

The light finally turned green, and I had to wait a few seconds while the guy in the car in front of me made up his mind to move. I honked a couple of times and he finally lurched forward.

"Now, promise you won't peek..." – I cautioned her with a mock serious tone, and I proceeded.

"Don't worry, honey, I won't look, I promise." – She said.

I resumed singing out loud while Rosa playfully and obediently lowered her head, shielded her face with her hands and closed her eyes.

Forever.

CHAPTER 18

A blur, a flash, a sudden, brief, angry, terrifying screech of protesting rubber and a horrific blast, a deafening boom, an ear-splitting detonation like the explosion of a bomb, like the thundering crack of a lightning strike in your backyard, like the simultaneous clash of a hundred, of a thousand cymbals, like the blast of a car crashing broadside into your car.

That's all I remember.

It's a booming blast that, to this day, still jolts me awake at night now and then. Rosa was killed instantly, or so I was told and want to believe. I was luckier – I survived. I was in a coma for over two months, but I survived.

Yes, I was lucky! That's what all my friends and relatives kept telling me over and over – I was lucky. Ironically, they were saying it without irony – they really meant it. They really believed I had been lucky!

If by lucky they meant I didn't have to worry about the unbelievable heartaches my relatives had to go through to cope with the aftermath of that tragedy, then – yes! – I suppose I had been lucky.

As for what I went through, both physically and emotionally, that's another story. Even the expression 'I wouldn't wish it on my worst enemy' seems trite and grossly inadequate.

Oh, I did wish it on the motherfucking son-of-a-bitch goddamned prick asshole teenage punk speeding away from the cops. I wished that and a hell of a lot more on him. But he got lucky too, that cock-sucking son-of-a-bitch! Yes, he got really lucky – he was killed instantly also.

The months that followed were so excruciatingly painful, so totally draining in physical and emotional strength and will to live that daily I literally begged doctors to let me die.

But those goddamned bastards wouldn't, of course, and they stubbornly kept me alive. And I cried, and I screamed at them, and I cursed them and the nurses, openly displaying my hatred for them all and for the entire universe.

Even when I was finally declared to be out of danger, I was so despondent, so unresponsive, so completely uninterested in living, that I had become practically catatonic, just staring in space motionless for hours and hours on end, just breathing.

Yes, I had been lucky!

When the crash occurred, my brother was in my front yard with Ange waiting for my car to appear. They heard the noise of what sounded like a crash but didn't see it because of the curve on Millcreek Road. Soon, however, they heard the sound of sirens as ambulances and police cars rushed to the scene of the accident.

Filled with foreboding, Mimmo ran to the accident scene himself. The road had already been closed to all traffic and the accident area had been cordoned off. He didn't recognize my car at first – it was just a piece of mangled metal overturned in a ditch. On the opposite side of the road another car lay askew, totally demolished, its engine pushed deep into the passengers' compartment.

Two bodies covered with tarpaulin were on the ground and a team of paramedics was frantically working on a mangled body on the side of the road. They were trying to resuscitate me, as I had gone into cardiac arrest.

Mimmo again looked at the mangled car in the ditch, and only then recognized it as mine. And then he began screaming, and he kept on screaming as he desperately rushed toward the paramedics, wanting to help me out. Having completely lost his head, he even began fighting with them and with the cops who had to physically restrain him.

Incoherent with grief and shock, he somehow managed to identify himself as my brother, but still they wouldn't let him come near me.

Babbling frantically, he provided the police with our names and
address adding that we were returning from our honeymoon in Italy
where we had married. Only after he saw them placing me in an ambulance he rushed home to inform Ange.

I can't even begin to imagine how he and all my relatives must
have felt, the emotional upheaval they were undergoing, their helpless-
ness, their desperation, their disbelief.

I am now convinced that the immediate relatives are much, much
worse off than the victims of a tragic accident. They are the ones who
have to cope with all the aftermaths of the tragedy, they are the ones
who have to inform other close relatives, they are the ones who must
make funeral plans, make daily visits to the hospital and deal with the
victims' day-to-day affairs. And they must do all that on very short notice, without any idea of what needs to be done first and frequently even
without the necessary skills. To further compound their agonies, they
are forced to perform all those tasks while they also grieve and have
their own affairs to tend to or jobs to go to.

Victims, on the other hand, are just dead or in a coma. In either
case, they have nothing to worry about.

Mimmo rushed to Wilmington General Hospital where I had
been taken. With enormous relief he was told that I was still alive. Despite his wretched pleas, he was not allowed to see me as I was in the
Intensive Care Trauma Unit.

Pacing restlessly in a hallway, he chain-smoked a full pack of
Marlboro. After a wait of several agonizing hours he managed to corral
one of the doctors, identified himself and pleaded with him to let him
know my conditions.

The guy pulled no punches. Going from head to toe, he detailed
all my injuries – a fractured skull with bleeding and swelling of the brain,
fractured jaw, fractured collar bone, several cracked ribs, collapsed lung,
a broken arm, open fracture of one leg and closed fracture of the other,
still undetermined internal injuries, plus multiple and severe lacerations

on my face and rest of the body where I had scraped the pavement when I was thrown out of the car.

"I'm sorry to have to tell you this," – was his glum prognosis – "It's a miracle he is still alive and, quite honestly, I don't think he'll make it."

I don't know where my brother found the strength to cope with all that. He hardly ever drinks, a beer or two at the most, but he says that when he went home he drained a water glass full of whiskey to steady himself, that's how bad he was shaking.

When he stopped shaking, he began to mobilize friends and relatives. There was no way of contacting the folks in Italy because they had no phone. He therefore immediately sent our parents a telegram saying "*Gravissimo incidente auto. Rosa deceduta. Lillo gravissimo. Arriverò Lunedi per informare i Donato*" (Very serious car accident. Rosa dead. Lillo very critical. I will arrive Monday to inform the Donatos).

He asked his father-in-law to claim Rosa's body, give it a proper funeral and provide a temporary burial place while waiting to decide what her parents might want to do.

Ange and the kids moved into my house to be near me. She came several times daily to the hospital, but didn't get to see me until after my brother's return from Italy as I was not allowed any visitors.

My nephew Pietro, now a young man of 14, was assigned the task of calling the bank first thing on Monday to let them know about the accident, although my name would surely appear in the papers on Sunday.

After contacting the New Castle County Police Department, Mimmo made arrangements for somebody to retrieve the luggage we had in the car and have it taken to my house. He then called Pan Am Airlines to make reservations to leave for Italy the following day.

Next he called Jack Ravello in New York, shocking him with the news of the tragedy, and asked him to meet him at the airport the next day with his brother Tony so he could leave his car with them.

Jack was so stunned that at first he had actually thought it was some kind of a prank call or a bad joke, and believed him only when he realized that Mimmo was crying on the phone. And then he also cried.

After drinking another half glass of whiskey, he tried to get some sleep, all to no avail. Carrying just a small suitcase, he left on Sunday night. He arrived in Torre Faro on Monday evening and went straight to our parents' house.

He could have saved himself the cost of the telegram as it had been delivered just about one hour before he got there.

He found both mom and dad literally in shock, too dumbstruck to cry. When they saw him coming through the front door they began wailing uncontrollably, wanting, demanding information about me, about Rosa, about everything.

He managed to calm them down a bit then somberly explained what had happened. He translated for them a front-page article from the Wilmington paper he had bought before departing.

A huge headline stated "**ITALIAN BRIDE KILLED IN TRAGIC CAR CRASH**" while a sub headline stated "**Husband near Death**". The article made it clear that a speeding car pursued by the police had gone through a red light crashing into our car. It went on to say that the teenage driver of the car had also been killed along with the newlywed Italian bride, and also mentioned the heartbreaking detail that the bride and groom had just arrived from Italy and that it was Rosa's first day in the United States.

He told my parents I was still alive when he had left, but he couldn't assure them if that was still true. He related the conversation he had with the doctor at the hospital and his pessimistic prognosis. Somberly, he urged them to be prepared for the worse.

Informing the Donatos was the worst thing he ever had to face. After consulting with our parents on how to address the situation, they decided that the best course of action would be for him to go to their house by himself to inform them of the tragedy. Our parents would then follow about 15 minutes later to help them deal with their grief.

It was about 9 in the evening when my brother knocked on the Donatos' front door. My father-in-law opened the door and, seeing my brother, was visibly shocked.

"Mimmo!... What are you doing here? What happened? Is something wrong?" – He asked apprehensively.

My brother swears that when *mamma* Lucia heard her husband call his name she came rushing out of the kitchen all agitated and shrieking wildly: "Rosa is dead! I knew it! I knew it!... I told you something happened! She is dead! She is dead!"

Now it was my brother's turn to be shocked. As my mother-in-law kept shrieking, both men tried to calm her down and forcibly made her lay down on a sofa.

My brother looked at my father-in-law questioningly, wondering if and how my mother-in-law knew about the terrible news.

In turn, my father-in-law looked at my brother with a desperate, pleading look, hoping, begging for a denial. But Mimmo just nodded.

My father-in-law then heaved a long, painful sigh. As my mother-in-law sat on the sofa wailing desperately, he explained slowly, in a daze.

"Two nights ago... It was around midnight. My wife had been tossing and turning restlessly in bed when suddenly she began first moaning and then screaming wildly in her sleep, jolting me awake. It took me forever to wake her up and calm her down. When she stopped shaking, she began whimpering unintelligibly, very scared like, terribly agitated, with a horrified look in her eyes. And she then told me about this horrible dream she had had. She was walking on a solitary country road, she said, when in the distance she saw a funeral cortege coming toward her, a funeral cortege led by a black carriage pulled by four black horses. And a long, long, long line of people stretching as far as the eye could see was following the hearse, and they were all dressed in black. She asked one of the mourners who had died, and the woman told her 'Don't you know? It's your daughter. She is dead.' My wife just laughed at her and told her 'No, no, what are you talking about? You are mistaken, Rosa left just yesterday to go to America'. But the lady shook her head and told her 'No, no, no, she is dead'. And then other people in the cortege began a chorus-like chant saying somberly 'Yes, she is dead, she is dead...'. And that's when my wife began shaking, and moaning and crying so wildly that I had to wake her up. When she did wake up she was so terrified, so distraught I had a hard time trying to calm her down, and she then told me about the dream."

He just stared vacantly for a few seconds, still incredulous, then added: "I told her, Lucia, go back to sleep, it was just a stupid dream. She did try to go back to sleep, but she couldn't get that dream out of her head and has been disturbed since then, for the past two days. And now, and now..."

And his words just trailed off as he shook his head disconsolately.

My parents walked in soon afterwards, and they all began wailing and grieving, tearing their hair out.

As Mimmo described the details of the tragedy, my in-laws – even as they grieved about their own daughter's death – were just as devastated when they learned about my conditions, expressing heartfelt concern as if I was their own son. My brother told them all he knew and what the doctor had told him, adding he didn't know if I was still alive.

Soon neighbors, hearing the heart-rending cries, began piling in. Within minutes news of the tragedy had spread all over Torre Faro, and for several hours friends, relatives and acquaintances were streaming in and out of the house, all of them wailing with cries of disbelief, sorrow, condolences, and mostly anger at the unfairness of life and destiny's cruelty.

When everybody finally left, my brother inquired where he could find a phone to call home to find out what my conditions were.

Despite the late hour they decided to go to Messina, the nearest place where there was a public telephone exchange with an oversea operator. It was closed, of course, and they had to return home.

They returned early in the morning when the office opened at 8 AM. At that hour – when it was 2 AM in Delaware – they managed to get through to my house.

Ange answered and told them I was still alive, but in a coma and still in very critical conditions. She informed them I had been given the Last Rites and that they still wouldn't let her or anybody else see me.

She was clearly relieved hearing it was them calling, thinking that a call so early in the morning could only have been from the hospital to announce I had passed away.

Both sets of parents wanted to come to the United States immediately, and here, may I say it one more time?... **God bless America!**

The next day they went in a rented car to Palermo where the nearest American Consulate was located. My brother, an American citizen, explained the situation to the American consul. With one phone call they verified that the information was correct, and they immediately issued a visitor visa for my parents and my in-laws.

But they didn't stop there – pulling some strings with their Italian counterparts, they managed to get my parents and my in-laws Italian passports in just three days, a feat unheard of in those days. Or even today, for that matter.

On August 2nd, they flew to New York and that same evening they were at the hospital. They still weren't allowed to visit me, but they managed to get a glimpse of my cast-enclosed and heavily bandaged body when a nurse came out of my room.

Nick Ravello had claimed Rosa's body and had it transported to a funeral home in a closed casket. Knowing my parents and my in-laws would be coming soon, he had wisely waited for their arrival before holding a funeral service.

They didn't have a viewing – her body, her beautiful face, had been brutally disfigured by the accident. God spared me the pain of being there, the only pain I was spared.

They held a religious service at St. Anthony's Church, the church of all Italians in Wilmington. I was told that the church was packed with people who had never known her but who knew me.

Her body was then taken to a morgue until a decision would be made on where she should be buried. My brother made that decision for me – her body was going to be flown back for burial in Torre Faro's cemetery when her parents returned to Italy.

While my in-laws agreed and were indeed grateful for that decision, they respectfully told my brother that, as her husband, I had the right to have her buried in the United States and they did not want to usurp my right to have her laid to rest near me.

My brother pointed out that a) I was in no position to make a decision; b) according to the doctors there was a good chance I would not survive; and c) even if I did survive, the doctors had declared I might not come out of the coma for a long, long time. If ever.

He finally convinced them by saying that he took full responsibility for his actions.

"Rosa was born and lived in Torre Faro all her life, and that's where she belongs." – He told them – "I am absolutely sure Lillo would agree that's where she should be buried."

My in-laws and my parents remained in Wilmington for one full month staying at my house and making daily visits to the hospital. Either my brother or Ange would pick them up and drive them to and from the hospital once or twice every day.

One week after their arrival they were allowed to come by my bedside and they were encouraged to talk to me, to call my name, to try to induce me out of my coma. They desperately wanted to be there when I came out of the coma to help me deal with my grief, but doctors couldn't give them any indications of when – or even if – I would ever come out of the coma.

They decided to return to Italy only after the doctors told them my conditions had stabilized and I was not in any immediate danger.

In early September, when the doctors finally assured them they were confident they could keep me alive, my parents and my in-laws left for their sad journey back home, taking Rosa's body with them.

I was told another funeral service was held in Torre Faro. The entire town and even people from nearby hamlets followed the hearse, people who had never known my Rosa but had learned of the tragedy through the local newspapers. They were so moved that they felt they had to be present at the funeral.

It was the longest funeral cortege in anyone's memory, all for my Rosa. And I will always thank God for sparing me the heartache of seeing her buried, for sparing me the grief of seeing *Papà* Filippo crying, for sparing me the agony of seeing *Mamma* Lucia tearing her hair and hearing her screaming over and over and over again.

"No!! No!!... It's not true!... This can't be true!!... Please, please, somebody please tell me it's still that nightmare!! Please, please, tell me it's that horrible nightmare!!"

CHAPTER 19

Beep... beep... beep... beep...

It's a faint, distant, barely audible sound – a constant, steady, annoying sound. It has been there forever, certainly since you've been there, certainly ever since you can remember, although you don't remember when or how you got there, or why you are there. In fact, you don't even know where you are. The sound's cadence and volume have been so regular, so precise, so uniform, that you now know it will never go away. It's there, you know it will be there, it will stay there, it's part of the landscape, part of the dream or nightmare, part of the phantasmagoria you are living. And you have no other choice but to accept it.

Beep... beep... beep... beep...

It's dark, very dark. You are used to that darkness, but despite the darkness you can see what's happening around you. But nothing much seems to be happening, just an unending series of orderly, repetitive movements. And more than seeing those movements, you feel them, you sense them. In that murky darkness, you can vaguely make out indistinct masses slowly advancing and retreating, moving sideway, left to right, right to left, rising and falling, blending in very slow motion, like molasses inside a rolling barrel.

Beep... beep... beep... beep...

You observe. You are part of the picture, but you are also separated. You are both participant and spectator. You cannot control anything that is happening, but you don't really want to control. In fact, anything could happen, but if it did it would be of no importance to you. So you just look.

Beep... beep... beep... beep...

There is another sound. It's a flowing, rushing sound, like the sound of water falling from a showerhead, like the sound of a brook flowing around a rock. It's a whispering sound, a gurgling sound, a soothing sound, not unpleasant at all, very relaxing in fact. And you absorb it, you luxuriate in it, it almost cancels out that annoying beeping sound. But not quite.

Beep... beep... beep... beep...

You do see and you do hear. But you don't know you are seeing or hearing. You just do. Your other senses – smell, touch, and taste – are not active at all. They seem to have been incapacitated, or maybe they simply do not exist. There is nothing to smell, you don't even know what smell means. And what is there to touch? Or taste? What is touch? Or taste? You are there, but it could just as well be your shadow, a shadow with visual and auditory powers. But just a shadow.

Beep... beep... beep... beep...

You feel no emotions, you have no feelings. Love, hate, fear, envy, anger, joy, sadness, jealousy, sympathy, grief, anguish, despair, misery, worry... you have never felt any of those emotions, you don't even know what they mean. Hunger, thirst, lust, pain or pleasure, they do not exist in your world.

Beep... beep... beep... beep...

That is your world, that has been your world since... since when? How long have you been there? An hour? A day? A week? A month? A year? Forever?... You don't know. Or care.

It's an unchanging, uninteresting world, but it's not boring. You could stay there another day, another week, another month, another year, or forever, and it wouldn't bother or concern you at all. It's your world, the only world you know. You feel comfortable in that world, it's your private nirvana. There, you are totally and completely at peace with the world. With this world.

Beep... beep... beep... beep...

And then, at some point, something occurs to disturb the perfect monotony of your world, something that wasn't there before, something so foreign, so alien, that it forcibly draws your attention.

The murky darkness is suddenly stabbed by a distant point of light, as distant and as small as a star, but more brilliant, more luminous.

This point of light seems to be moving rapidly, it moves a very short distance sideways, no more than an inch or two, left to right, then right to left, then left to right again. And then it seems to bounce or jump a slightly longer distance, from one side of the space you are occupying to the other, where it then resumes the same short, left to right, right to left, and left to right rapid movements.

Beep... beep... beep... beep...

Though still far and very tiny, this new attraction is a bit annoying, and you would like to avoid it. And you do try to avoid it, to evade it, to ignore it, but you can't. You are powerless to affect or influence anything that's happening in that dark, yet serene place.

Yes! It's annoying and it bothers you. At the same time, though, you can't help paying attention to it. It's a nuisance, yes, but it's also a magnet, a distraction, and you hypnotically follow its quirky, rapid movements.

Beep... beep... beep... beep...

And now something else invades your world. It's a new noise that slowly merges with the constant and annoying beeping sound and the whispering, soothing, relaxing sound you are used to. But this new noise becomes stronger, it gets the upper hand, until both sounds that were part of your world become imperceptible background noises.

This new noise is an indistinct murmur of what sounds like human voices. *Human voices.* Your world has no concept of what is animal, vegetable, or mineral, it doesn't know the 'humanity' of things, of beings, of voices. And yet it knows, and you do know that the buzzing noise you hear is the sound of human voices.

It's not a conversation. No, it's just snatches of words, some soft, some loud, all of them incomprehensible, like the verbal flotsam one would hear at a crowded outdoor market or at a stadium. You hear but you do not listen.

Beep... beep... beep... beep...

The tiny point of light has now become definitely annoying. For that very same reason, however, it also becomes even more enticing. You somehow become aware it is seeking you – intentionally, it seems. You know it is seeking you in that dark corner where you stayed, suspended in space. Its intense, bright beam totally destroys the peaceful tranquillity you were immersed in. Its movements seem to vary now from sharp, left-to-right linear, to small concentric circles, to a perfectly still point. And each variation seems to occur at faster, more precise, and more deliberate intervals.

Beep... beep... beep... beep...

"His pupils are dilating..." are the first distinct words you hear, but they are meaningless, there is no point of reference, no logical continuum. They are like snatches of dialogue you would hear if you were turning the Tune button of a radio while rapidly scanning for specific station.

Beep... beep... beep... beep...

"His pupils seem to be focusing... Yes, I think he is responding."

Those are the next spoken words you seem to understand. But they are still meaningless. You now sense more movement, more shadows appear, the light becomes more intense, closer, fiercer, almost hurting.

Beep... beep... beep... beep...

"Call him! Call out his name! He may respond faster to the voice of someone he knows..." – Someone says.

Who is talking? Is he talking to you? You feel totally engulfed in a dense fog. You are like a skin diver deep under water, blindly striving to break through the surface, but unable to discern if he is going up, sideways, or further down.

Beep... beep... beep... beep...

"Lillo! Lillo!" – You now hear someone call you in a quiet tone of voice at first, and then, with rising intensity.

"LILLO! LILLO! *MI SENTI? SVEGLIATI!* (Can you hear me? Wake up!")

Yes! Somebody is calling you, from a distance at first, then closer and closer, and louder and louder. There is urgency in that voice, there is hope, worry, expectation, encouragement.

Beep... beep... beep... beep...

It's a voice you know. Where have you heard it before? You struggle to remember, to attach a face, a time, or a place to that voice. You want to find out, you need to find out who is calling you with such insistence. And, somehow, you realize you can't do it unless you exit your world.

With considerable effort, and some reluctance, you know you must leave the peaceful cocoon where you have nested since the un-determinable time you had roosted in it. You know you must leave the soothing sound of rushing water, the tranquil darkness. You know you must leave your world to find out who is calling you.

Beep... beep... beep... beep...

Exiting your world is disorienting.

Like the traveller who, waking up in a hotel room somewhere, occasionally experiences the unsettling sensation of not knowing where he is, how he got there or why he is there, you are also totally unaware of where you are, and how or why you are there.

The traveller, however, can quickly regain his bearings summon-ing up all the relevant circumstances, recollecting where he came from, the mean of transportation he used to get to his present location, and the business that brought him there. Unlike the traveller, you have no such points of references. You do have vague memories of your former self. You do know your name is Lillo, and you do know that the voice calling you is familiar. But you have absolutely no clue as to where you are or how or when or why you got to your present location. You are disoriented.

BEEP... BEEP... BEEP... BEEP...

That distant and faint beeping sound has now become much loud-er, much closer. And while before it was almost cancelled out by the pleasant, gurgling, watery sound, now it can't be ignored. It's there, it's real, and it's also very annoying and distracting, but you just can't turn it off, and it won't allow you to concentrate on recognizing that voice. You want to tell someone to shut the damn thing off, but you can't. You are still powerless to do or to say anything.

BEEP... BEEP... BEEP... BEEP...

Some molecules in your brain activate and you now have an olfactory perception of something pungent. You don't know what it is, but it's so intense that it activates your other senses.

Your eyes go in and out of focus, and you begin to see what look like several blurry figures, indistinct shadows, shadows gathered around you, shadows that slowly acquire consistency. They seem to be people peering down at you. You also see a strange white towering column suspended in front of you, and that attracts your attention.

You have a fuzzy yet fairly specific understanding of what those figures are. They are people – anonymous people, but people. You know that, so you feel no need to further scrutinize, to further investigate, to determine what or who they are. But the white towering column rising in front of you confuses and intrigues you, so you ignore the figures and concentrate on that column.

What is it? Why is it there? You struggle for a while trying to understand what it is, but you can't figure it out. Unable to solve that riddle, you then return your attention to the figures around you.

BEEP... BEEP... BEEP... BEEP...

"LILLO! LILLO!" The voice is now very loud, almost shouting, there is a hint of a command in it, a command you feel you should obey. You know it's calling out your name, so you pay more attention to it.

BEEP... BEEP... BEEP... BEEP...

The figures have now become bodies with faces, and they all seem to be looking down at you. But the first few faces you see are unknown faces, they belong to people you have never seen before.

Who are all these people, anyway? You slowly move your pupils around. You scrutinize every face, one by one, until on your left side you see a familiar face. It's the face of the one who is shouting "**LILLO! LILLO!**" at you.

You recognize him, it's your brother, it's Mimmo, and you also recognize Ange who is standing right next to him, and she is also calling out your name, though not as loud as Mimmo. In recognition, you instinctively want to smile and say "Hi, Mimmo", "Hi Ange", and the corners of your mouth imperceptibly do move down as you try to say it, but no sound comes out of your mouth.

BEEP... BEEP... BEEP... BEEP...

Someone standing right across from Mimmo is now speaking. His voice is controlled but loud and has a hint of authority. Slowly, you turn your eyes in that direction. You don't understand his first words.

"**...YOUR... NAME?**" – But he then repeats slowly what he first said, clearly enunciating each word.

"**DO... YOU... KNOW... WHO... YOU... ARE?... DO... YOU... KNOW... WHAT... IS ... YOUR... NAME?**"

Bewilderment. Whoever is speaking is someone you don't know. He is a man dressed in some kind of white garment, and he is asking you something. Why is he talking so loud? Why is he shouting at me? He asked do you know who you are? Do you know what is your name? Of course I know who I am. I am Lillo... my name is Leo Vadalà.

I try to say yes, I know who I am, I know my name. Still, no sound is coming out of my mouth, so I try to move my head up and down.

That same person speaks out again: "**DO YOU KNOW WHERE YOU ARE?**" And he then enunciates each word again.

"**DO... YOU... KNOW... WHERE... YOU... ARE?**"

No, I have no idea of where I am. My eyes slowly wander around the room; I'm more than ever disoriented. Where am I? I try to say 'no, I don't know' but, still, no sound comes out, so I try to shake my head.

"**YOU ARE IN A HOSPITAL... YOU... ARE... IN... A... HOSPITAL!**" – that same man says.

He pauses now, and there is a brief moment of silence, except for the now very loud BEEP... BEEP... BEEP... BEEP...

"YOU WERE IN A CAR ACCIDENT... AND YOU WERE HURT BADLY... THAT'S WHY YOU ARE HERE!" – The guy says, following with a word-by-word rendition of the same phrase.

There is silence for what seems like several minutes. Slowly I begin to understand, the people around me, the cast on my leg slanting up like a white column, the beeping sound of a heart monitor. And I nod my head. Now I understand.

Then, suddenly, explosively, one thought comes to mind – **ROSA!**

And with panic-stricken eyes I look at my brother and whisper, or shout, or scream – **"ROSA!"**

Still, no sound comes out, but from my startled expression and from my lip movements my brother makes out what I am trying to say. He sadly shakes his head, and I see tears rolling down his face.

And then I do scream, and this time a long, uneven ululation comes out, a raspy, anguished, hysterical shriek. The beeping sound immediately accelerates and quickly becomes a steady, dangerously fast **BEEP BEEP BEEP BEEP BEEP...**

There is quick movement among some figures, and a voice barks out rapid orders followed by a peremptory **"STAT!!"**

And then darkness, sweet darkness, blessed darkness returns.

BEEP... BEEP... BEEP... beep... beep... beep... beep... beep...

It was Sunday, September 29, 1963.

A brain scan done two days earlier had shown some unusual patterns, and the doctors had alerted my brother that it might be an indication I might be coming out of the coma.

For the past two days Mimmo and Ange had practically camped in my room. For the past several hours they kept calling my name to jolt me out of my long sleep.

And their patience, their perseverance had been rewarded – I was now awake. But learning of Rosa's death had caused an unacceptable and dangerous acceleration of my heart rate and, as a precaution, the doctor had promptly ordered the administration of a sedative to put me back to sleep. But the first important step had been accomplished – I had come out of the coma.

The next day I awoke fully, and my private Via Crucis began in earnest.

I was in a full body cast, with another cast on my right leg rising at a 45 degrees angle and suspended with some kind of hook from the ceiling. Yet another cast was on my lower left leg, and still another on my right arm. The full body cast also immobilized my left arm.

All the casts were for injuries doctors considered non-life threatening. I had also suffered severe internal injuries, to the brain, lungs, liver, etc. that had worried doctors far more.

Extremely serious as they were, my physical conditions were far better than my emotional conditions.

Foremost on my mind was one thought and one thought only – Rosa was gone! Nothing else mattered, not my broken bones, not my internal injuries, not my physical pain, nothing. Absolutely nothing!

Rosa! My Rosa! The woman who loved me, the woman who had married me, the woman who had followed me to the United States, the woman I had deeply fallen in love with one minute before she was killed, the woman who almost surely was carrying my baby, our baby!

Rosa! Gone! Gone forever!...

I would never, ever, see her again, I would never touch her velvety skin, never kiss her warm lips, never inhale her heavenly scent, never hold her in my arms, never make passionate love to her... Never!

Gone! She was gone! My Rosa was gone! Gone, gone forever!

But how could it be? How was it possible? One minute we were two incredibly happy young people, full of life, rejoicing, laughing, the world at our feet, and the next... **Dead! She is dead! Gone forever! Rosa is dead!** And me, me... me a helpless wreck in a hospital bed.

I didn't know the exact extent of my injuries, but just a glimpse at all the casts holding my body together, one glance at my disfigured face, one look at all the needles piercing my body to keep me alive was enough for me to know I was in for the long haul, a year, maybe two before I could return to a normal life.

A normal life? What normal life? A normal life without Rosa? How could life be normal without Rosa?

Had my injuries been ten, fifty, a hundred times worse than they actually were, they would still have been preferable to the idea of a life without Rosa.

The idea? What idea? The **FACT**... the **ABSOLUTE CERTAIN-TY** that the rest of my life would be without Rosa.

Mimmo and Ange were by my bedside when I awoke the second time, and they were the ones who wiped my tears, the endless flow of tears that kept coming out of my eyes, tears I couldn't dry because both my arms were in casts.

Both of them did all they could to console me, to encourage me, but the tears kept flowing, gushing out like groundwater-fed springs. And the wailing, the uncontrollable wailing, the screaming out loud, the shrill cries sounding like the desperate bawling of a baby who has fallen and skinned his knees. God! What I went through! In my wretched grief, I didn't give a damn if anybody saw me or heard me. And that went on and on for hours, for days.

Mimmo informed me that our parents and my in-laws had come to America to see me and had already returned to Italy, and he also told me he had authorized the return of Rosa's body for burial in Italy. He was worried I might not have been in agreement with that decision but, through my tears, I managed to tell him it was a good decision, and I thanked him for it.

To alleviate my intense emotional state, they administered more sedatives. I fell asleep again, but it was a troubled sleep teeming with frightening nightmares and vividly detailed dreams.

One hazy detail of one horrific nightmare still haunts and jolts me awake now and then at night, even after all these years.

In this dream, Rosa was being sucked in a fast spinning vortex of muddy water, and while her body kept spinning around I was desperately trying to hold her afloat by grabbing her long, golden hair.

Holding her twisting hair, I was pulling her up and had almost managed to drag her to safety when, suddenly, her scalp detached from her head and remained in my hands.

As I looked horrified at the twisted mane of hair in my hands with the torn, bleeding scalp at one end, Rosa fell and disappeared in the vortex, but not before giving me one last, desperate look, a look that seemed to express not so much fear of dying, but her deep disappointment in my failure to rescue her. And that last look still haunts me.

And then I had this one incredible dream, still so vividly etched in my mind that to this day I remember every single detail of it, the sights, the colors, the movements, the sounds, everything, even the smells.

I was floating-like up in the sky, and I could see below me a vast expanse of fields, an undulating terrain with wonderful vistas of picture-postcard bucolic scenes resembling those outrageously beautiful countryside views of Tuscany.

I was floating, and I somehow had the capability of zooming in and out at will on whatever attracted my attention, so that I could swoop down from any height, from a mile high, or even higher, to half a mile, to fifty yards, or even down to ground level, and I could change that distance whenever it suited my fancy.

The day was crystal clear with not one cloud marring a sky so blue that it seemed unreal, faked, artificial, like the vivid blue sky in a Technicolor cartoon.

As I surveyed the huge expanse of land below, one patch of ground of circular shape caught my attention. It was a creamy white perfect circle amid irregularly shaped fields of green grass, yellow wheat, and tilled land of different shades of ochre.

Its unusual color and its perfect shape were so odd and distinctive that I immediately zoomed in to see what it was, to see why it was so different from the other patches. To my surprise, I saw that it was a field of lilies gently undulating in the breeze.

Zooming in closer, I could see each gently curving white petal, I could smell their sweetly cloying odor, I could even glimpse vividly green blades of grass growing among the many stems.

I zoomed a bit higher, and once again the field of lilies became an even circle of creamy white milk. As I hovered above, I began to notice here and there spots of colors slowly trying to break through that foamy sea of white, like chicks hatching through eggshells.

And all these emerging spots were of incredibly brilliant colors – hundreds and hundreds of specks of every hue of green, blue, yellow, orange, indigo, violet, red, amber, pink, brown, and several other shades of color.

As they slowly forced their way through the level white surface of the lilies, I could make out that they were flowers, beautiful multi-colored flowers of intricate, kaleidoscopic shapes. And I somehow knew, somehow understood that all those flowers were vying with each other to show off their beauty, that they were having a contest to determine which one was the fairest flower.

And suddenly, among the swarm of competing flowers, in the exact middle of the now speckled white circle, one red flower emerged from the lilies, growing rapidly as if it was being pushed out of the ground. It was a rose, a ruby red rose with delicate, diaphanous petals, and it kept growing and growing until it was almost within reach of my hands.

It stopped growing for a few seconds and slowly began to rotate, seemingly uncertain, as if to orient itself. It then resumed its growth – purposely in my direction it seemed – as if it was seeking me out. And when it was within reach of my hand, it stopped growing completely.

It was now so close to me that I could even smell its fragrance, an intoxicating fragrance that made me dizzy.

And there it stood, so splendid, so magnificent, so superiorly overwhelming in its loveliness, that all the other flowers – tacitly acknowledging its peerless beauty – slowly began retreating until they all disappeared under the milky surface of lilies.

Totally mesmerized, I reached with my hand to touch the rose's velvety, translucent petals so that I could transfer and always retain some of that fragrance.

Just as my hand brushed it, however, I heard an eerie sound, a musical but hauntingly ominous sound of violins, a sinister sound, like in the movies when something menacing is about to happen.

Startled, I looked around to see who or what had made that sound, or where it was coming from, but I didn't see anything. Yet the sound kept playing, more menacing, more ominous, more threatening than ever.

Timorously, I withdrew my hand, and immediately the sound stopped. Unable to resist the allure of that rose, I again tentatively reached for it, but just as I was within an inch or two of touching it, the musical sound began anew, this time accompanied by the pressing rhythm of beating drums, a rapidly accelerating rhythm presaging impending doom.

Again, my hand retreated and once more the sound stopped. Bewildered, I looked around to see where the sound was coming from, but nothing was there.

Uncaring of any danger, I adamantly reached again for the rose and touched it, but at the same instant that my fingers brushed its petals, a sudden gleaming flash appeared, followed by a sinister whooshing sound, like the rustling of tree branches bending to a sudden, violent gust of wind.

And in one appalling instant, the rose plus a ten-foot wide swath of lilies fell to the ground, cut down by an enormous scythe swung by an invisible force. In front of my dismayed eyes, the stems and pearly petals of the lilies began rotating in extremely slow motion in the air and gently began their soft descent to the ground in precise movements and cadence, as if dancing a funereal pavane. And as they settled on the ground, they laid in precise formation, like perfectly lined graves at military cemeteries.

The rose, instead, seemed to have exploded, torn apart from the stem by the force of the blow. Totally spellbound, I stared as each ruby red petal and each pistil also began to descend to the ground twirling gracefully in that same extreme slow motion, accompanied now by the dulcet tinkling of a spinet, until they all finally settled quietly on top of the cut lilies, resembling drops of blood on an immaculate sheet. And when the last crimson petal came to rest, they all immediately began withering and shrinking rapidly, soon resembling scabs of multiple scraping wounds.

And then the music ended. An eerie, disturbing silence followed, a silence perfectly in tune with my stunned disbelief at the sight of the sudden, savage, senseless destruction of all those innocent flowers.

The annihilation of the rose in particular, the shattering of that flower so overwhelming superior in its beauty, seemed to me absurd, wanton, outrageous – it simply defied comprehension.

The dream was so vivid, so detailed, so graphic, so real, that I remember questioning myself – even as I was dreaming – whether I had been dreaming. Had that barbaric slaughter really happened? Had I just imagined it? Had I dreamed it?

I can still recall the appalling feeling of standing there wide-eyed and open-mouthed, unwilling to believe I had been witness to such absurd savagery, wanting, desperately forcing myself to avert my eyes from that cruel butchery, and yet being unable to look away from such wholesale carnage.

And then there was this other even more bizarre part of the dream. My brother had suddenly materialized next to me, and in my dream I was telling him about the strange dream I had just had, about the field of lilies, the emerging flowers, the rose, its superior beauty, its scent, the creepy music, the scythe. Everything, every shocking detail.

And I was urging him to please make sure he would remember all of it, because I never remember my dreams, and I absolutely wanted to remember this one. And at my urging, he dutifully took out a notepad and began jotting down all the details I feverishly described.

But the really weird part of this last portion of the dream is that I wasn't just describing the dream or giving him instructions in ordinary words or normal conversation.

No! No! I was declaiming everything, as if I was reciting a play or a poem, using ample, theatrical gestures, and alternately lowering or raising my voice.

Yes! I still remember that dream!

CHAPTER 20

Torture. My next three months can be summarized with that single word. Plain and simple torture, both physical and mental.

Being in a body cast means being unable to do or perform the simplest, most ordinary daily tasks one does automatically, unthinkingly, like washing, scratching, feeding yourself, blowing your nose. Even for those simple and most ordinary tasks, you are totally dependent on others. And all the more so with the intimate tasks like urinating, defecating or wiping your ass. Yes, even that has to be done for you.

These common, everyday tasks – normal occurrences when performed routinely on your own in the privacy of your home – are so downright humiliating when done by others, are so embarrassing that one can't help feeling dehumanised. But you have no choice – it has to be done for you.

Several weeks went by before I would get used to the simple fact I just couldn't do it on my own – in fact, I never really did get used to it. Until I left the hospital, I always felt shame and embarrassment when a nurse, male or female, had to handle my privates.

The itching, the unbearable itching – in and by itself a rather insignificant matter – was probably my worst torment, certainly more aggravating than my physical miseries. An itch is just a skin irritation that one can relieve simply by scratching himself, of course. But how do you scratch in places covered by a cast? And how do you scratch when both arms are also immobilized?

I remember crying, crying, crying in frustration because of unrelieved itching. I remember begging nurses and doctors to please put me to sleep, to let me die, anything that would put a stop to the unrelenting and frequently intense itching. I remember screaming at them, cursing them, cursing a chaplain, cursing God, even cursing my poor brother – no one was immune to my wrath, to my helpless rage. I just had to vent my frustrations on whoever was available and near me.

And how can one describe my mental state? I was a wreck, that's it, plainly and simply a wreck. Just as bad as my physical state, I would say – possibly even worse.

The accumulated weight of Rosa's death, my physical afflictions, plus the pervasive anger and despair caused by the clear injustice of what had befallen me had taken its toll. I fell into a deep depression, a depression so intense, so acute, so total that I literally did not care if I lived or died. I was indifferent to whatever happened around me, it hardly registered on me.

I refused to take pills or even to eat and drink. To counteract my refusal, doctors began feeding and medicating me intravenously, forcing nourishment and drugs into me through dripping bottles with needles attached to various parts of my body.

And then, perversely, I tried to remove all needles stuck in my body, a difficult task indeed since – strapped as I was in a body cast – I couldn't reach them, but I did try to dislodge them by twisting and turning. And they were then forced to immobilize me, strapping my arms and legs to the bed.

This went on for about a week until even I realized that being strapped was the worse choice. They removed my straps only after I promised not to try to remove needles and other stuff.

It will sound ridiculous, I know – and it was in fact ridiculous – but just to show how insanely desperate I was, for a time I even consciously tried not to urinate, hoping my bladder would burst and kill me. But I couldn't, of course – like it or not, nature forces it out, I guess. But just out of sheer rage and plain spite, I did not notify the nurses when I had to go, and I just urinated in bed.

They quickly realized that my incontinence was intentional, and to counter it they inserted a catheter to do the job.

Of course, it didn't take long for them to become aware of my increasingly unstable mental state, and a psychiatrist was called to evaluate and treat me.

The sessions with the shrink were more or less like a physical therapy session, a routine affair that had to be done because the doctor had ordered it. I have no recollection of what, if anything, the guy did, what questions he asked, or what answers I gave. Just like physical therapy, it may have done some good in the long run, but when I left the hospital my mental state was still bordering schizophrenia.

God! Was I messed up! A small but significant example of how disturbed I was should provide a clear measure of how totally unconcerned, how utterly catatonic I had become about my surroundings or whatever happened around me.

President Kennedy's assassination occurred about a month before my discharge from the hospital. In addition to being a historical occurrence of major magnitude, it was also a tragic event that deeply affected the nation and the entire world. To me, it didn't mean diddley squat.

I didn't grieve along with the entire nation, I didn't express any emotion one way or the other, I just didn't give a damn – a very strange turnaround for me, considering I had been one of his most enthusiastic supporters when he had run for President, even doing volunteer work distributing his pamphlets to passers-by during the election campaign.

Two of my fractures had not healed properly. That meant more operations to reset the bones, to apply some screws, and whatever the hell else needed to be done to make me whole again. That meant more casts and – God damn it to hell! – more itching.

When all the fractures had finally healed properly and all the casts removed, they then started plastic surgery operations to repair part of my face, badly disfigured as it scraped the pavement when I was thrown out of the car.

Physical therapy – a painful, tiring, repetitive, and excruciatingly boring twice-a-day routine – started as soon as I could stand up.

I obstinately refused to go and, on a daily basis, I engaged in a futile verbal sparring with those poor nurses who, I'm sure, would have gladly – and justifiably – let me croak. They literally had to drag me there because, quite simply, I didn't care whether I would ever walk again properly or not.

On Dec. 21, 1963, nearly five months after the accident, I was finally discharged from the hospital. My weight had dropped from 185 to 138 lbs. and I still needed crutches or a cane to walk. All doctors, however, assured me that, with a few more months of intensive physical therapy, I could look forward to a near normal life. As if I gave a shit.

My brother forced me to stay at his house in Rising Sun for the first three weeks after my discharge from the hospital. I had refused, of course, I wanted to go home, my home, but he wouldn't take no for an answer.

He knew, of course, that I couldn't hack it on my own, not in my present physical or mental condition. I knew it too, but I just didn't care – I would have been perfectly happy to be left alone at my home where I could peacefully let myself crumble into oblivion.

Mimmo wanted me to stay at his house longer, in fact begged me to stay with him at least until spring, but around mid-January I stubbornly decided to go home.

I needed, I craved loneliness. The Christmas holidays – always the most joyous time of the year for me – had become a prime source of aversion and grouchiness. The Christmas carols I used to delight in singing were now an irritating noise to my ears, an outright nuisance, an additional reason to hate the entire human race, the whole creation.

I spent the holidays practically shut in my former room, exiting only to answer Ange's pleas to join them for dinner or to just keep them company. The presence of people physically bothered me, the sound of voices, even the joyous screams of delight of children opening their Christmas presents or their happy giggling at play grated my ears.

My only semblance of comfort came with the silence of the night, the long, long nights spent staring at the ceiling.

Against my brother's persistent advice, I insisted on returning to my house. He finally agreed to let me stay on my own only after extracting from me a sworn promise that I would allow him to come see me any time he wanted, even unannounced. And he did indeed show up at my doorstep practically every day.

Returning home was almost like walking into a new home, one I had never been in before. I hadn't set foot inside my house in seven months, since June 14, 1963, the day I had left to go to Italy.

Upon my departure, the only furniture in my house was the bedroom set my brother had given me, plus a living room set and a Formica kitchen table with four chairs I had purchased shortly after I had bought the house.

There was now another bedroom set purchased by my brother to accommodate my parents and my in-laws when they had come over from Italy. I wanted to reimburse him, of course, but Mimmo wouldn't hear of it.

Inside the house, neatly stacked on the kitchen table I found about a dozen piles of unopened greeting cards, each pile held together by rubber bands. I estimated them to be well over 500 cards. I just opened maybe half a dozen of them – they were sympathy cards and Get Well cards from relatives, friends, colleagues, bank customers, and some even with names that didn't ring a bell. I just gathered the entire bunch and threw them in the trashcan outside.

I didn't have a car, and even if I had one I couldn't drive it – in fact, I wouldn't drive it. The day Mimmo took me to his home from the hospital, stepping inside his car had been a traumatic ordeal, a terrifying ordeal. They had to drag me in there. Literally.

God, what a scene that was! Oddly, while my brother was taking care of my discharge papers and even while I was being taken out of the hospital room in a wheelchair, my mind hadn't dwelled on the fact that I would be going home in a car.

A male nurse had pushed the wheelchair from my hospital room into an elevator and then to the hospital lobby. After completing the discharge routine, Mimmo went to get the car in the annexed parking garage while Ange and I waited inside the lobby, as it was quite cold outside.

When Mimmo eased the car near the curb to pick us up, he blew the horn to alert us he had arrived, and that's when the reality of having to ride in a car hit me. Like a punch in the stomach.

I still shiver thinking about it! Too panic-stricken to speak, I said nothing while the male nurse pushed the wheelchair outside, but I remember furiously gritting my teeth, gripping the wheelchair's arms with all the strength I could muster, desperately wanting to brake, to stay bonded to that chair. And then, as we approached the car, I began moaning. And shaking. And then I began pleading.

"No! No! No! Please Mimmo, I don't want to go, please don't make me!" – I kept begging and screaming. And to Ange, as I hugged her, as I buried my face on her shoulder to avoid even glimpsing at the car: "Please, please Ange! You tell him! I'll die, we will all die... Don't do this to me... Why are you doing this to me?"

Dear God, the petrifying dread I felt, the deep foreboding of impending doom, the teeth-gnashing reluctance to enter the car! Pure and simple terror, that's what it was.

Mimmo and Ange gently yet firmly kept urging me to slide in, and they quietly assured me that everything would be OK, but I was literally terror stricken. Seeing I wasn't getting anywhere with them, I even pleaded with the obviously embarrassed male nurse to take me back to my room in the hospital.

And when they finally convinced me – and that took forever – I adamantly refused to sit next to my brother on the front seat. And the ride home... O God! I'll never forget riding all the way home, shaking, moaning, crying, bent in half, my arms covering my face, my eyes tightly shut, and Ange maternally holding me and whispering words of encouragement. God, what a trip!

When we arrived in Rising Sun, my clothes were totally sweat-drenched. Fearing I would get pneumonia in the wintry chill, Ange considerately rushed inside to get a heavy blanket to cover my body.

That particular phobia lasted for quite a while. It gradually alleviated and finally disappeared, but not until after several months had gone by.

My brother stopped by my house five or six times a week to take me for physical therapy as well as to bring provisions from grocery stores and medical supplies from a pharmacy.

For the next six months my curative routine consisted of one hour of physical therapy three times a week, plus another hour of daily walking on a treadmill Mimmo had rented. And I performed this last exercise only because my brother stood there next to me, forcing me to do it. On the occasional days when my brother couldn't come to see me, I invariably skipped the treadmill routine.

Local, national, and world events meant absolutely nothing to me. Inside me dwelled just total emptiness along with an inability, an unwillingness to connect with people. Nothing interested me. For the entire six months I never once turned on the television or the radio, never even glanced at a newspaper, and never put on one of the many, many records I had, the music I used to love so much. Absolutely nothing.

For the entire six months I don't remember ever cracking a simple smile. My face was constantly a mask of deep, obstinate sullenness punctuated by bursts of desolate, hopeless crying. Emotionally, I just lived, I existed, I was there, a breathing automaton.

One feeling and one feeling only festered inside me, a feeling that kept growing and growing daily to such enormous proportions that I knew I would go totally insane unless I dealt with it in some meaningful, some conclusive way.

It was a feeling of hatred, of pure, distilled, unadulterated hatred toward the damned bastard who had caused all my misery.

I knew nothing about him – his name, age, address, nothing. I just knew he had also died in the crash.

His being dead didn't assuage my feelings of hatred at all – in fact, it increased them. The motherfucking son of a bitch had practically gotten away scot-free, he hadn't suffered, he hadn't gone through the agony he had caused, the torment I had experienced, the hell I was even now going through. And he should have. Oh, goddamnit! – **GODDAM-NIT! GODDAMNIT TO HELL! YES, HE SHOULD HAVE! IF THERE WAS ANY KIND OF DIVINE JUSTICE, HE SHOULD HAVE! HE SHOULD HAVE SUFFERED THAT AND A HELL OF A LOT MORE!**

I had no idea of who he was or what he looked like, if he was white or black, young or old. To provide some substance, some flesh and bones foundations for my feelings, I had crafted a mental image of a white male, of a cocky young punk with long, unwashed and uncombed blonde hair, with bad teeth, a constant sneer on his pimpled face and with more than a few needle marks on his arms.

For no specific reason – as a diversion possibly, or maybe to pro-vide a new focus or a sharper image for my hate – I changed this mental image frequently. Inexplicably, the one constant feature I always main-tained was the race – I always imagined him to be white. Whenever it suited my fancy, every other feature changed – sometime I would picture him as older or younger, with different hair color or hair length, slim or heavyset, wearing varied garb or of different stature. But always white.

Thoughts of revenge were a constant escape valve for the intense hatred I felt. Unfortunately the guy was dead, of course, and I could not exact any type of revenge on him. As a cut-rate substitute for retribu-tion, I constantly tried to imagine his frantic panic, his helpless despera-tion as he tried to evade the police pursuit.

I can still vividly recall the build-up in my chest of a slow, steady, intense inhalation as the movie of his final and fatal journey began roll-ing in my mind.

The movie always started at the time the young prick saw the flashing lights of a police cruiser behind him. He had been surely speed-ing of course, doing well over 100 miles an hour on his hot rod, and I imagined – **SAW HIM!** – glance in his rear view mirror and immediate-ly realize the cop was after him.

And I then imagined – **HEARD HIM!** – spit out an angry "**SHIT!**" and saw him as he flicked out the car window the butt of the joint he was surely smoking, and then... Ah, yes! And then I even saw the sud-den, jolting backward and forward motion of his upper body as he determinedly floored the gas pedal, thus gaining a momentary advantage over his pursuer.

And that's when the cop turned on the sirens. I could hear their long, piercing, intimidating, frightening scream, and I could see the police cruiser lurching forward as the chase began, and I could hear the cop rapidly barking out detailed instructions in staccato fashion on his car radio to other law enforcement officers in the area. And then the real chase began. Ah! **Yes! Yes! Yes!** The chase, the chase itself...

And my body tightened and would weave along as it followed the rapid, wild maneuvers of the creep's car as he – uncaring of any danger now – recklessly passed at breakneck speed every vehicle in his way, and brakes shrieked, and car horns screamed angrily as cars and trucks going in the opposite direction veered sharply to the road shoulder to avoid a collision, and dozens of cars going in both directions quickly scurried out of the way and unto the shoulders to allow the pursuers to catch the prey.

And the suspense – the **DRAMA!** – kept building up inside my chest to the point of near explosion as the crescendo of the constant, frightening wails of the cops' sirens intensified, as the action sequence I was witnessing neared a conclusion that **I KNEW** would end with his total, complete, absolute, and totally deserved destruction. And now... **Yes! Yes! YES!**

Now the young punk wasn't feeling so cocky, so confident anymore. No, sirree! I sensed, I felt the change of emotions in his heart. His initial angry defiance and cockiness had turned first to worry and was now sheer anxiety. And at this point I would silently start mocking him: "Well, well... Poor little baby... You are not so cocky now, are you? Are you scared? Do you want your mommy?"

And his anxiety was now morphing to mawkish self-pity.

"What have I done? Why are they always picking on me?" – I could hear him whimper.

And finally... **yes! Yes! YES!** Finally it was total panic. And he was now darting quick, terrified glances in the rear view mirror, left and right, front and back, left and right again, as he frantically sought avenues of escape. And... **OH GOD!** The arousing elation I felt as the movie of his last journey neared its end. The wicked joy! The sense of triumph! As I visualized, as I even **HEARD** him screaming that last atrocious shriek, that last horrified scream of terror, a scream drowned out by the angry screech of protesting rubber, one second, one instant prior to the crash, a visceral scream cut short by his own instantaneous death...

AAAAAAAAAAAAAAAAAAAHHHHHHHHHHHHHH!

And in that instant, the instant of his sheer, final, total, utter destruction, I would unbosom an explosive exhalation, an exhalation of almost orgasmic rapture.

But even that wasn't enough.

One day I called a cab and went to the Main Library in Rodney Square in Wilmington. Hobbling inside that grandiose Beaux-Arts style building, I asked a library attendant for the microfilms of the "Wilmington Morning News" papers for July 28, 1963, the day after the accident, as well as the ones for the next couple of days.

The attendant solicitously helped me set up the microfilm machine, showed me how to use it and graciously even offered to search for whatever I needed. I thanked her and declined her offer.

The article, accompanied by two chilling photos of the scene of the accident, was front-page news. The sight of those pictures jolted me to the bone. For the first time I heard again that horrific blast, the blast that – to this day – occasionally jolts me awake at night. I had to cover the photos with my hand so that I could continue reading the article about the accident.

Skipping the part about Rosa and me, I looked for and quickly located the part about him. The guy's name was Everett McKee, 19 years of age. He had had a couple of minor drug-related convictions as well as several previous traffic violations and he was running away from the police, a fact I already knew.

To a remarkable degree, it seemed to corroborate the mental image I had made of him.

The obituaries of July 29 listed the tragic and untimely death of

Everett McKee who lived in Westgate Park, an upscale development less than a mile away from my house. He loved music, played guitar and always helped his neighbours. He was survived by his grieving parents, an older sister, a younger brother and assorted relatives. The obituary went on to say that there would be no viewing and services were going to be private.

The last paragraph stated that burial would be in Silverbrook Cemetery, just outside Wilmington's city limits and not far from the scene of the accident.

The next day I again called a cab and asked to be taken to Silverbrook Cemetery. At the office, I identified myself as a friend of the deceased and gave them the date of death and burial. I made up a cock-and-bull story about having been in Vietnam when he died, explained I wanted to pay my respects and asked where he was buried.

They bought my story, told me where he was buried and gave me directions to the grave. Leaning on my cane, I slowly made my way there and had no trouble finding it. It was a simple grave with a small oval-shaped marble headstone bearing his name, his date of birth and date of death.

Without even bothering to see if anyone was looking, I opened my fly, pulled out my dick and pissed on his grave.

I then hissed: "I hope you are doing a slow roast in hell, you motherfucker. You and your fucking guitar..."

Then, after shaking the last drops, I put my dick back in, pulled up my zipper and turned to walk away. I took two steps, then turned around, went back, and spat on his grave. I then left.

By the time I reached the cemetery gate I already felt like a piece of shit, so totally ashamed and sick of my execrable and profane act that I suddenly began to experience a series of violent dry heaves.

Leaning against the stone column of the gate, I first began belching loudly. Then I just couldn't hold it in. And right there, my eyes bulging out of the eye sockets, I barfed up everything that was inside my stomach.

I heard some grossed out passer-by muttering a disgusted: "Goddamned drunken bum!", but I felt too sick and really too bummed-out to even care. Furthermore, I felt I definitely deserved it.

But what was done was done and – small consolation! – the intense feelings of hatred for that young man seemed to have disappeared. Now I could luxuriate and continue to indulge in my total lack of feelings for everything else

How did I spend most of my days, in fact, all of my days? That's easy enough to answer – I spent all of my days, every last one of them, sitting down on a recliner and reliving the trip from Italy to Wilmington, inch by inch, foot by foot, step by step, mile by mile, hoping, wishing, wanting, desperately trying to gain or lose one second, one little miserable second that could have prevented the accident. One second.

That's what I did all day long. Yes! All day long! Even when I nibbled on some food, even when I sat on the hopper, even when I retired for the night, especially when I retired for the night!

One goddamned little second! Somehow, I believed, I wanted to believe, I made myself believe that one minuscule second, just one second plus or minus, could have changed the outcome. No, no, no, that's not quite right... **SHOULD** have changed the outcome. No, no, that's not quite right either... Crazily, insanely, I even made myself believe that it really **WOULD** change the outcome. That's how fucking cuckoo I had become! I made myself believe that if I succeeded in finding, in gaining or losing one meaningful second of that trip, it would somehow miraculously suspend, cancel out the tragedy and everything would return to normal.

One second, and **ZAP!** We would all be reunited, we would all go around doing our daily chores, we would all be laughing and behaving as if nothing had happened. I mean – yes! – we would all, of course, be aware we had escaped by the skin of our teeth, but we wouldn't dwell too much on it. We would all quietly acknowledge that the miracle was my just reward for finding that one second.

In psychological terms, in my desperate obsession to bring Rosa back and to return to the idyllic moments we had shared, I was consciously blocking out reality.

310

Finding that one second became my reality, my only reality, a new reality that would cancel out the real reality. I know, I know, it's off the wall, I'm not making any sense, but nothing made sense to me, and playing that game became my life, my reason for living, my only reason for living.

Yes! I knew Rosa was dead! Of course I knew Rosa was dead! I knew perfectly well that nothing could bring her or the past back! And I knew I was crippled, of course I knew I was crippled. But oh... how satisfying it was, how hopeful, how uplifting, how rewarding it was to constantly play and replay this 'what if' game.

Except that to me it was not a game – it was a way of life, it was what literally sustained me for weeks. For months.

And to make this game, this fantasy even more realistic – more attainable if you will – I would bargain with God, with destiny, or with whoever would listen. Just give me Rosa back – I would propose – and all my injuries could remain. OK, God?... And all my sufferings wouldn't have to be alleviated either, OK?... And then I would raise the ante – all the problems I had had as a direct result of the accident, they too could remain, they could even be intensified, tenfold, twenty fold, a hundred fold, I would propose. As much as you want, God, just so that one single unalterable event could be altered. Please, please, I beg you God, please, dear God... please. Are you listening, God?

This "one second" game, this way of life always began the same way, with me reliving the moment Rosa woke me up in her father's house on July 25, 1963, our last day in Torre Faro.

She had awakened me with a kiss. I was already half awake and I was expecting that kiss – she always kissed me in bed in the morning, a practice I adored! When she kissed me, I had reached out, grabbed her and held her close to me, rubbing my nose on her breasts and getting all aroused in the process.

We had not made love the previous night – as a matter of fact we had not made love at all during the nights we had stayed in Torre Faro. We were staying in her parents' house, and she was scared and embarrassed that they would hear us moaning.

I had assured her I would be quiet, I even remembered telling her jokingly that she was the one doing all the moaning anyhow, but she was uneasy and had repeatedly asked me please, please let's don't, promising me she would 'reward' me for it when we would be on our own. I wasn't too happy about it, but I had agreed – I understood how she felt and, to some extent, I even shared her concerns.

We had spent the previous three days packing our suitcases and entertaining friends and relatives who had come visiting to say goodbye and to wish us good luck when we started our life together in America.

Her parents had already packed all our wedding gifts and most of Rosa's wardrobe and dowry in two trunks that they were going to ship later.

That last morning in Torre Faro – I remembered – we were both excited and sad. On the upside, we both looked forward to the trip and to our life in America; on the downside, we also knew that saying good-bye to her parents was going to be a heartbreaker.

Many tears were going to be shed before and after that final em-brace – we both knew that – especially before and after the parting be-tween Rosa and her mom. They would be clinging to each other crying their hearts out, not wanting to let go. And that's exactly the way it went – they did cry their hearts out. We did in fact cry, all of us.

A cab had picked us up, and I relived every single minute of the trip from Torre Faro to Messina, and then from Messina – where we boarded a train – to the time when we arrived in Rome and checked in a hotel.

Scavenging my memory for every little detail, I first reviewed the time it took for the cab to take us to Messina. I remembered Rosa's last longing look at Torre Faro, my worries, her reassurances, how long it took to get to the railroad station, the mini-squabble I had with the cab-driver who had tried to stiff me for some extra fare, the train that left fifteen minutes late, the arrival at the Termini station in Rome, the time we spent looking for a cab. I remembered the friendly chat I had with the cabdriver and him accurately guessing that I lived in America. I remem-bered tipping him, then the check-in at the hotel, Hotel "Artemide", tipping the bellhop who had helped carry our two suitcases in the hotel lobby, everything... even the elevator ride to our room, room No. 311, and the time it took for me to find some change to tip another bellhop who had escorted us to our room.

We had freshened up, relaxed for a couple of hours, and we had then gone out to get a bite to eat. We had asked the hotel clerk – a pretty and very courteous brunette with a pleasant Roman accent – if she knew of any good restaurants or small *trattorias* in the vicinity of the hotel.

The hotel did have a decent restaurant, she had told us, "but if you want real Roman cuisine I recommend you go to *"Antica Boheme"*, it's a small *trattoria* only about two blocks away from the hotel."

It was a real find, a cozy and intimate hideaway with about ten small tables and a delightful aroma of cooked food. We had a superb late dinner there – a fabulous antipasto of cheeses, cold cuts and olives, *carciofi alla giudia* (Jewish style artichokes), *abbacchio* (roasted lamb), garden salad, a bottle of Frascati, espresso, a shot of Sambuca for me and an *amaro* (bitter) for Rosa. The bill had been ridiculously low too, about 15,000 lire, the equivalent of about twenty bucks.

We had finished rather late and we had then strolled around the neighborhood for a while to help us digest the food. We had finally returned to the hotel.

The next morning a cab had taken us to the airport where we had boarded a Pan Am plane that had landed in New York about ten hours later.

Plenty of opportunities there to find or lose much more than one second, even an hour, but eventually I deleted this portion of the trip from my fantasy. I had decided that it was useless, it just didn't belong. The entire trip by cab, by train and by plane was an entity apart, totally beyond my control, and couldn't therefore have any essential influence on my pursuit of that vital 'one second'.

My quest for that precious fragment of time could only begin after I got my car in New York from the Ravello brothers.

Minchia! Che bella pupa! Tony had said, no wonder you stopped coming to New York, you were saving yourself for her, and then what did Rosa say, and what did I say, we had bantered jokingly with the two brothers for several minutes but, Christ, much as I try, I remember only snatches of that conversation but not all of it, but was it necessary, surely that bit of banter could have been avoided, or maybe prolonged, and anyway, we then left to come home and I made a wrong turn and wound up in Manhattan, and why the hell did I decide to roam through Manhattan, to show her the sights, the Radio City Music Hall, Times Square and the stupid Camel ad, yes, even that stupid Camel ad, just to see if she would have the same reactions I had had, if she would experience the same high I had experienced twelve years before, oh hell all right let's move on, the Lincoln Tunnel, you know Rosa, we are underwater, and wouldn't you know, she had the same response I had, down to the same exact words, and the New Jersey Turnpike, same wide eyed exclamation of marvel, but there, on the turnpike, the opportunities to gain or lose one second were so plentiful, so damn plentiful, one hundred and ten miles of turnpike for God sake, take your pick, increase your speed just one mile an hour, or even ten or twenty, get a fucking ticket if necessary, oh I wish I wish, instead, what do I do, every time I saw one of those goddamned Chrysler cars the cops drove I slowed down, even if I was within the speed limit, and why didn't I pass that stupid truck on the right, since when have you been observing road etiquette, Lillo, and then what did I do, what did we do, let's see, yes, we stopped at Howard Johnson's, the pit stop, I went to the Men's Room, she went to the Ladies Room, OK nothing much I can gain or lose there, and then, then, then, yes, then I called Mimmo to let him know more or less what time we would be home, and I dialed his home phone by mistake even though I knew damn well he and Ange were at my house, was that stupid or what, could have gained at least two minutes there, and then, are you hungry Rosa, would you like a hamburger, no thank you honey she said, I'm not hungry, then she reads "Milk Shake" on the menu and she asks what is a milk shake, it's a drink made with milk and ice cream I explained, oh, it's a frappé, she said, I never tried one, you never did I said, it's delicious, do you want to try it, and I don't even wait for her to say yes, I just order one for her, a strawberry milkshake, why didn't I ask her what flavor she wanted, she may have demurred a while trying to make up her mind, you know damn well women always take their time deciding something, but no I just have to go ahead and decide for her, I had to be the decision maker, why, to show off, to impress her with my savoir-faire, imagine, me, a decision maker, when I can't even make up my mind on what color socks to wear, there is your second, your minute even, and what did we do then, we went to the gas pumps, and I got on the left side of the pump, I had forgotten on which side of my car the gas tank door was, and wouldn't you know it, it was on the left side of the car, so the attendant had to go around the car to fill it up, more time lost, OK let's move on, the toll booth, we got to the toll booth, and where is the goddamned ticket, keep that fucking ticket on the dashboard where it belongs instead of looking all over the fucking car to find it, and why didn't I have my money ready, why didn't I get the wallet out of my pocket ahead of time, like I did at the Delaware Memorial Bridge toll just a couple of miles down the road, and after the bridge then what did I do, I made a small detour, a small detour hell, it was about five miles out of my way just to drive by Union Street, why did I drive by Union Street, just to show her where I worked, you see that building there honey, that's where I work, that's the branch I manage, for crying out loud did you have to show it to her now, you can show it to her Monday, Tuesday, next week, whenever for God's sake, you have the rest of your life to show her that, drive straight home you asshole, and then my worries, my damn worries, I was worried, and I slowed down, purposely slowed down, and then I stopped, why did I slow down, why did I stop, because I was too worried, worried that she might not like it here, well that's too damn bad, just keep moving, why didn't I stop to think about that when we were in Italy, better yet why didn't I stop to think she might like it here, no I always have to think the worst, and not only I have to think the worst, I even have to tell her, damn idiotic jerk that I am, honey we are almost home and I am worried, and what did she say, worried about what, that's what she said, I remember the exact words, well, I am worried you may not like it here, that's what I said, or some stupid thing like that, and I hesitated when I said that, tell her quickly, you jerk, don't mumble, don't make long pauses in between your bumbling words, and then what did she say, I know I will love it she said, yes, I remember exactly what she said, word for word, I will never forget what she said, she said I'll love being anywhere as long as you are there with me, those were the exact words, and those words, oh those sweet, sweet *words, those sweet words that melt my heart, and the way she looked at me, oh God how she looked at me, she gazed at me like I was her God, totally adoring, totally worshiping, and me, me thinking why me, what have I done to deserve this, am I worthy of this, and she makes me fall in love with her so deeply, so totally, so helplessly, so irretrievably, so completely, that I simply say, I have to say, I am forced to say, spontaneously, it just comes out like a breath I must exhale, I say I love you Rosa, you don't know how happy you have just made me, I couldn't help saying that, and now... oh I wish I hadn't said it... God I wish I hadn't said it... no, no, no, **NO, NO, NO, ROSA,** forgive me, I didn't mean that, I don't wish that, I'll never take that back, I just wish I had said it sooner, in New York, on the plane, in Rome, in Torre Faro, on our honeymoon, in my letters for Christ sake, why, why didn't I ever, **EVER, GODDAMMIT,** why didn't I ever tell her I loved her, you dumb asshole sonofabitch, because technically it might have been a lie, that's what I told her, can you imagine, technically it might have been a lie, so what, you idiotic nincompoop, big deal, a technical lie, why do I have to be the knight in shining armor, why do I have to be so fucking sanctimonious, because I have to be honest to myself and to her, oh shut the fuck up will you, stop being so conceited, what's a little white lie, especially when it's not a lie at all, you did love her, Lillo, you just didn't know you did, you are so fucking stupid you are in love and you don't even realize it, and then what did I do, I start this foolish, this long, this garbling excuse, couldn't I have made it a bit shorter, or since I was already embarrassing myself, couldn't I have made it a bit longer, ten, fifteen seconds longer, and then that stupid, that infantile bit, close your her eyes Rosa, for the surprise, **COME ON, LILLO,** that's childish and you know it, was that really necessary, well no, maybe not, maybe not, maybe it wasn't necessary, certainly not, but because of that she had made me oh so happy, she had given me such joy, yes that's when she said she might have a surprise for me, no, no, no, I don't want to change that, no, no, that can stay, that must stay, I wouldn't change that, I would never change that, it was too beautiful, but did I have to stop again, well I guess I had to, I was too excited to drive, might hit somebody, so what, even a fender bender would have been a blessing, and if I hadn't stopped I probably could have, no, I surely would have made the green light at the Newport Gap Pike, we would have made it across safely, we would have been home in about ten, fifteen, twenty seconds at the* *most, but really, my chance, my best chance, my only chance, my only real chance was at that red light, the jerk ahead of me didn't move when the light turned green, didn't move for how long, three, four, five, ten seconds, how long was it, I don't know but it was too long, and I had to lean on the horn, a couple of times I did, and he finally moved, and I followed him, I followed him... oh God I followed him... I followed him... oh God why did I follow him... why did I follow him... and me, me crazily, wildly, happily singing "Wonderful, wonderful" out loud....*

And my quest didn't end there. As I relived, as I flashed back to my car slowly entering the intersection, I – sensing the impending catastrophe – would actually desperately stomp with both feet on an imaginary brake with such rapidity and with such force that the lurch of my legs in thin air would cause a sharp pain to my injured body. And the sharp pain would immediately jolt me out of my hopeful search for that miraculous second and plunge me back into the desolate reality of a lonesome, crippled man sitting on a recliner in a desolate and lonely room.

And to quickly evade that bleak, that painful reality, I would immediately substitute it with another tender illusion.

This new fantasy had me on that same recliner reading a newspaper and sipping a cup of coffee. It's a weekday evening or perhaps a Saturday or a Sunday morning. Rosa, already settled in the American way of life, is quietly puttering around the house dusting or vacuuming.

The louder hum of the vacuum cleaner tells me she is gliding by my recliner. And as she does, I almost absent-mindedly reach out, grab her somewhat chunkier backside and pull her to me. And I then press my nose and my ear to her swollen belly and listen to my son kicking inside her, and I smile contentedly as I savor the strong but not unpleasant odor of her body.

And tears of pure joy trickle down my eyes as my arm indeed moves to reach out for her. But the reality of my private Golgotha cruelly resumes when, as I try to pull her to me, my arm embraces only empty space. And then more tears, tears of pure grief would pour out of my eyes in streams, tears I couldn't stop, tears I wouldn't even try to stop.

How many times did I go through that routine? How many times did I go looking for that one precious second? How many times did I find it? How many times did I discard it? How many times did I discover other, better opportunities, wanting, desperately wishing to change the outcome, to cancel out, to wipe out, to alter that one, indelible, inalterable event? How many times did I reach out to embrace her? How many times did I experience the bitter disillusion of embracing empty space?

A hundred times? A thousand times? More, many more times than that, I am sure. Daily, ten, twenty times a day, God knows how many times every day, while sitting on my recliner all day long staring in space, and then in bed at night until the wee hours of the morning when plain exhaustion finally closed my eyes for a few hours. It was a recurring theme with just slight variations brought on by other particulars, other forgotten bits that now and then surfaced here and there in the mazes of my memory, but always with the same ineluctable result – I did follow that car... oh, God, why? Why, why did I follow that car?

Months later, when it finally dawned on me that finding or losing that one second was a pointless waste of time, when I had to acknowledge that reaching out for her only added intolerable and unneeded grief to my already tormented life, I began to slowly wean myself away from those fantasies until I finally gave them up entirely. Reluctantly.

But my troubled mind needed an outlet, an activity, some fuel, anything that could keep me from facing reality. And I therefore replaced those obsessions with another one, an even more severe, a more harmful, more lethal obsession than the first one.

I began to experience – or rather, I assigned myself – morbid feelings of guilt for the occurrence of the tragedy itself. I intentionally assigned myself the ultimate responsibility for Rosa's death. I began to believe that Rosa had died because I had come into her life.

That assumption was easy enough to make because, technically, it was correct. If I had resisted the urge to go to Italy, if I had graciously declined the offer to correspond with her or if I had not followed through with it, she would still be alive.

But I had gone to Italy out of curiosity, hadn't I? And I had met her, and I had encouraged her to write to me, and I had answered every one of her letters, and I had decided she would be a good choice for a wife, and I had asked her to marry me, and I had in fact married her, and I had taken her to the United States, and I was driving the car. *Ergo,* **I** was responsible for her death.

And this feeling of guilt reached an even higher plateau when, inevitably, it found its natural twin. I began to believe that, without a doubt, my in-laws felt the same way I did and would never forgive me for being the prime, the foremost, the **ONLY** agent of their daughter's death.

My depression had become so deeply entrenched, my obsession so fiercely intense and my spirits so profoundly abysmal that – as befits a man who has something to hide, something to be ashamed of – I purposely refrained from communicating with my in-laws.

For that matter, I even refrained from communicating with all my relatives in Italy, my mom, my dad, my sisters. But I felt no qualms about that, that was another matter entirely, that was due to sheer apathy, I knew that. The only relative I kept in touch with was my brother and his family, and then only because he practically forced himself on me, bless him!

During and after my hospital stay I didn't write one single time to my parents, to my in-laws, to my sisters, or to any of my friends. But the only ones I really would have wanted to contact – even more than my own parents – were my in-laws whom I loved just as much as my own folks.

In my mind and in my heart I had wronged them and owed them at the very least an explanation, some kind of apology. But how do you approach someone who holds you responsible for the death of their only daughter? Just writing them a few lines that essentially said 'Gee whiz,

I'm sorry' seemed to me a totally inadequate way to address the problem or to allay their belief that I – and I alone – was responsible for their daughter's death.

I knew they had written to me personally at my brother's address and I knew, of course, they had come all the way from Italy right after the accident. Mimmo had also told me they kept writing to him, always inquiring about my health, wishing me a speedy and complete recovery and always asking why I didn't write.

Mimmo was aware I was depressed but was unaware of the exact cause of my self-inflicted torment. He always answered their letters informing them that physically I was coming along fairly well, and he vaguely tried to excuse my long silence saying I was still too depressed about the loss of Rosa. He also always added he was sure I would reply when I felt better.

My self-inflicted morbidity, however, made me believe that their inquiries about my welfare were just perfunctory. In my heart I knew that in their hearts they had to feel I was guilty, they had to hold me responsible, they had to consider me irredeemable.

They had to feel that way because in my own eyes, in my own heart, I felt guilty, I felt responsible, I felt irredeemable. And since I had hurt them, since I had caused irreparable harm to these people I loved, I desperately wanted to make amends. They were my closest link to Rosa.

This need, this desire to reconcile with them became the only thing that mattered to me, even more than my own health and welfare.

Oh! If I could only obtain their forgiveness… And I began to bargain with myself about the degree of absolution I could aspire to attain. Outright forgiveness? No way! Outright forgiveness was a goal too outlandish, simply unattainable. Forgiveness? Are you kidding, Lillo? Get out of here! Forgiveness? Dream on, guy! That's way, way too much to ask for.

Oh! If I could only get them not too hate me… That's it! If I could only get them to just resent me a tiny little bit maybe, that's more reasonable. If I could only get them to at least not view me with contempt, with suspicion. Oh! If I could only get them to look at me, say, the way they saw me that first time, nearly two years ago. That's it, the neutral way they saw me the day when they had invited me to dinner. Yes, that's it, with the affected cordiality one shows to a distant relative who comes visiting, one you have invited just to be polite yet you don't really care if you ever see again. Was that too much to ask or to hope for?

My daily crucible, my daily occupation was to discover a way to make them accept me in a neutral way. No love and no hate, just neutral – I could live with that.

Reconciliation and affection, a return to the loving, familial status we enjoyed when we left Torre Faro seemed a wildly unrealistic goal, a pipe dream, a castle in the air. If I could achieve a "neutrality" status, if I could obtain, let's say, something like an armistice – that's it! An armistice! – a huge burden would be lifted off my shoulders, and I might even begin to believe life was worth living.

But even the constant lowering of my hopes and expectations seemed a hopeless dream, an impossible dream.

I kept asking myself over and over again, a hundred, a thousand times: "Would I be willing to forgive someone who was responsible for my only daughter's death?"

And the answer was always no, no, one thousand times no, no.

NO.

CHAPTER 21

On the evening of the 3rd of July 1964, Mimmo called me to tell me he was coming to pick me up the next morning. He had organized a 4th of July picnic at his house and he wanted me to be there.

Of course I had told him no, I did not want to go, I did not feel like going, the 4th of July didn't mean shit to me, and I would rather stay home. And, of course, he wouldn't take no for an answer, and he had come to pick me up anyway.

To this day, I don't know how my brother managed to stand by me, to love me and to help me way beyond what any reasonable human being would have done.

I still vividly recall those days and, in retrospect, I know I must have been a royal pain in the ass. No, no, no! 'Must have been' doesn't quite cut it! I most definitely **WAS** an insufferable pain in the ass.

Granted, I had plenty of reasons, ample justification for acting the way I did but still, I was a pain in the ass, I know that! And yet Mimmo stood by me, loved me and helped me through thick and thin, bless him!

He came to pick me up and took me to Rising Sun. The kids, Pietro, Nick, and Leo, were overjoyed to see me. They hadn't seen me in a while and they eagerly gathered around Uncle Lillo, fussing excitedly.

Back in the good old days I used to play catch with them in their huge backyard, or I would bat some fly balls for them to catch. On this day, they timidly asked me if I was up to throwing a few pop flies at them. Not wanting to disappoint them, I tried, but the best

I could do was lob the ball a few times. And of course I was unable to catch the ball when they threw it back, unless it was thrown directly at me.

My motion was still severely limited and I could only walk slowly and with a limp. I had discarded the crutches a couple of months before, but I still had to use a cane to walk any kind of distance.

Before the accident I used to be a decent athlete. I played soccer for a local semi-pro team, and I was also quite proficient at tennis, racquetball, and table tennis.

My inability to catch the pop flies reminded me that, for all practical purposes, I was now finished athletically. The thought that I would never again be able to engage in any significant sports activity was so dismal, so dejecting that I felt like crying. Not wanting to upset the kids, however, I managed to hold back my tears, even as I told them to keep themselves in shape, as I would be ready for them in just a few months.

We had our picnic, Italian style, of course – Ange had prepared an enormous tray of lasagna with meatballs and *braciole*. As a token gesture to the American tradition, she had also grilled hot dogs and hamburgers on an outdoor grill.

Later in the evening the whole family went to Rising Sun where they had the traditional firework display. But I was in no mood for that either. My depression wasn't just a fun inhibitor for me – it also made me hate seeing other people enjoying themselves. The dazzling display of pyrotechnics meant fun to a lot of people. And for that very reason I wanted no part of it.

Finally, shortly before midnight, all the festivities were over. Mimmo persistently had asked me to sleep over at his house but I – annoyed with the entire 4th of July shenanigans – inconsiderately asked him to take me home. I didn't even think or care about inconveniencing him and having him make a fifty-mile roundtrip at that late hour. I just insisted that he take me home – and he did, without a word of protest. Before leaving, Ange packed for me enough leftover lasagna and stuff to feed me for at least a week.

When we got home, Mimmo helped me out of the car and walked me to my front door and didn't leave until he was sure I was safely inside.

When I walked in I noticed immediately that the house felt uncomfortably warm. After placing the leftover food in the fridge, I checked the thermostat. The indoor temperature was indeed 82 degrees, even warmer than outdoors. Clearly, the air conditioning was not functioning right.

Shit! What do I do now? At that late hour – and on a 4th of July weekend to boot – there was no way I could get any service.

Mimmo had already left. I would just have to suffer until Monday when I could call somebody, or maybe I would bother my brother first thing in the morning – he was quite handy with appliances and tools.

Resigned to spending an uncomfortably warm night, I started opening a few windows to let in some fresh air. But then I thought the problem might be just a fuse, the air conditioning fuse might be off – I thought – so I started looking for the fuse box.

Of course I had no idea of where that damned fuse box was. I looked for it in every room but I couldn't find it. Where the hell is that goddamned fuse box? There had to be one somewhere in the house, that much I knew. I figured it had to be downstairs in the basement.

I hadn't been anywhere downstairs since I had returned home. In the six months since my discharge from the hospital, the only rooms I had ever used were my bedroom, the kitchen and the living room, plus the bathroom, of course. I had never set foot inside the two other bedrooms and the dining room upstairs, or the recreation room and the basement downstairs.

Hobbling slowly down the stairs, I entered the basement where I was greeted by a strong musty smell. And there the goddamned fuse box was. All the fuse switches were plainly labeled and I immediately saw that the one for the air conditioner was in the "OFF" position. I flicked it on and immediately the air conditioning unit started humming.

Thank God for little thing!

Heaving a sigh of relief, I turned around to go back upstairs. And, right beside the basement door, I saw two suitcases.

I had no idea whom they belonged to or who had placed them there. Puzzled, I lifted one and then the other – both of them obviously contained something. I then saw the "Pan Am" tag on both handles with my name and address and I realized they were our suitcases, the luggage we had when we had returned from Italy.

I had no idea how they wound up in my basement but, obviously, somebody – probably my brother – had retrieved them from the wreckage of my car and had brought them here.

Not without difficulty, I took both of them upstairs and placed them on the kitchen table. I tried to open the smaller suitcase first, but it was locked and I didn't have the key. With the aid of a small screwdriver, I managed to pop the flimsy lock open.

With some trepidation I lifted the lid – a white negligee, Rosa's negligee, was lying on top. Immediately a wave of dizziness hit me, a wave so strong that I had to lean against the wall to sustain myself.

I remembered she had worn that negligee the night we had spent at the hotel in Rome, and instantly a flood of exquisite, painfully beautiful memories rushed into my head.

We had made love that last night, twice, once when we had first gone to bed and then again early in the morning. Afterwards, she had removed her negligee and had placed it in the suitcase, right on top where I found it.

I closed my eyes recapturing, reliving those last moments of pure bliss. Fleeting images of her tenderness, of her initial shyness and of her subsequent passionate desire gratified my senses.

I recalled how with trembling fingers I used to softly caress the velvety skin of her arms, her breasts, her thighs; how I would then grab her and squeeze her tightly in an impetuous paroxysm of pure lust; how, even those few seconds it took for her to remove this same negligee seemed an unbearably long time; how, panting heavily with desire, I would excitedly help her remove it; how once – in Florence – I had unintentionally hurt her as, in my yearning to become one with her, it had caught one of the earrings I had just bought for her as it cleared her neck and her head; how I would then just blindly fling the negligee away; how we would afterwards lay side by side in bed for five, ten, fifteen minutes, totally spent but still embraced; how she would then silently dismount from the bed, pick up the negligee, and slip it on before returning to quietly nestle in my arms; how she would rub her nose on my shoulder, my neck, my cheek, hungrily relishing my scent; how we would finally fall asleep.

I reached for the negligee to touch it. It was silky, just like her skin, and I began to caress it slowly, cherishing, savoring, almost tasting those moments.

Impulsively, I grabbed it, lifted it up bringing it to my nostrils and inhaled deeply.

Incredibly, impossibly, there was still a faint fragrance of her perfume, that indelible aroma, that bewitching, unforgettable fragrance I had first smelled, I had first inhaled on our wedding night. There was even a faint scent of her skin and of her body.

I buried my head in it breathing deeply to capture every last drop, every last molecule, every last atom of her essence. For one brief, magical moment it felt like she was in my arms again.

From the depth of my whole being emerged first an anguished moan, and then a howl, a long animal howl of both pain and pleasure, and I began weaving and staggering all over the kitchen. I began calling out her name over and over, I felt her presence near me, around me, inside me, I heard her repeatedly calling my name, I heard her telling me, asking me to go see her.

I couldn't let go of that faint but heavenly scent. Still clutching that precious garment and holding it up to my nose, I feverishly looked up the Pan Am number in the directory and then went to the phone. Fumbling the telephone dial with trembling fingers, I misdialed several times until I finally managed to dial the right number.

It was nearly 1 AM, but I managed to talk to somebody in some department. I asked the lady who answered if I could get a ticket to Rome for the next day – that same day actually. She put me on hold for several minutes while she checked and she then informed me that I couldn't, the flight was all sold out. I then started calling other airlines hoping to find a seat, any seat, even first class, I didn't care.

I knew I was flush with money. Since the day of the accident the bank had continued to pay my salary, stopping only when I had gone on disability. And of course, WSFS management had also assured me my job would be waiting for me whenever I felt ready to return.

A few weeks after my discharge from the hospital, I had asked my brother to take me to the Union Street branch that I managed. I was in no condition to do much of anything, and I wanted to give him Power of Attorney to handle all my financial affairs.

My staff hadn't seen me in several months. When we walked in – me leaning on a cane and holding on to my brother for support – nobody recognized that skinny crippled man waiting in the customer lounge.

A new employee was in my office, a middle-aged lady waiting on a customer, either a temporary manager or somebody sent to help out Kathy Clark, my assistant manager, during my absence.

Kathy was in her office located right next to mine, and she was also waiting on a customer. I recognized three of my tellers and there was also a new one I didn't know.

When Kathy was through with her customer, she politely thanked him, shook his hand and held the office door open for him. After he left, she then turned to us and cordially invited us to step in her office with the traditional "May I help you?"

She briefly glanced at my brother and me, and then turned around motioning us to enter her office before her. Then, suddenly, she stopped and twirled around. She looked at me again, and then did the classic double take – in one split second her face dramatically changed expression, from pleasant, business-like cordiality to startled astonishment.

"LEO!?!?!..." – She literally screamed. I motioned her with my hand to keep it down, and I even tried to smile but only managed to grimace.

Her scream, however, had alerted all the tellers. They immediately excused themselves with the customers they were waiting on and they all rushed to see me, to touch me, to embrace me, all of them literally in tears. Some of the customers also were friends or acquaintances of mine and they all gathered around me, wishing me good health and anxiously asking me when I would return to work.

I thanked them for their good wishes and assured them I would be back as soon as my body allowed me to do so, possibly within the year I told them, although I didn't really believe it myself.

We then proceeded to assign Power of Attorney to my brother, and it was then that I found out I had a sizable amount of money in my account.

Some of it was from the accumulated and mostly unspent monthly salary. Additionally, the young man who had killed Rosa came from a wealthy and heavily insured family. Through an attorney my brother had managed to collect a very large sum for Rosa's death, for my bodily injuries and sufferings, for my potential future disabilities and loss of earnings and for the destruction of my car.

The settlement had been more than enough to pay off the mortgage on my house, with a tidy sum left over to indulge in the kind of expenditures I could only dream of making on my salary only.

The bank health insurance program paid all my medical expenses, past present and future, and my household expenses were minimal. I was not exactly a tycoon, but I certainly could afford to go first class. And that's exactly what I did.

I found a first class seat on a flight leaving that same day from Philadelphia with a stopover in London, and I booked it immediately. I was so excited, so frantic, that at 2 AM I called my brother – scaring the hell out of him – to tell him about my plans and asking him to please take me to Philadelphia before 5 PM that same day.

The trip to Rome took about 13 hours because of the layover in London. Thank God I had gone first class because the seats were very comfortable and my body was far from being OK. I still needed a cane to walk any long distance; at the airport, they had even offered me a wheelchair that I had proudly – and foolishly – refused.

My only luggage was a small gym bag containing a change of underwear for a few days, one pair of pants and two shirts. In my rush to depart, I hadn't even thought about bringing a toothbrush or shaving gear.

Unsure of how long I was going to stay in Italy, I had bought an open ticket and had to pay a premium for that. But I didn't care, I had to go, I had to go even though I didn't know why I was going. I just felt this burning need to be there, to see where Rosa was buried, to talk to her. While there, of course, I would also talk to her parents – if they would even deign to speak to me. And I would beg their forgiveness, and try to patch things up.

In Rome I took the train to Messina – first class again. On the evening of the 6th of July I arrived in Torre Faro. My parents would normally have been there by now – they always came down from Genoa around the end of May. Mimmo had told me, however, that they had remained up north because one of our sisters was expecting a baby any day and mom wanted to be there to help her out when the baby was born.

A taxi took me straight to the Donatos' house – I paid the driver and saw him leave.

I was literally trembling because of some emotion I can't even describe – uncertainty, guilty feeling, fear of rejection, I just don't know. I approached my in-laws' house and pressed the doorbell button. I heard the inside chimes ring and waited, but nobody came to the door. Again I pressed the doorbell button and also knocked on their front door. Still, no answer.

It was almost 9 PM but it wasn't quite dark yet. Maybe they had already gone to bed, I figured. If they had retired for the night, I would be in a bit of a jam. There were no hotels that I knew of in Torre Faro, and I had no idea of where I could spend the night. There was my parents' house, of course, but it was closed, and they had the key. I would have to walk all over town hoping to find some relatives who could put me up for the night. I wished I had told the cabdriver to wait, but it was too late for that.

I pressed the doorbell button and knocked one more time, louder this time, and waited several more seconds. Just as I was ready to leave, I heard a faint voice inside say in Sicilian *"Trasiti!"* (Come in!)

Slowly, I opened the door and stood on the threshold without entering. I peered in the dark front room; a small table lamp in a corner cast a tenuous light, barely bright enough to outline a few pieces of furniture arranged differently from what I remembered.

When my eyes adjusted to the semi-darkness, I saw two old people sitting on two easy chairs placed at right angle to each other, their knees almost touching. Except for the fact that I knew I was in their house and I knew who they were, I would never have recognized them.

My father-in-law, a tall, portly man in his mid-fifties when I had last seen him, looked now like a frail and shrunk old man in his seventies. My mother-in-law, a very attractive woman in her mid-forties only a year ago, looked now like a feeble old lady with gaunt, deep set, circled eyes, and no make-up at all. Her once glorious honey blonde hair was now almost completely gray and unkempt, and her face was a mask of utter sadness and desolate resignation.

It was July and quite warm, yet both of them wore wool shawls on their shoulders. And there they were, sitting silently in the dark.

"Posso entrare? (May I come in?)" – I asked hesitantly.

"Cu siti? (Who are you?)" – My father-in-law asked in Sicilian, thrusting his face forward and furrowing his eyes to see who was this intruder coming at this late hour.

"Sono io... Lillo..." (It's me... Lillo...)" – I mumbled, almost apologetically.

"Lillo chi? (Lillo who?)" – My father-in-law inquired suspiciously, almost confrontationally, and the tone of his voice made my heart sink.

Tears came to my eyes.

"Sono io, Lillo, vostro genero. Per favore, fatemi entrare. (It's me, Lillo, your son-in-law. Please, let me come in.)" – I asked pleadingly

There was silence for what seemed to me an inordinately long time. Had they heard me? Had they understood who I was? Were they unwilling to let me in?

Then, at the same time, they both said: "**Lillo?!?!**", and there was shocked astonishment in their voices.

"*Si, sono io...* (Yes, it's me...)" – I said crying softly – "*Vi prego, fatemi entrare.*" (Please, let me come in.)

Then, without even waiting for their reply, I just walked in and hobbled to where they were sitting. Laying my cane on the floor, I managed to kneel in front of them and, embracing their knees, I began pleading with them.

"I know I have hurt you a lot, but I did not mean to do it, it was not my fault." – I sobbed out loud – "It just happened. I am so sorry... Please, please, please forgive me!"

Neither one moved or said a word as I, clutching their legs, my head on their knees, kept on crying unrestrained tears.

Then suddenly my father-in-law came alive. Rising rapidly from the chair, he lifted me to my feet and embraced me, squeezing me so hard that I gasped in pain. My mother-in-law also jumped up and began hugging and kissing me.

"Lillo! Lillo! *Non può essere!* (It can't be!)." – She kept screaming – "*Madonna Santa!* (Holy Mother of God!). You look terrible! How are you?"

My father-in-law then grabbed me by the shoulders. Looking at me in the eyes, he shook me violently.

"Is that why you never wrote to us?" – He sternly questioned me – "You thought we were mad at you? Is that it?"

I nodded, still crying without restraint.

"Oh, *mamma... papà...*" – I blurted out, then, fearful I had committed a gaffe of some kind, I added timorously: "Can I still call you *mamma* and *papà*?"

"**CAN YOU CALL US MAMMA AND PAPÀ?**" – My father-in-law literally shouted at me, scolding me – "**OF COURSE YOU CAN!!** Why shouldn't you? I insist! We both insist! Nothing has changed! You are our son! We are your *mamma* and *papà*!"

I hugged them both and just kept mumbling over and over:

"Thank you! Thank you!"

Then, trying to justify my long silence, I said dejectedly: "Yes! That's why I never wrote. I was going crazy. No, I **HAVE** gone crazy. I am such a miserable mess, I had convinced myself you hated me, you had to hate me, I had convinced myself you thought I was responsible for Rosa's death. Oh! *Mamma...Papà!...* You can't even imagine what I have gone through for the past year."

They both gave me an expressionless look and nodded slowly. And instantly I felt like a goddamned idiot – I couldn't believe I could have been so grossly insensitive, so totally lacking in dignity.

Here, in front of me, were the parents of my late wife – they had lost their only daughter, they had gone through the agony of losing her and burying her. Except for the physical pain of my wounds, surely their pain was at the very least equal to mine. I could see with my own eyes what they had been through, they both looked like me, worse than me, and here I had the audacity, I had the fucking nerve to tell them they couldn't imagine what I had been going through. Goddamn me! What a boorish horse's ass I was!

Grabbing their hands, I brought them up to my lips to kiss them.

"Oh, God! I am so sorry, *mamma, papà* ... Please, forgive me, I didn't mean what I just said." – I begged, shaking my head – "I am just a foolish young man. Yes, I have suffered a lot, but I know, or I should know that you have suffered just as much as I have, and even more. Please, please forgive me!"

My father-in-law just smiled a wan smile.

"No apology is necessary, Lillo." – He reassured me, patting me on the shoulder. – "We both know you didn't mean to belittle our sorrow."

My mother-in-law then started acting like a mom.

"Lillo!" – She exclaimed – "You look so terrible, you are so skinny."

I had lost nearly 50 pounds during my hospital stay and had regained maybe 5 in the six months at home. I had no interest in myself or anything else, including food.

I don't recall one single time in the last six months, or in the last year for that matter, when I felt hungry or had a craving for any kind of food.

I used to be a big-time pasta lover. Since my discharge from the hospital, however, the only times I ate pasta was when Ange would come over bringing me a tray of lasagna or some other special dish she had prepared. And to make sure I ate it, she would sit at the table with me and force me to eat it, practically spoon-feeding me.

When on my own, I survived on cereal, salads, and the occasional large pizza I would have delivered. I would eat one or two slices then place the rest in the fridge, and that would be my meal for the next few days.

I embraced my mother-in-law smiling – my first smile in one year.

"*Mamma...*" – I told her. And God, it felt so good calling her '*mamma*' – "I don't even remember the last time I was hungry, but I am hungry now. Is there anything to eat?"

I was home.

CHAPTER 22

In less than half an hour *Mamma* Lucia had an ample and tasty meal in front of me – pasta with a deliciously flavored marinara sauce, grilled steak, garden salad, cheese and sliced salami, plus a bottle of home-made red wine. Both of them sat down at the table watching me as I ate hungrily. And as I ate, we talked and talked.

There was so much ground to cover, so many blank spaces to fill, so much information to exchange. Conversation was fragmentary and disjointed with questions quickly following one after the other, even as an answer was being given. We would often interrupt each other blurting out bits and pieces evoked by a sudden memory related or even unrelated to what we were talking about.

Fragments of our conversation did concern or marginally involve Rosa but, by common and silent agreement, we purposely refrained from talking specifically about her – that subject was too painful for all of us.

When they mentioned their trip to the United States and their daily visits to the hospital, the attention shifted to my medical problems and me. At their urgings, I told them about my physical sufferings, my broken bones, the resetting of my fractures, the plastic surgery, everything.

As I detailed them, however, they kept asking repeatedly what the chances of my regaining good health were. It became clear to me that I was distressing them, so I purposely tried to minimize them.

To mitigate their concerns, I assured them that all doctors agreed I would be in decent shape in just a few months, after some more intensive therapy.

Papà Filippo informed me he had taken early retirement immediately after Rosa's funeral. His pension, his savings and some income he received from farmland he owned and leased to others allowed them to live a quiet and dignified existence. Since he considered me family – his only family! – he even disclosed private financial details, confiding to me the actual amount of the pension and the farm income.

Somberly he told me that for the first six months after Rosa's burial they visited the cemetery every single day. Since March, however, they had cut down the visits to once a week, the only times they ever left their house except for grocery shopping.

On my part also, I felt unburdened. I dealt with them exactly the way I dealt with my own brother – they were my family. I could talk with them openly, and I did not hide anything. I poured out all about my deep depression, my precarious mental state, my feelings of guilt, and my lack of desire to go on living. I even told them about my intense feeling of hatred toward the guy who had caused the accident and about my visit to his grave.

When I disclosed the urinating incident, my father-in-law shook his head and looked at me sharply, visibly upset.

"Lillo! You shouldn't have done that. You don't expect me to approve of that, do you?" –He told me sternly.

"No, *papà*... No!" – I told him, deeply ashamed – "I expected, I even wanted your disapproval. I felt like a worthless scum myself as soon as I did it. I haven't been to church since the day I got married, but right after I did that I prayed God to forgive me for that cowardly act."

He gently touched my arm to let me know he understood.

"I just mentioned that episode to let you know how far down I had sunk. No, how far down I still am." – I said, shaking my head disconsolately – "That has been my life since that day. And I don't see any way out yet."

"We know what you have been through, Lillo." – My father-in-law said – "As you can see, we went through the same heartbreak ourselves."

After a brief pause he then went on, shaking his head slowly: "I wish I could tell you we are resigned, I wish I could tell you we have accepted it, but we haven't, really, not yet, anyway, and God knows if we ever will, if we will ever be resigned. I don't even know if it's possible, if it can be done..."

And his words just trailed off as he kept slowly shaking his head just staring in space. He then suddenly shook his head more forcefully, as if trying to erase a memory or to focus on a more important matter.

Looking at me, he frowned and then told me with a peremptory tone: "But we are old people, Lillo. We don't have much to look forward to... But you, you..." – and he repeatedly jabbed me on my chest – "You are still a young man and it's now time for you to go on with your life. You can, you must start a new life for yourself."

That statement jolted me – you must start a new life, he had said. Start a new life meant starting a new life without Rosa, a new life with another woman. The idea seemed so absurd, so nonsensical, so irrational even. And yet it was not, I knew it was not – widows and widowers do remarry all the time, it's a perfectly normal occurrence. For others.

"I know you mean well, *papà,* and you are probably right." – I told him halfheartedly – "I just don't know where to start. Or how to start."

"Where or how will come to you." – He told me with that same peremptory tone – "It's when to start that is important, and you can start right now. You can start today."

"Maybe today was a good start." – I told him quietly – "I got a huge load off my mind knowing you were not mad at me and you still love me. But without Rosa, I just don't know... ". And I couldn't finish talking.

There were a few seconds of embarrassing silence as I tried to keep my feelings under control. I quickly glanced at both of them and then cast my eyes around the room.

Every single feature in that house, their countenance, their physical appearance, their clothes, their posture, the unnatural silence, the air, the atmosphere itself, even the walls and furniture, everything spoke of the intense suffering and despair they had endured and were still enduring. Everything mirrored the heartbreak that had now taken sole possession of their home.

Squeezing my eyes shut to block out, to erase that gloomy mood, I consciously tried to forcibly substitute it with a recollection of something pleasant – anything, anything agreeable, or even neutral.

The last pleasant, indeed joyful event in my life had been my marriage and honeymoon – but I couldn't, I wouldn't think about that. That didn't count – that had been the direct cause of our common heartbreak.

And other pleasant events – my first trip to Italy, the night at the beach, my correspondence with Rosa, my engagement – they didn't count either. They were all common threads to the tragedy.

Other joyful events in my life seemed to be so far removed, so out of touch with the present wretchedness as to be downright risible. My promotion to a managerial post? Big deal!... My week-end excursions to New York? Whoop-de-do!

I finally settled on the most recent event. I concentrated on the warm and loving reception I had just received from my in-laws and held on tightly to the thin layer of solace I felt receiving it. Holding on to that fragment of comfort, I changed the subject and switched my attention to both of them.

"You know," – I remarked – "You are worried about my conditions, and I appreciate that, and you encourage me to go on with my life, and I appreciate that also, but what about you? You really don't look all that well yourselves."

"I know... Just like you, we were crushed." – My father-in-law murmured. He then quietly corrected himself. "No, we still are crushed."

He paused for a while. As if to justify their abject conditions, he then raised his head to look at me.

"But like I said, we are old people, Lillo," – He added firmly – "and we got nothing to look forward to, but you, you..." – and again he jabbed me repeatedly on my shoulder – "You are still what... Twenty-eight? Twenty-nine? You still have your whole life ahead of you! You have plenty of time to make a new life for yourself, to start a new family."

Start a new family! God, what a subject! Oddly, when he had first suggested starting a new life, I had just envisioned – and dismissed as improbable – the picture of a life with a new companion, without even associating this new union with its natural and complementary benefit, sex.

But now, his statement about starting a new family brought to my mind a fleeting image of a bedroom scene, and the thought literally made me shudder. It seemed improper, if not outright lurid. Sex was something that had been totally out of my mind over the past year and – now that he had indirectly brought it in the picture – I realized it was a subject I didn't even want to consider. Still, I was touched.

"Thank you *papà*. I know you both mean well and want me to go on with my life, and I will try, *papà*. Maybe some day I will try, but not right now. I'm just not ready yet." – I told him – "The way I've been feeling, the way I am right now, I haven't even thought about it. It seems to me it would be an insult to Rosa if I even just thought about it. Eventually, who knows? I know it will take months, maybe years before I can forget and return to a normal life."

"Lillo, believe me, we know how you feel," – *papà* Filippo said – "and I'm not pressing you, you know that. I just want to make sure you understand we would have no objections, and I'm certain Rosa would have no objections either. We want you to be happy, she loved you and she would want you to be happy. You have a right to some happiness, especially after what you've been through."

We remained silent for a while, just staring at the floor. Then, raising his head, my father-in-law suddenly asked me point blank: "Lillo, what made you decide to come back now, just like that, all of a sudden?"

"I don't know, *papà*." - I answered him, and I proceeded to detail all, about the suitcase, the negligee, everything.

"This may sound crazy" – I went on – "but when I held Rosa's negligee in my hands I felt like she was calling me, I felt like she was telling me to come to see her."

339

I paused for a while recalling the emotions I had experienced when I held the negligee in my hands, and again I felt like crying but managed to hold it back.

"The only thing I know, *papà*, is that one minute later I was on the phone making arrangements to come to Italy." – I continued – "And here I am, and first thing tomorrow morning, please take me to the cemetery. I want to see… I need to see her grave."

"Of course, of course…" – He said softly, and he patted my hand sensing I was near an emotional outburst.

And tears did, in fact, start falling. Much as I tried to stifle my sobs, I began to cry, and they both joined me.

And sitting around the kitchen table, we cried silently, three wounded souls trying to alleviate our common grief the only way we could, the only way we knew how.

The next morning I got up late. The warm and loving welcome I had received from my in-laws had soothed the turmoil that had obsessed me for the past several months. Additionally, the long trip and the jet lag had tired me out, and I had slept well.

After a breakfast of *caffelatte* and *biscotti*, my father-in-law and I left to go to the cemetery. *Mamma* Lucia stayed home to prepare lunch.

It was a long walk – just over a mile – with the last half-mile up a steep road that ended right at the cemetery gate.

Because of my disability, my father-in-law wanted to call a cab, but I stubbornly refused and insisted on walking.

"I need some exercise, *papà*, and walking will do me good." – I told him, and he relented. It took us well over an hour to cover a distance that could normally be covered in about thirty minutes. We had to stop several times to allow me to catch my breath and to allow my aching limbs to rest, and at each stop I wished I hadn't been so stubborn.

The Torre Faro cemetery is located on a hill rising just outside town. Before entering the cemetery we paused to look at the magnificent view one can enjoy from that summit. It's a breathtaking scenery that includes the entire Strait of Messina, the coast of Calabria and, in the distance on clear days, even the Aeolian islands of Stromboli and Vulcano.

I had never visited that cemetery before, had never seen that magnificent view that embraces seas, mountains, islands, cities, villages, as well as the quiet, irrevocable finality of a graveyard. One look at that gorgeous scenery and I understood why my dad always said he wished to be buried there when he died.

In a ramshackle stand just outside the cemetery walls, a florist did brisk business selling flowers to cemetery visitors. My father-in-law bought a bunch of lilies, and we then entered the cemetery and started walking in the direction of Rosa's grave.

As he weaved along the narrow gravel paths – with me following right behind him – *papà* Filippo occasionally stopped to point out the graves of some of my relatives – my grandparents, a few uncles and aunts – some of whom I hardly remembered.

He then stopped suddenly and did not point to any relative's grave – we had arrived. A fleet glimpse at a grave of pink marble shocked me, literally paralyzed me. I couldn't move, I found myself incapable and powerless to even look at it.

When my father-in-law pointed to the grave, I abruptly turned away from it, moaning loudly, refusing to face that reality. Burying my face in my father-in-law's shoulder, I then burst into tears and began sobbing uncontrollably, unable and unwilling to turn around and look at the grave.

My father-in-law let me vent my grief for a while then, patting me softly on my back, he quietly murmured: ""*Su...Su... Lillo, fatti coraggio.* (Come on, come on, Lillo, have courage.)"

And he kept gently exhorting me, physically trying to turn me around to look at the grave.

I at first tried to sneak a few quick, furtive looks. Then, gathering all my courage, I turned around sharply and faced the grave.

Its stark vision, the plain symmetry of the marble slabs, the inscription on the upright slab, the utter finality of its significance, made me lose all composure. Literally hurling myself on the grave, I began shouting her name repeatedly, sobbing unashamedly, kissing the cold stone, begging Rosa to talk to me.

My father-in-law again let me vent my grief then gently picked me up and embraced me as he kept whispering soft words of encouragements. Listening to his soothing words, I managed to compose myself.

Again I turned to look at the grave. In the center of the upright slab there was her likeness in a large porcelain oval. It was a picture I had never seen before, a picture of Rosa in her bridal gown.

I hadn't seen any of our wedding pictures – the wedding album would have been sent to us when completed, but it was never sent of course.

In the picture, Rosa looked incredibly beautiful and radiantly happy, a happiness so genuine, so true that it melted my heart.

The grave was decorated simply. Etched on the marble slab was one rose with a long, curving stem and with sharp thorns piercing deeply inside three broken hearts. In the middle of the slab, in a beautiful flowing script, the inscription said:

Rosa Donato in Vadalà
20 Gennaio 1938 – 26 Luglio 1963

Below, in the same script, was the following verse:
Rosa, soltanto ieri,
Tu, come un giglio pura,
Il più bel fiore eri
Di tutta la natura.
E come fior di campo
Fu la tua breve vita,
Un improvviso lampo
T'ha colto, e sei appassita.

(Rosa, only yesterday,
You, pure as a lily,
Were the most beautiful flower

In all of nature.

And like a field flower

Was your brief life,

A sudden bolt of lighting

Struck you, and you withered)

What beautiful verses! They captured precisely Rosa's essence and the tragedy of her untimely death.

As I read them, though, I felt inside an uneasy feeling, a confused feeling I couldn't quite express. That strange sensation lingered for a few moments until it finally crystallized. Yes! –There was something vaguely and at the same time distinctly familiar about those verses. Where had I seen them or where had I heard them before?

I struggled trying to remember why they seemed familiar, but I just couldn't place it. Glancing intermittently at those verses, I kept murmuring them trying to jolt my memory, all to no avail.

It was a feeling like hearing a musical refrain you have definitely heard before, a refrain you know, something you are very familiar with but can't quite put your finger on it. Much as you try, you find yourself unable to attach lyrics to it, or name the singer who sang it, or the movie it came from. It's a maddening pursuit that ends either when it finally hits you or you give up the chase.

Unable to solve that nagging feeling on my own, and yet unwilling to give up the chase, I turned toward my father-in-law.

"Those verses are so beautiful." – I remarked – "Who wrote them? Who commissioned them?"

"But…" – He stammered, obviously perplexed, almost confused by my question – "I thought… I'm sure your brother said… Mimmo sent them to me. He wrote to us saying you had composed them and wanted them on her grave. He said you had dictated them to him while you were still in the hospital."

"**WHAT?!?**" – I blurted out, totally befuddled.

I thought I hadn't heard right or maybe he had misunderstood my question, and I actually started to repeat it. But just as the first words came out of my mouth, my eyes happened to fall on the bunch of lilies *papà* Filippo was carrying. Immediately a vision flashed in front of my eyes.

I grabbed my head with both hands and began shaking it.

Alarmed, my father-in-law put his arms around my shoulders and looked at me.

"Lillo, *che c'è, non stai bene?*" (What's the matter? You don't feel well?) – He inquired, visibly concerned.

I just waved him off. A series of pictures kept flashing in my mind, clicking rapidly, like in a slide show – the landscape, the lilies, the rising flowers, the competition, the rose, the music, the flash of a blade, the cut flowers... No, no! It can't be! Yes! Yes! That must be it! That has to be it!

I slammed my forehead with my hand.

"*È IL SOGNO!!!* (IT'S THE DREAM!!!) – I shouted, startling my father-in-law with my outburst. *È IL SOGNO CHE HO FATTO!!!* (IT'S THE DREAM I HAD!!!!)"

My father-in-law now became really agitated. Bewildered, having no idea of what I was talking about, he frantically started looking around for some help. Seeing no one, he then tried to calm me down probably thinking I was having some kind of seizure.

Struggling to regain some composure, I managed to calm down. I then began telling him in garbled words about the dream I had – or had it been a dream? – about the fields, the lilies, the emerging flowers, the beauty competition, the growing rose, the scythe mowing everything down. Talking in spurts, babbling literally, I tried to explain as well as I could – with bumbling words and mimicking hand gestures – what I had experienced.

I am not sure he understood what I was saying, or if I was making any sense at all. I wasn't sure myself if I was making any sense, but it seemed pretty obvious to me that I had somehow translated that dream-like experience into those verses for my wife's grave.

Yes! Of course! I clearly remembered telling my brother in my dream about the dream itself, and I also recalled urging him to take notes so I could remember the dream later. And then the clincher – I remembered telling him about my dream not in ordinary words, but declaiming them, as if I was acting in a play or reciting some verse.

Is that what I was doing? Was I composing and dictating a poem, an epitaph for my wife's grave? Was I asleep or awake?

God! How utterly bewildering and confusing it all was! So far out, so improbable, that for a while I didn't know what to think or believe.

Was I dreaming now? Was I really in a cemetery? Was I in front of Rosa's grave? Had I gone completely nuts? But there it was, the epitaph was right in front of me, and my father-in-law swore my brother had written the precise instructions I had given him, requesting that those verses be engraved on Rosa's grave.

Several minutes passed before I fully recovered from my astonishment, from my disbelief. *Papà* Filippo then removed a few withered flowers from receptacles attached to the sides of the upright marble slab and replaced them with the fresh lilies he had purchased. We lingered there for a few minutes to recite some silent prayers and we then began to slowly make our way home.

The rest of the day was uneventful. I managed to get in touch with my parents in Genoa and told them I was in Torre Faro. Stunned and overjoyed, they were ready to make arrangements to come down to Sicily immediately, but I insisted that they stay in Genoa to help my sister.

I explained why I had come and told them I would be returning to the States in just a couple of days, three at the most. I assured them I was in pretty good shape and also promised I would come visiting as soon as my therapy was over.

After dinner, we sat outside on their *"bisolu"*, a cement stoop facing the Strait of Messina. A soft evening breeze was blowing and gaining strength by the minute. I had left Wilmington totally unprepared, practically wearing just the clothes I had on my back, knowing that Torre Faro in July is usually as hot as Florida.

Concerned about my health, *Mamma* Lucia went to get one of her husband's jackets to protect me against the evening chill. It hung loosely on my skinny frame, but I thanked her for it and put it on.

A full moon shone a glimmering path of gold on the sea. Two

"*lampara*" boats (boats equipped with a fishing lamp) trolling for fish near the shore caught the moonlight glimmer and seemed to redirect it to the bottom of the sea. Silhouettes of a few anglers with fishing poles were visible at the water's edge, and a scant number of beach visitors were slowly rounding up their belongings, preparing to return home.

We spent the late evening filling in the details of each other's lives since that awful day. I related the low points of my depression, while they went over the anguish of Rosa's funeral in Torre Faro as well as their own equally heartbreaking agonies.

Bad move! Each wrenching detail of her last journey only added fuel to my still unstable and vulnerable state of mind. But no matter how painful the details, I urged them to continue, I wanted to know everything, I needed to know everything. Perversely, I needed to feed my sadness with even more sadness.

It was nearly midnight. Visibly tired, *Mamma* Lucia embraced her husband and me and got up to retire for the night. Not quite ready for bed yet, *Papà* Filippo and I just lounged on the front stoop a while longer. After conversing for a few more minutes, he then suggested we go for a walk.

We walked in silence for less than half a mile in the now deserted Via Torre – the town's main drag – till we got to the little square in front of the town church.

Across the street in front of the church, a low wall separates the square from the beach – the locals call it '*u murettu da chiesa*', the church wall.

Since it was built – God knows how many years ago – that wall has been the traditional gathering place for the entire town. During the day and every evening until late at night, weather permitting, you will always find dozens of people of all ages sitting there just chatting, the topics of conversations covering the gamut of everyone's daily life – whining about family or work related problems, debating sports news, deploring the constantly decreasing fishing catch, complaining loudly or sighing resignedly about the empty local and national government promises, or simply gossiping.

Even at midnight, when we got there, about a dozen town folks were sitting on that wall, some facing the church, others facing the sea.

My father-in-law stopped briefly to say hello to a couple of acquaintances who greeted him warmly, clearly surprised to see him out at all, much less at that late hour. Understanding my need for privacy, he did not bother to introduce me, but I noticed that they all scrutinized me with some curiosity. I'm quite sure, however, that none of them recognized me or guessed who I was.

We moved a few yards away from them and sat on the wall, facing the sea, that beautiful and dangerous sea that for centuries has provided a living for half the people in town.

The evening breeze had now become a gusty wind.

"*Sta facennu sciroccu!*" (The sirocco is blowing!) – *Papà* Filippo said in Sicilian, referring to the 'sirocco' wind, a constant, oppressive southeastern wind – predominant in most of Sicily – that usually starts as a pleasantly gentle and warm breeze, but then starts blowing hard and it frequently lasts for days, becoming downright maddening, irritable, even influencing a person's mood, always in a negative way.

After a stronger than usual gust, we debated returning home but we decided to linger a while, turning up our coats' collar to protect against the night chill. We sat there silently for long while, staring at the sea and listening as the sirocco wind slammed fragmentary waves on the sandy shore.

It was a long, almost embarrassing silence that neither of us seemed able or even willing to break. We kept glancing occasionally at each other as if ready to start a conversation, but we then quickly stared back at the sea.

Papà Filippo finally broke the silence. Reminiscing about the first time I had returned to Italy, he asked me quietly: "Lillo, do you remember that first time when you came for dinner at our house. When was it?... In 1962?"

Yes! It had been a short two years, yet it seemed like an eternity had passed since then.

"Of course I remember, *papà*, I even remember the date. It was a

Sunday, Sunday, August 19th. I even remember what Rosa had cooked for dinner." – I mused. And, with a sad smile, I then proceeded to recite every dish she had prepared.

He looked at me wistfully, impressed and yet sadly touched by my recollections.

"Yes, I remember how she fussed all day long over every dish." – He then said – "She wanted to make sure everything was perfect because she wanted to impress you. She was so much in love with you..."

Puzzled, I looked at him sharply – clearly he was mistaken, he had to be mistaken.

"Did you say she was in love with me? Even then?..." – I corrected him gently – "No, *papà,* it can't be. You are mistaken. That can't be right. How can that be? She didn't even know me then. You must be thinking about some other time."

"No, no, Lillo." – He murmured, shaking his head sadly. Then, nodding, he added: "I know what I'm talking about. When you came in '62 she was already very much in love with you. She was in love with you long before you even arrived."

That just didn't make any sense.

"But how can that be, *papà?*" – I asked him, puzzled. – "I don't even remember meeting her, if I ever did meet her at all, when I was here in 1950."

Trying to clear my doubts, I then added: "And even if I did meet her, she had to be what?... Only about eleven or twelve maybe."

"That's right." – He said, nodding quietly – "She began having feelings for you when she was twelve. Twelve and a half to be precise."

Now I was really bewildered.

"But... but, I don't understand. How is that possible? Why? – I asked – "It just doesn't make any sense. How could that be?"

He gave me a quizzical look, as if he didn't quite believe what I had just said. He then asked me: "You mean she never mentioned anything to you?"

"No, no, I swear to God, *papà,* Rosa never said anything at all." – I told him emphatically – "This is all new to me. Please tell me."

He nodded slowly and smiled a sad, wistful smile, visualizing and recollecting those distant days. Placing both hands on the wall as if to sustain himself, he hunched his shoulders and raised his head staring straight ahead at the Calabria coast across the Strait. He then began narrating.

"I don't recall exactly when it happened, but she came running home one day when she was about twelve, twelve and a half..." – He turned to look at me – "When did you say you were here? Was it the summer of 1950?"

I nodded, and he went on: "Well, it was during that time. She came running home one day, and we could tell she was all excited. She was acting like she had a big surprise for us, like something big had happened. My wife of course asked her why she was so excited. At first she didn't want to tell us, but eventually she did tell us. And the big secret, the big surprise was that she had decided whom she was going to marry when she grew up."

Smiling softly, he continued: "Of course we played along, paying mock attention to this important decision. You know how it is with kids – when they make an important decision or announcement, nothing else counts. Anyway, it was you, she had decided she was going to marry you, and that was it. You know the way kids state things, firmly, decisively. She had made a final decision, and that was it."

Chuckling at the memory of his pre-pubescent daughter acting like a grown-up, he then went on: "And the way she said it, it was clear she kind of expected us to raise some objections, and she was telling us in no uncertain terms there was no use trying to change her mind."

I couldn't help chuckling myself.

"Rosa wanted to marry me?" – I asked, a bit confounded – "That's really funny. But why, what had I done?"

"Well, it was a culmination of things, actually." – He proceeded. "Even before making her 'absolutely final' decision, she already liked you a lot because you got her a ride on Nick Ravello's car. Oh, you can't even imagine how excited she was about that. She came home raving about that car. She went on and on listing all the details, the seats, how big they were, the radio, the air conditioning, everything. And Lillo did this, and Lillo did that, and anyway she liked you and was very grateful to you for that."

OK, that part I remembered – that is, I remembered being instrumental in getting rides for a lot of local kids, boys and girls, plus the ice cream cones and sodas. I remembered that back in 1950 many young kids used to hang around me precisely because they hoped that Nick would take us for a ride in his Pontiac. I remembered how it made me feel important because of the influence I yielded. But that hardly justified a twelve-year-old girl getting a crush or falling in love with me.

My father-in-law seemed to read my mind because he quickly added: "But that was not all, of course. She decided she was going to marry you because you helped her out in a difficult situation."

"I did?!?" – I asked, all the more puzzled – "And what was that?"

"I bet you don't even remember," – he said – "but when she was eleven we had braces put on her teeth, and she still had them when you were here on vacation. And anyway, she looked awful, and all the kids used to make fun of her."

"No, I don't remember that at all either." – I admitted. "Heck! I don't even remember meeting her."

"Yes, I know..." He went on – "But, anyhow, when she announced she was going to marry you, we were naturally curious about why she had chosen you. She didn't volunteer any particulars at that time, but my wife later talked to her, in a confidential way... you know, a private matter between women, you know how it is."

"And what had I done for her?" – I asked.

"Well, she told my wife that once, when kids were making fun of her because of her braces, you stood up to them and made them stop. You scolded them, you told them they should be ashamed of themselves, you told them that making fun of somebody, anybody, is a terrible sin, and it's even worse if they make fun because of a physical problem." – He explained.

I didn't remember that part either but it did sound like something I could have done – and no, not because I was a saint. I knew from personal experience what it was like to be made fun of. All the kids in Genoa used to make fun of me on account of my stupid names, and because of that I have always hated and confronted any type of malicious teasing or ridicule.

"But that's not all." – He went on – "She also said you took her aside and taught her an important lesson."

That kind of threw me off. "Who, me?" – I asked, intrigued. "An important lesson? And what was that?"

"You really don't remember, do you?" – He said, a bit surprised himself.

"No, *papà*." – I answered emphatically – "Honest to God, I don't know what this is all about."

"Well... She said you taught her how to fend off anybody that made fun of her." – He explained. "You advised her that the best way to stop others from making fun of you is for you to make fun of yourself first. You assured her that if they see you making fun of yourself, they would know their barbs couldn't hurt you."

I didn't remember that part either, but I privately acknowledged it was something I could have told her. Long ago I had somehow discovered that poking fun at myself was a most effective way of deflecting razzing from others.

Papà Filippo looked at me then, nodding slowly, added: "And, by the way, Lillo, I would like to compliment you because, for a boy of fifteen, you were exceptionally mature."

Shrugging my shoulders, I murmured a soft: "Thank you, *papà*."

I then explained: "I don't know if it was a question of maturity or not, but I learned at an early age what it's like to be made fun of, mainly on account of my first and last names. The name Letterio may be pretty common around here, but it doesn't mean a damn thing up north. And I don't even have to tell you about Vadalà. In Genoa, all kids in school used to make fun of me because of it. *Vada là... Vieni qua...Baccalà...* (Go there, come here, baccalà). You know how it was, and I had to learn to fend it off."

I smiled a sad smile remembering those days.

"I couldn't even tell you how I learned to defend myself that way, but I did. It was either that or I would have had to come to blows with somebody just about every day." – I explained. – "It works, though, I do it all the time, even when nobody is making fun of me. It has come in handy in many other circumstances."

"I understand, I understand." – My father-in-law said – "Still, it was good advice. She said she tried it, and it worked."

He snorted slightly, pleasantly amused by that recollection, then he went on.

"Oh, Mother of God! You should have seen her, you should have seen how excited she was when she tried it. The next time she was out playing with kids, she said she took the initiative. What she did, she had laughingly told them she had a mousetrap in her mouth and showed them her braces. And she even started opening and closing her mouth fast, clicking her teeth, like it was a mousetrap. And they all laughed… But they were not laughing at her, they were laughing with her. And after that they even started showing her off to other kids as if she was someone important. And since that day nobody made fun of her again."

He paused and shrugged his shoulders.

"And anyway," – he went on – "not only had kids stopped making fun of her, but she had instantly become popular, an attraction almost, when only a few days before she was being ridiculed. And because of that, because of what you had done for her, you had made such an impression on her that she had absolutely decided such a sensible and good boy would be the only one she would want for a husband."

So that was why she loved me. His account of her juvenile infatuation for me brought a faint smile to my face. At the same time it also triggered a memory, a fleeting flashback of a seemingly insignificant episode that had taken place the year before, just prior to our marriage. I recalled the loving smile of appreciation she had given me, and how she had tousled my hair when I was regaling them with my adventure with the Korean con man.

I had thought nothing of it at the time. Just an affectionate gesture of amused disbelief – I had thought – a good-humored way for her to verbalize silently "Dear Lord, look what kind of scrapes my man gets in."

But it was clear to me now that was not the case at all – it hadn't been just an amiable sign of affection. She had smiled at me and had tousled my hair because, as I was telling the story, I was poking fun at myself. I was displaying that same quality that had made her fall in love with me.

That poignant memory filled me with a wonderful, suffused feeling of tenderness and warmth that instantly turned to an icy, stabbing, heart-piercing pain as I realized she would never smile at me again and I would never again feel the soft touch of her caress. And the pain was so sudden and so real that I actually gasped and by reflex action raised my hand and covered my heart.

"What's the matter, Lillo? Are you feeling OK?" – *Papà* Filippo immediately asked, alarmed.

"Yes, yes, *papà*, I'm fine. Don't worry, it's just some gas."– I lied, not wanting to upset him – "I ate too much of that eggplant *parmigiana* mom made, but it was too good to pass up."

"Yes, I love it myself." – He agreed – "But it's true, it does come up all the times."

"Please go on, *papà*." – I urged him – "I want to know all about this."

Reassured, *papà* Filippo went on.

"Of course, at first we laughed about her 'absolute and final decision' to marry you. Just a schoolgirl's crush, puppy love, we thought. And, anyway, the next year you went to the United States."

He raised his hands and shook them in the air to indicate the consternation my departure had caused.

"Oooooh, God! She was heartbroken..." – He continued. "When she found out you had left she was crushed. But after a while she seemed to be the usual Rosa, the twelve-year-old schoolgirl, thirteen now... and anyway, we were sure that was the end of that. But we were wrong, we were totally wrong. You remained very much on her mind, and in her heart... Only we didn't know."

Pausing a while to brush off some windblown sand from his pants, he then resumed his narrative.

"When she was nineteen, she was already the beautiful girl you married. I am saying this not because she was my daughter, but she was a real beauty, absolutely. You know that..."

I nodded morosely. Then, almost imploring, I asked him: "Please, *papà*, don't remind me of that."

"I'm sorry, I should have known that might be painful, I didn't mean to hurt you." – He said patting me on the shoulder. "Anyway, when she was nineteen, the mayor's son, Giacomo Arena, came to my house... I'm sure you don't know him."

I shook my head – no, I didn't know him. And he went on.

"Well, anyway, he came to my house and asked me for my permission to become engaged to her, he asked for her hand in marriage. I didn't even know they knew each other, but I figured he probably knew her from school and they were secretly sweet on each other. To tell the truth, I was a bit upset because... well, you know how protective we Sicilians are, especially with our daughters, and I would have wanted to know from her that they were in love with each other. Still, here was a good young man from a good family, he had just graduated from the University of Bologna, he had a law degree, he had a good future, and I figured he was a good match for her... no offense to you. And I had no objections, that is, if she wanted him."

"She turned him down I guess." – I interjected.

"Of course she did." – He confirmed – "But I thought nothing of it, I figured maybe she thought she was not quite ready to settle down and raise a family. And that was OK with me also. She was still young and – what can I say? – I didn't mind having her home with us a while longer."

Then, spreading his arms open, he frowned.

"But then... Then the same thing happened about two years later when Dr. Longo's son – his name is Filippo, like mine – I'm sure you don't know him either. Well, anyway, he also asked me for her hand in marriage. I asked her if she agreed to it and she turned this young man down also."

And here he made a long pause, hunched his shoulders and stooped slightly. His eyes wide open, he thrust his lips forward to indicate his astonishment at her refusal to even consider this second proposal.

"I mean, she said she knew both boys well, and she even got along well with them." – He remarked – "So it wasn't a case of her disliking them. But no, she just had no intention of marrying either one."

He shook his head bewildered and then resumed talking.

"I discussed this with my wife and asked her to find out what, if anything, was the matter. I mean, here we have two outstanding young men, both from good families, nice looking boys both of them, with a good future. Giacomo is an attorney, and Filippo was studying medicine, in fact, he became a doctor just a few months later. He just opened a new clinic with his father who is a doctor also. You know what I mean, no young girl in her right mind is going to turn both of them down, not in Torre Faro anyhow, that's how I saw it. Again, no offense to you."

Mamma Lucia had talked to her, of course, and Rosa had shocked her, and him of course, by telling her: "*Mamma*, I told you a long time ago. The man I want to marry is Lillo, Lillo, Lillo Vadalà. He is the one I have loved, and I still love him."

They were both astounded. They had tried to talk some sense into her.

"Rosa, he has been in America for God knows how many years. He may already be married for all you know, you don't even know if you will ever see him again. You've got to grow out of that childish fantasy, you can't throw away your future like that, you can't waste your life because of a juvenile infatuation."

"Oh, she was furious." –My father-in-law stated – "We had a hell of a row. She cried defiantly, she screamed at us in no uncertain terms, she yelled 'It is not a childish fantasy. It never was a juvenile infatuation. I love him, do you understand? I love him.' and then she threw in, 'and, anyway, I know he is not married'. I guess she had found that out from your mother. And, anyhow, she said she was going to wait for you and marry you."

"We tried to reason with her." – He went on. "But what if he gets married in America? Or if he never comes back? Then what? Are you going to remain an old maid? Are you going to become a nun? Have you thought about that?"

"In that case, and in that case only, I will consider marrying somebody else." – She had said firmly, and that was that.

My father-in-law kept on shaking his head.

"Lillo, believe me, we were dumbfounded. Both my wife and I had thought that story about you was over years ago, when she was twelve or thirteen. We didn't think it was anything serious to start with, just puppy love, that's what we thought it was, and here we discover you are still not just **IN** the picture, you are **THE** picture, the one and only picture. We just didn't know what to do, we were totally baffled, totally at a loss on what to do. But there was no question about it. I mean, we had no doubts she meant what she had said."

"And how did you resolve that?" – I asked, more curious than ever.

"Well…" – He said, and he scratched his head. – "That was a tough one. I didn't know how to handle that. We both didn't know how to handle that. But then my wife had a great idea. She said why don't I talk to Pietro, your father. You know your father and I are not only third cousins. We are also best friends, more than best friends really, we respect each other, and if we have any problems, we can confide in each other. He is more than a relative, more than just a friend to me. To me your dad is like a brother, like a big brother."

I just nodded. I knew how everyone in both families seemed to have an almost reverential regard for each other. *Papà* Filippo went on.

"And so I took her advice, and I went and talked to your father about this problem we were having. To tell you the truth, though, much as I respect your father and will always ask for his advice, this one time I really was reluctant to do it."

He grimaced and audibly inhaled through clenched teeth to express the discomfort he had felt.

"I was reluctant because I didn't want to burden him with this problem." – He explained – "I was embarrassed because… well, you know what I mean... it was a private matter, a delicate matter. I mean, how do you tell somebody, even somebody you love and respect, how do you tell him 'Hey! Guess what, my daughter wants to marry your son'. I mean, it's bad enough if it's the other way around, that is, my son wants to marry your daughter, but when the proposal comes from the girl's family it's... oh, I don't know... it seems inappropriate. And, anyway, I knew it would put your father on a spot, and I didn't want to put him on the spot, or in any kind of uncomfortable position. But I did manage to tell him anyhow, apologizing for taking such liberty, and I asked him if he had any suggestions."

This was getting more and more interesting as well as enjoyable.

"And how did my dad take it?" I asked, eager to learn all the details.

"Well, to my great relief, he really surprised me." – He said – "You know what your father told me?"

"No! What did he suggest?" – I asked.

"Yes! He really surprised me!" – My father-in-law repeated. "When I finished telling him the predicament I was in, he told me these exact words, I still remember them word for word. He said 'God, I wish that would come to pass. I would be the happiest man in the world if my son married Rosa'. Those are the exact words he said."

He paused for a few seconds then added: "God! Was I relieved when he said that! Mainly because I had not put him on the spot, of course, but also because he would be pleased at this union. Anyway, I assured him that on my part I would have no objections either, I would be very happy also."

Pausing again briefly, he then looked at me almost apologetically.

"I'll tell you the truth, though, I didn't know what kind of a young man you were." – He acknowledged. – "I mean, I had only seen you a couple of times when you were a young boy of fifteen, and I never paid much attention to you. But knowing you were the son of Pietro Vadalà was good enough for me, really!"

He shrugged, then added: "Furthermore, it would make Rosa happy, and that was the main point. And they all lived happily ever after, as they say in fairy tales."

He again paused for a while, but I urged him to go on.

"Then I asked your father how that could come about, what with you in America, and so on." – he continued. "And he just said 'Let me handle it, Filippo'. He could not guarantee anything, of course, but he said he would try to do something about it. He just needed some time to think about it."

This tale was getting better and better and – like Alice in Wonderland – I was getting curiouser and curiouser by the minute. I couldn't wait to hear what came next.

"And then... and then what happened?" – I urged him on.

"Well, the solution he came up with was to talk to your mother. He asked her to write to you suggesting you come back to Italy for a visit." – He went on. – "He figured that was the most important part, to get you here... And he was right of course... Then once you were here he thought we would let nature take its course. But at that point the practical thing to do was to get you back, just to get the ball rolling."

I almost had to laugh. My dad, the marriage arranger! Imagine that! Did I say something about all marriage arrangers being females? Scratch that!

And that brought to mind one question I had never really resolved – had Rosa been privy to all this?

"And how?... How did Rosa feel about this..." – I asked hesitantly as I couldn't think of the right word – "...about this plan, this arrangement?"

My father-in-law immediately thrust his hands in front of him, palms facing forward, as if to refrain me from even considering that thought.

"Oh, no, no, no! Stop it right there, Lillo! No! No!... Believe me, she was entirely left out of it." – He exclaimed earnestly – "Are you kidding? Had she known we had tried to arrange something, anything, she would have been furious. No way!!... She was in love with you, yes! And she wanted to marry just you. Yes! Absolutely!... No questions about that! But I am also absolutely certain she wanted you to fall in love with her."

He kept waiving his hands in front of him to emphasize his denial.

"No, no..." – He went on – "I can tell you she was overjoyed when she found out you were returning, because she loved you. And I'm sure she hoped something would happen while you were here. But I swear on my honor that she thought you were coming here just for a vacation, and..."

Shaking my head, I interrupted him.

"This is so odd, *papà*." – I said – "I never told this to anybody, not even to Rosa, but when I came to Italy in '62, it was for a vacation, yes, but it was also out of curiosity. Yes, personal curiosity! I knew my mother was trying to match me up with Rosa."

Then I corrected myself: "Well, actually Mimmo had figured it out, not me. He is much more Sicilian than I am. But, anyway, I knew a marriage arrangement was in the works. But I wasn't interested at all, precisely because it was an arranged marriage. I have never been a fan of arranged marriages. Still, I came because I was sort of curious. I mean, I figured if my mother was arranging something for me, the prospective bride must have been someone really special, and I was curious to see what this would-be bride of mine looked like, what she was like."

Then, lowering my head, I murmured: "And my mother was right, of course. Rosa was really special."

My father-in-law just nodded in agreement.

"Yes! She was, she was really special." – He said quietly.

Trying to break the somber mood, he shook his head and continued: "Anyway, I know your mother wrote to you and she shrewdly also mentioned something about Rosa sending her greetings."

He paused, then chuckling he added: "Women! They really do have better intuition, I must grant them that. At first I thought that was a bit too obvious, and I bet Mimmo figured it out precisely because of that. But it worked out just fine, you did come, and nature did take its course."

Oh yes! Yes, indeed! Nature had taken its course – I thought bitterly – and her destiny had been set.

We remained silent for a while. I looked around – we were now the only two persons sitting on the wall.

Staring straight ahead, I heaved a sigh. Then, lowering my head, I spoke to him in a hushed tone of voice.

"I must tell you something, *papà*..." – I confided – "I hope it won't add to your grief, but I think you have a right to know... I am quite sure Rosa was pregnant when she died."

Patting me lightly on the shoulder, he nodded quietly.

"Thanks for telling me, but we knew that already, Lillo." – He said – "She had told my wife the day she left Torre Faro. But, of course, we wanted her to be the one to tell you."

"Yes! She did tell me." – I said shaking my head disconsolately – "She told me less than a minute before she died." And bitter tears started falling.

Yes! Now, more than ever, it was firmly rooted in my brain – nature had indeed taken its course. And because of that, Rosa was now dead.

Poignant as well as enjoyable as it was, my father-in-law's revelation of how a childish love had turned into a mature love, and the plotting of our parents to get us together, ultimately plunged me even deeper into my sorrow and my despair.

The bottom line still and always remained the same – Rosa was now dead because she had chosen to love me and only me. And nothing would ever change that.

My feelings of guilt, somewhat abated by the loving reception I'd received from my in-laws, resurfaced stronger than ever. I could feel it wrapping its cold coils around my heart, my chest, my soul, my entire being.

My dejection, my despondency was now complete. Had I been alone, I know I would have gotten up and walked slowly into the sea to disappear.

Sensing my despairing mood, my father-in-law kept glancing nervously at me sideways.

"Maybe I shouldn't have mentioned all that to you." – He murmured. "Please forgive me if I have hurt you in any way, Lillo. You know that's the last thing I would want to do."

I just kept staring silently at the murky sea. Abruptly, my father-in-law got up from the wall.

"I think it's time for us to go home." – He said quietly.

Silently, we walked home.

CHAPTER 23

Sleep, I needed sleep. God, how I wanted to sleep! I prayed for sleep, I begged for sleep. But on that long night sleep just wouldn't come.

Lying silently in bed, I was unable to even close my eyes. Constantly tossing and turning, I wished for some kind of sleep, any kind of sleep, even the eternal sleep! Staring at the ceiling, the walls, the window, the door, the furniture, every nook and cranny of the room, I prayed. I prayed for something, anything... anything that could have broken the constant pounding in my head, the leitmotif that kept repeating over and over and over again that I was responsible for Rosa's death.

All my thoughts, all my ruminations, all my conjectures, all my explanations, they all led, by a direct or by a circuitous route, to the same result or conclusion – if I had not come into Rosa's life, she would still be alive today. But I **HAD** come into her life and Rosa was now dead. And that led to the same inescapable result or conclusion – I and I alone was responsible for her death.

Had I done something wrong when I had reprimanded the kids taunting Rosa because she had braces? Hell, no! Of course not! It was a nice gesture, but if I had kept my mouth shut or, better yet, if I had joined the chorus of taunting, Rosa would have disliked me. And she would still be alive today.

And what about the advice I gave her on how to stop the taunting? What was wrong with that? There was nothing wrong with that, of course not! Even my father-in-law had complimented me for my maturity. But if I had kept my mouth shut, Rosa wouldn't have become infatuated with me, and her infatuation would not have turned to love. And if she hadn't fallen in love with me she would probably have married one of her suitors. And she would still be alive today.

And ditto with me coming to Italy in 1962, what was so bad about that? Well, Lillo, come on! Your curiosity about this arranged marriage really was one of your reasons for coming, wasn't it? Of course, it was! In fact, don't deny it, it was the main reason, wasn't it? And, if you hadn't come, she would still be alive today.

And singing to her, and agreeing to correspond with her, and answering all her letters, and liking her, and asking Mimmo for advice, and proposing to her, and marrying her, and taking her to the States, and falling in love with her, and driving the car. Who did all that, Lillo? You, you, you, you, you, you, **YOU DID ALL THAT, LILLO!** And if you hadn't done all that, she would still be alive today.

You did all that, Lillo! And Rosa is now dead! And you are still alive.

Yes! Even the dream I had – the field of lilies, the rose cut down as soon as I touched it –wasn't that also a subliminal sign of my guilt? Of course, it was! I had touched her, I had made her mine, and she had died!

Yes! She had died and I was still alive, and that – I was now absolutely convinced – just wasn't right. That was a reality, a morally unacceptable reality that foreshadowed another reality, an even bleaker reality – I would spend the rest of my life constantly blaming myself for Rosa's death. Could I spend the rest of my life doing just that? Would I want to spend the rest of my life doing just that?

No, I could not and would not. The answer came to me promptly, with no hesitation. And that promptness told me I had reached the end of the line.

Death, my own death, had become a liberating thought, and I began to accept it as the easiest way out of my troubles.

But how? How does one who has made up his mind to end it all decide what is the appropriate way, the most convenient method to put an end to his life? A firearm? Gas? Hanging? Poison? Cut his wrists with a razor?

Never, never in my wildest dreams, never in my most bizarre suppositions of what the future might have in store for me, would I have thought that a time would have come in my life when I would actually have considered that very question. And yet, there I was, thinking just that. How do I end it all? What's the easiest method? The least painful method, the least messy method?

I quickly decided that the simplest and easiest way of ending my life was only a few yards away – just go out and walk into the sea. I was a poor swimmer, barely able to stay afloat, and the Strait of Messina is known for its fierce and treacherous currents.

Drowning! That matter was settled! Now it was just a question of finding the courage to act it out.

Courage? What courage? On that endless night I came to understand that suicide does not require courage. Quite the opposite, in fact – I came to terms with the certitude that suicide is proof of cowardice, it's the crowning admission of weakness. I learned it was a way – the ultimate way – of acknowledging my inability as well as my reluctance to bear the burden of my accumulated troubles.

Tossing restlessly in bed, I heard every quarter hour pealed by the church bell tower and every foghorn wailed by every passing ship.

I silently prayed and begged Christ, the Virgin Mary, I even prayed to Rosa for some type of relief, for some semblance of tranquility, even for absolution for my guilt feelings, but all my prayers, all my supplications did nothing to loosen the tense knot of remorse I felt in my chest.

The night sky had begun to discolor. Just as the church bell tower began pealing the quarter hour past three, I abruptly sat up on my bed.

For a couple of minutes I just sat staring at the wall in front of me. Then I quietly got up and put on pants and shirt, and for the most absurd reason – I didn't want people to see me in my underwear when and if my body would be recovered. Furthermore, I could fill my pant pockets with stones to make it difficult for me to surface, just in case the survival instinct would make me change my mind.

Tiptoeing to the door, I opened it slowly to minimize any squeaking noises and I silently crossed the threshold. But just as I did, I heard rustling sounds coming from my in-laws' bedroom.

I quickly retreated into my room.

Papà Filippo's quiet footsteps sounded first in the hallway and then in the kitchen. Shortly thereafter I heard the faint sound of running water – it sounded like he had gone to the kitchen to get himself a drink of water.

Quietly I waited for him to return to his bedroom. His unseen presence, however, planted in my mind a question I hadn't considered at all – what would the consequences of my gesture be?

His involuntary interruption forced me to think of the consternation my extreme gesture would cause. My death – worse yet, my suicide! – would surely generate untold pain to my parents, to my brother, and to my sisters, but most of all to the Donatos. And yes! Even more than the pain it would cause to my own blood relatives, I dreaded just the thought of the additional pain it would cause to my in-laws.

I had already broken their hearts once, yet they still loved me. They considered me like a son, to them I **WAS** their own son. How could I even think of breaking their hearts a second time? Was I capable and willing of committing an act of such savage and needless cruelty? No, absolutely not, I could not! And instantly I resolved I would not. Going on with my suffering was a preferable choice.

Was my rapid change of mind due to the natural instinct to survive that's in all of us, or possibly a lack of courage on my part? Yes, I did think about that, and I cannot rule it out completely, but I am sure that those factors, even if they existed, only marginally influenced my decision to go on living.

Quietly, I undressed and returned to bed, but I still couldn't sleep, of course. And neither did my father-in-law or my mother-in-law, I am sure. I heard either one of them getting up two other times, presumably to get a drink of water or to go to the bathroom, but I felt pretty sure they were also checking on me.

When morning came, it was windy and uncomfortably warm. The sirocco wind had picked up in intensity and swirling sand was now beating against the windowpanes. You could hear the wind's howling as it passed through the high voltage electric lines strung on the enormous pylon erected on the beach to carry electric power from the mainland.

Long, intermittent howls lacerated the early morning quiet, sounding not unlike the mournful cries of a Greek chorus, the anguished laments of a mother mourning the death of her son or, for that matter, the despairing wails of a husband mourning the death of his young wife.

After breakfast, I quietly informed my in-laws I wanted to visit the cemetery again.

"Sure. I'll come with you." – *Papà* Filippo said agreeably. – "Only, this time let's take a cab, OK?"

"No, *papà*." – I told him somberly – "If you don't mind, I want to go by myself. I need some time alone with Rosa."

My father-in-law looked at me sharply. He then resolutely approached me and grabbed me by my shoulders.

"Lillo!" – He asked me harshly, looking at me straight in the eyes – "You are not thinking of doing something foolish, are you?"

Hearing her husband's sharp questioning, *mamma* Lucia left the sink where she was washing the breakfast dishes and approached us timidly. Looking at me apprehensively, she placed her arm around my waist. She then began caressing my hair and shoulders, her face suffused with anxiety and worried tenderness.

"Please, Lillo…" – She pleaded gently, her eyes filling with tears. – "Please, try not to think about her. Please, we have had enough grief already."

I forced myself to smile at her reassuringly.

"Please, don't worry, *mamma*. I am OK" – I told her.

Then, turning toward my father-in-law but avoiding his gaze, I told him: "No, *papà*, don't worry."

He wasn't convinced.

367

"I want you to give me your word of honor, the word of honor of the son of Pietro Vadalà, that you will return here safe and sound by noon." – He dictated peremptorily.

"You have my word of honor, *papà*." – I assured him quietly.

"Just remember!" – He said, still with a stern, authoritative voice – "If you do not come back I would never forgive myself, and I would never forgive you. And I know Rosa would never forgive you or me."

"Don't worry *papà*; I will be here before noon." – I pledged softly. Then, trying to ease the tense moment, I added: "And maybe this time I'll take your advice and get a cab. OK, *papà*?"

Seemingly reassured, he left to call a cab from a nearby bar's phone. *Mamma* Lucia seemed reassured also.

"Lillo..." – She asked me hesitantly, with a tentative smile – "Would you like something special for lunch?"

"Anything you cook is always special, *mamma*, you know that." – I told her smiling. And I hugged her.

A cab took me to the cemetery. The cabdriver asked if he should wait, but I told him it wasn't necessary – I was pretty sure I could negotiate the road downhill on my own. I paid the fare and he left, leaving me alone outside the cemetery walls.

No one was around, not even the custodian, but the cemetery gate was unlocked. I entered and slowly began walking toward Rosa's grave.

A weight of unrelenting pain ravaged inside me, but not a simple emotional heartache – it had now become a real pain, a heavy physical pain, a pain made all the more oppressive by the now indelible belief that Rosa had died because she had chosen to love me and no one else but me.

I had to tell her, I needed to tell her I was deeply sorry about her fatal choice and, at the same time, how grateful I was for the happiness it had given me. I needed to tell her how much that happiness had meant to me. I wanted her to know that the happiness she had given me – brief as it had been – more than compensated for the immense pain and despair that followed.

Just like the previous day, as I approached the grave I knew that I wouldn't be able to face it. And to steel myself, to prepare myself, as I walked along the gravel paths I consciously tried to occupy my mind, glancing here and there, looking at the sky, the gravel, the grass, the other graves, the inscriptions on the graves, anything that could divert my attention. And when I got within about ten yards of her final resting place, I began moving forward slowly, even walking almost sideways and with my head turned sharply to my right to avoid looking at it.

Still, when I finally reached her grave I couldn't bear to look at it. For several seconds I faced away from it, almost expecting to find the solace of my father-in-law's arms. But no one was there, and I knew I had to deal with it on my own.

Slowly I turned to face the grave, my eyes clenched tightly shut. I then gradually opened them, just a slit at first, and finally wide open.

The sight of her grave again jolted me, but then I looked at her picture on the marble slab and her radiantly happy smile filled me with a soothing sensation. With that joyous smile she was telling me I had made her immensely happy on that magical day, and that smile was my reward.

"Rosa!... Rosa!... Rosa!..."

Softly, I kept murmuring her name as myriad different emotions swirled through my head. And I kept whispering her name over and over and over, unable to think of anything else to say. In subdued, apologetic tones, I finally managed to articulate garbled, confused words.

"Rosa, Rosa... *mi senti?* (can you hear me?)..." I whispered and I suddenly stopped, bewildered. I realized that, unwittingly, I was parroting the very last words of *"Prima notte"* (First night), one of Pirandello's most beautiful short stories, that heart-rending "Nunzia', Nunzia'... *mi senti?*" (Nunzia', Nunzia'... can you hear me?) whispered by a grief-stricken husband kneeling on his wife's grave, simple words imbued with immense pain, simple words that I had read and reread many times, simple words that never failed to upset me emotionally. And here I was, echoing those very same words in the same precise circumstances.

With a somber grimace I resumed talking to her.

"It's me, Rosa, It's me, it's Lillo, it's your Lillo. Listen to me Rosa, please... I am here, I am here talking to you. I know you can hear me... I know you died because of me, you died because you loved me, I know that. And part of me has died also, you know that... You died because I told you I loved you, I know that. You would still be alive and with me if I had never told you that... God, I wish I had never said that, Rosa, and yet... yes Rosa, and yet I am glad I said it, because I wanted, I needed you to know that I loved you. It came from my heart, I had to tell you... You understand that, don't you, baby? I had to tell you, I had to tell you... When I found out I was in love with you I felt a joy I had never felt before... Forgive me for saying this, baby, but I don't think, even if I had known that saying what I said was going to take you away from me, I don't think... I don't know if I could have stopped myself from saying it. I believe... no, no, I know, I am certain it would have come out on its own... Yes! I'm sure it would have come out on its own... It was as natural as my heartbeat, as natural as breathing, as the sun coming out in the morning, it was like the rain falling. You understand, Rosa, don't you?... Please, baby, please, tell me you understand, baby, please..."

I looked at her picture hoping to see something, wanting to see something, even expecting – yes, expecting! – to see something, looking for some sign that she heard, that she knew, that she understood. But nothing was there, everything remained the same.

No, Rosa would never let me forget she had sacrificed her life for me – that's what her silence meant. I fell sobbing on her grave, tears streaming down my face, and again I began pleading, out loud now.

"Rosa! Rosa! Please, baby, please, please forgive me... I loved you, I still love you and I will always love you... I will never, I can never say I am sorry I told you I loved you. You gave me the only real happiness I have ever known in my life... You were carrying my baby, I know you were carrying my baby, our baby. Please forgive me. Please do it for our baby..."

And just as I said that, I thought I heard a sound, a soft cry of someone calling out at me. Raising my head sharply, I looked around but saw nobody.

The wind, I thought, it had to be the wind. I figured a sharp gust of sirocco wind whistling through the electric lines had produced a noise that sounded like someone calling my name.

Somewhat puzzled, I turned back toward the grave, but just as I did I thought I heard that same ululating voice calling my name again.

"*Lillo!*" – It seemed to whisper – and then some garbled phrase, something that I made out as "*Adesso basta!.. Devi ricominciare a vivere!*" (Lillo, that's enough! Now it's time to start living again!).

I know, it's unreal, it's fantasy, it's science fiction, and yet, yes! I swear to God! I swear to God I thought I heard someone say something that sounded like that!

It was not Rosa's voice. No, it was not the fresh, silvery voice I remembered, the voice that always carried a hint of laughter, the voice with that subtle touch of teasing irony, the voice that never failed to turn me on as it murmured sweet words of love in my ears, the voice that told me she would always be happy living anywhere as long as I was there with her. No, it wasn't her voice, and I couldn't even tell if it was a man or a woman's voice. But I was sure I had heard someone whispering those words, I'll swear on a stack of Bibles I did.

Startled and more than a bit frightened, I looked all around me. Slowly, I searched the entire area looking at nearby graves, the withered flowers in the receptacles attached to the marble slabs, the cemetery chapel, the sky, the cypress trees, the cemetery walls, the graveled paths, but no one was there.

Surely, in my desolate grief, I had imagined hearing something that simply wasn't there.

My teary eyes finally settled again on her picture, and that's when my heart nearly stopped. Rosa was looking at me, but her face was not smiling now. It had a stern, an almost scolding expression.

Despite the warm, stuffy weather, I felt a sudden chill. Clenching my teeth, I covered my eyes tightly with my hands.

"Oh God! No! No!" – I softly began to growl almost in a panic – "Please, no!... This can't be... I am losing my mind!"

By nature I am not a particularly courageous person. In fact, I have always tried to shy away from direct confrontations. I can only recall a couple of times in my entire life when I had to scrap and swing my fists in anger, both times as a youngster and both times against the same kid, a neighborhood bully – Luigi – who later became my best friend.

No, I will acknowledge that I am not a particularly courageous person, but I am confident that, if the occasion calls for it, I can summon the courage to face up to a clear danger or foe. But the unknown is an invisible foe, and its very lack of shape or form is what makes it a formidable foe, a terrifying foe.

I thought I had heard unexplainable voices, and I was now seeing unexplainable things, and I was scared. I could feel waves and waves of fear crashing over me.

Trembling and definitely frightened, I jumped to my feet and turned away from the grave, intending to flee, to bail out of there.

There is no doubt in my mind that, had I been whole, I would have been tearing out of there like the Roadrunner. Crippled and leaning on a cane as I was, however, a fast flight was out of the question. Being handicapped was what gave me – if not the strength and the courage – certainly a valid motive to remain. I just stood there, holding my breath, numb, frozen, just plain and simple terrified.

I don't know where I found the strength to confront that situation. I've read somewhere that in moments of serious crisis, if shock does not incapacitates you totally, your body will always try to find an outlet to vent your fears, to deal with the situation at hand. After God knows how much time – two, three, five minutes, I don't know – I somehow managed to lower my hands and open my eyes, and I just stared numbly at the surrounding landscape.

Far away, across the Strait of Messina, the uneven chain of mountains of Calabria formed the backdrop; in the Strait, a ship approaching the port of Messina was leaving a white foaming wake behind; one solitary *fulua* – a huge, tall-masted boat used to spot swordfish – bobbed jerkily in the choppy, sirocco-whipped sea and was slowly heading to port; dozens of smaller boats, normally out fishing, were now beached;

on the near shore, the village of Torre Faro lay quietly at the foot of the hill; glancing up the hill, I could see olive groves and vineyards separated by tall, impenetrable cactus hedges; several villas built below the perimeter of the cemetery dotted the countryside; and finally, just a few feet from Rosa's grave, rose the low cemetery wall.

In the stillness of that isolated hilltop, broken only by the rustle of the sirocco wind blowing through the tall and slender cypress trees undulating gently around the perimeter of the cemetery, I became aware I was all alone in that spooky cemetery.

A pervasive, almost uncontrollable agitation overcame me. My shivers had quickly turned to a frost. Fright brought to the surface of my mind the atavistic fears I felt as a child when mom or my sisters told me scary stories, stories of zombies, stories of ghosts, stories of dead people returning to haunt the living at night. And those memories, along with the lugubrious location and the inexplicable phenomena I had just been a witness to, increased my intense feeling of fright. It was now at the level of pure panic.

Glancing at nearby headstones, the grave faces of mustachioed men and austere looking women in the old, faded pictures seemed to look at me accusingly.

Panic was now giving way to terror, or something very much like it. I felt it grip me, overwhelm me, my stomach muscles contracting, my shoulders tightening, my teeth chattering. Clasping my hands tightly I began swaying nervously and moaning softly.

To my dismay and shame, I realized I was actually looking for, wishing for, hoping for, wanting the presence of some other human being, someone, even an animal, a dog, a cat, something, any living thing, anyone, anything that could tie me to reality, anything that could protect me.

Some minute part of my brain made me aware I was losing control. It kept scolding me, kept telling me I was acting like a child, kept urging me to snap out of it.

I placed the first knuckle of my right hand in my mouth and bit sharply. Then, closing my eyes again tightly, I began shouting out loud.

**"STOP IT! STOP IT, LILLO! GET A HOLD OF YOURSELF!
THERE'S GOT TO BE AN EXPLANATION FOR ALL THIS!!!"**

Whirling around to face the grave, I forced myself to open my eyes and looked closely at Rosa's picture.

To my almost ridiculous amazement, I realized that a flying insect had landed on the porcelain oval surface of the picture – right where Rosa's mouth was – causing, at first glance, what to my tear-filled eyes appeared to be a change in her expression from smiling to stern.

Totally exasperated, I screamed out loud in that sacred place: **"YOU GODDAMNED SONOFABITCHING IDIOT!"** And I actually punched myself in the head.

At the same time, even as I giggled at my own stupidity and heaved an immense sigh of relief, I began feeling a dizzying wave of elation, an explosive joy, a glorious sense of liberation.

Goddamned sonofabitching idiot, sure! Big time sonofabitching idiot! Absolutely! But I was certain – yes, without a doubt! – I was certain Rosa had sent me the message I wanted.

The voice? I thought I had heard a voice, I thought I had heard something. In my heart and in my mind at least I was certain I had heard it, but it was possible I had just imagined it. I will concede it was possible I had just imagined it. Yes! Surely I had just imagined it because those were the words I wanted to hear, the words I needed to hear, the only words that could have healed my troubled soul.

I do not know and will never know if I had actually heard those words. But that insect, that insect landing right there on her mouth? That insect that made me believe Rosa was scolding me? Yes! Maybe that was a casual occurrence also, a random occurrence perhaps, an amazing coincidence, I will concede that is possible also, OK? But I still believed and will believe to the end of my days that Rosa had sent me a sign.

A wave of my hand, and the insect flew away. Rosa was now smiling at me again.

"Yes, Rosa! I will start living again... I promise." – I whispered to her. – "If that is what you want."

I bent down to kiss her picture. Then I just straightened up and began walking a slow, steady, sure walk away from her grave. And as I walked down the gravelly paths among the graves, even the crunching sound of my steps on the gravel reverberated alive, decisive, reassuring.

Just as I reached the cemetery gates, a carillon in the cemetery chapel began pealing a song. I recognized the notes of Schubert's "Ave Maria", and I began humming the tune along with the bells. It was the first musical sound coming out of my mouth since that horrific day, that last day in the car.

Walking down the hill I felt light, buoyant. Nothing bothered me, not even the strong, at times violent gusts of wind bothered me. They seemed, in fact, to push me, to propel me toward a new life.

The unbearable weight of obsessive guilt I felt until a few minutes before seemed to have been lifted from my heart, and I could walk with an easy step, hardly feeling any pain. Except for the fact that I still walked with a cane, I felt like I could have skipped down the road like a kid, all the way to Torre Faro.

A new life was beginning, I could feel it! A new life worth living!

One hour later I was at my in-laws' home. I had decided not tell them what had happened, about the voice I thought I had heard, about the changing picture, about the insect. No, that was mine, that was all mine, that was something I couldn't share with anybody, it was something I wanted to keep for myself.

I was certain *mamma* Lucia would have cried out loud that some sort of miracle had occurred, that Rosa had spoken to me. While I did firmly believe I had received a clear message from Rosa, I didn't want *mamma* Lucia to become agitated over something that could easily have had a natural explanation.

I do not believe in the supernatural or in miracles. In the past I had in fact frequently made mocking remarks whenever someone hailed any strange happening as a miraculous occurrence. This one time, however, I felt absolutely certain something had happened. Maybe because I wanted it to happen – I'll concede that – but something... something unusual, perhaps preternatural, had occurred. I can't quite explain it but no, I did not consider it a miracle, but I was sure I had received a message. I know, I know, it doesn't make much sense, I don't believe in miracles and yet I felt like something closely resembling a miracle had happened to me. But that's exactly how I felt.

Both my in-laws, however, seemed to sense that something in me was different, something had clearly changed, and changed for the better. When I left their house to go to the cemetery, they were worried I might be suicidal – now, on my return, my mood seemed to be serene, almost cheerful. Clearly, something had happened.

The way they looked at me told me they were elated by this turn of events, but neither one pressed me for any detail or explanation.

Before sitting down for lunch, I informed them I had decided to return home within two days. Thanking them repeatedly for everything they had done for me, I again apologized for neglecting them since Rosa's death and I assured them I would be all right and would always be in touch with them.

When we sat down for lunch, *papà* Filippo spoke to me.

"Listen, Lillo." – He told me – "You know you are like a son to us." Then he corrected himself – "No, you are not like a son, you **ARE** our son, you became our son the day you married Rosa, and now that she is gone you are still our son, our only son."

"I know *papà*," – I interrupted him, touched. – "and you and *mamma* are like a father and a mother to me. No, no, you **ARE** my father and my mother. I know, I know, it may sound a bit foolish, but I really do feel like I have two sets of real parents."

"Lillo, what I am trying to say is that I want you… both of us want you to go on with your life." – He went on.

He paused briefly then added: "Before you leave, I want you to promise you will try to do that… No, no, I don't want you to just try. I want you to promise us you will do that. Can you promise me that? "

"I promise *papà*, I **WILL** start a new life." – I assured him, underscoring the 'will', and he knew I meant it. I almost added 'because I know Rosa wants me to', but I managed to hold it back. They would start wondering why I had said that, and maybe start asking questions about my visit to the cemetery.

"Good!" – *Papà* Filippo said – "I know you will. But that's not all. I also want you to make us another promise."

"Anything you ask, *papà*." – I said, and again I meant it. I was prepared to do anything humanly possible for these two precious people.

"At the right time, next month, next year, two, three, five years from now, when you find the woman who will make you happy, you must promise us you will bring her here," – he asked me – "if we are still alive, that is. We want to meet her, because to us she will not be just an acquaintance. She will be our son's wife, she will be like our own daughter. Can you promise us you'll do that?"

Tears just started flowing down from my eyes, but for the first time in God knows how long, they were not tears of pain or sorrow.

"I will! I promise I will!" – I told them sobbing. I then embraced him and *mamma* Lucia and added: "But I also want both you and *mamma* to make me a promise."

"What's that?" – He asked.

"I want both of you to promise me that on my next visit... and I will come again, and soon, you can count on that, that's my promise to you, with or without a wife, but I will be back. You must promise me that the next time I come I will find both of you close to the way you looked at the wedding. Can you promise me that?" – I asked, trying to smile through my tears.

"Well, maybe not quite the way we looked then, but we will give it a try." – He said, trying to smile also, and they both embraced me again.

And for a while, the three of us remained standing, embracing each other and crying. And – like mine – their tears were tears of relief mixed with just a faint whiff of happiness and hope, for. For a change.

Two days later I returned to the United States, eager to re-start my therapy, eager to get well, looking forward to going back to work. Eager to begin living again.

I bought a new car and forced myself to drive it, saving my brother the trouble of taking me to my therapy sessions. Three months later I contacted the bank and informed them I felt ready to return to work.

It was a joyous homecoming. The bank actually prepared posters for display at the branch announcing my return as manager after an absence of 16 months.

Everything was done without my knowledge, of course. To my amazement, a throng of over three hundred customers and co-workers, all happily cheering and applauding, was waiting for me inside and outside the branch when I arrived for work on Monday, Oct. 19, 1964.

The lobby floor was practically covered with an untold number of fruit baskets, flowers, cookie trays, bottles of wine, liquor, and assorted gifts all accompanied by "Welcome back" cards.

Not much business was conducted that day, as I spent most of the day crying and thanking all the well-wishers. The festivity went on for the rest of the week, a week that was meant to be a celebratory week anyway.

I spent the next two weeks being re-trained. Several changes had occurred at the bank over the previous year and a half, most of them of a technical nature – new computers, new teller machines, new bank products, and so on – and I had missed out on in-house training.

In mid-November I returned to my branch full-time, and in no time it was business as usual.

On April 30, 1965 I met Maria.

Love at first sight? Come on, guys, give me a break, that's the stuff of romance novels. And yet, and yet, and yet...

Well, technically it wasn't love at first sight. I had glimpsed this very attractive young lady several times before, always on a Friday evening, when she came in to cash her meager paycheck. Invariably, she always deposited about one third of it in her savings account.

To this day Maria playfully scolds me and swears that the first time she came to the bank I had refused to cash her paycheck because she did not have an account with WSFS.

I honestly do not remember that episode, but I always defend myself by saying that a) it couldn't have been me because I was not a teller, and only tellers cash checks, and b) maybe a teller had asked me to approve the check cashing and I had refused because bank's policy stated we couldn't cash checks for non-customers, and c) even if that was true, as a result of my refusal to cash her check she had opened an account with WSFS and, because of that, we got to know each other and we got married, so what are you complaining about?

After my return, I had seen this very attractive girl wait in line several times, but I looked at her as just another customer, with no ulterior motive in my mind. My "hunting" mood was, let's say, dormant. For one thing, I felt self-conscious about my appearance, still far from optimal – I had gained maybe 20 pounds, but I still looked scrawny.

But mainly, while Rosa's memory was no longer an obsession or even an obstacle, I just didn't feel an urgent need for companionship, of a permanent nature or even in the form of a casual date.

Sex? While in the hospital, of course, sex was the last thing on my mind. But even after my discharge, even after my return from Italy, and even after my health returned and I had become whole again, I simply did not feel any urgent need for it.

The idea of female companionship was not a constant fixation as in the old days – it wasn't even "on the backburner" so to speak. Maybe I was subconsciously still being faithful to Rosa's memory, but I just led a very normal celibate life, and I was OK with that.

After my return from Italy, my good friends, the Ravello brothers, had called me from New York on several occasions suggesting that I go visiting. In the old days, whenever they called to invite me over, our telephone conversations were always laced with sexual innuendos and raunchy bantering about how we would "kill" them, how many female scalps we would add to our belts, and that kind of nonsense.

Now their calls were deferential and respectful. They knew I still grieved over the loss of my wife, of course, and they respected my mourning and my sorrow. Whenever they called, they simply tried to provide some comfort, some solace, even by just suggesting a change of scenery. I am pretty sure that going 'hunting' with them was not what they had in mind. In any case, I thanked them but I always declined.

On the evening of Friday, April 30, this attractive young lady came in to cash her check and make a small deposit. This time, however, when she finished her usual transaction she did not leave the bank. She walked to the Customer Lounge and sat down – she had some additional business to transact.

A customer was in my office. When I finished with him, I stepped outside and asked who was next. It was she.

It was the first time I had seen her up close. She was about 5' 2", had a splendid hourglass figure, gorgeous dark blonde hair cascading down her shoulders, lovely brown eyes, and a perfect mouth with full crimson lips. She was wearing simple blue jeans and a loose flowery top that couldn't hide her ample bosom. She had hardly any make-up on and had obviously just come from work.

I asked her to step in my office, shook hands with her and held the chair for her; she sat down and told me she needed to buy Traveler Checks. She had a pretty heavy accent, but I couldn't quite place it.

Trying to make some conversation, I asked her: "Going on a trip?" She just nodded.

"Where are you going?" – I asked.

"Italy." – She replied quietly, and the way she said it, "Ee-taly", made it pretty obvious she was Italian.

"Oh! Are you Italian?" – I inquired.

"Yes." – She answered.

I then started speaking to her in Italian, and she was obviously overjoyed because her English was still quite tentative. We continued conversing in Italian. I found out she was from Abruzzo, a region on the east coast of central Italy. She had been in this country for about two years.

"How do you like it here?" – I asked her.

"Except for the language I like it very much." – She told me.

"Look, I'm sure you will learn how to speak well in no time at all, and then you'll see, you'll love it." – I told her – "The same thing happened to me when I came here in 1951. I had problems with the language myself, but once I got the hang of it, well, then it was all downhill."

She had come to the United States with her brother – she told me. They had a tough time at first, but were now doing OK. In fact, they had managed to bring over their parents, three other brothers and a sister.

Two other sisters, both married, had elected to remain in Italy.

Since she had mentioned she had been in this country for only two years, I politely inquired if she was going back because of family problems.

"No, no!" – She exclaimed – "I'm just going there on vacation."

What I said next came out in a bantering, almost joking manner, and I honestly have no idea why I said it.

"I bet you are going there to get married." – I blurted out with a smile.

"No, no, absolutely not!" – She replied earnestly. – "Why would I want to marry someone there? I like it here and I want to stay here. I have no intention of returning to Italy, except on vacation maybe."

Well, at least I had learned an important bit of business – she was still single and unattached.

The sale of Traveler Checks was over, but we continued to chit-chat some more. She told me her parents used to be farmers in Italy adding that, with eight kids, life was hard and everybody had to do their share of work, rising early at dawn and working until well after sunset.

By pure chance she had found out she could come to the United States as an American citizen. Her mother was born in the States but had been brought back to Italy when still an infant.

Life on a farm in Italy had nothing to offer except the opportunity to work very hard for very little reward, she said. Like millions of others before her, she lost no time seeking a better life. Seizing on the unhoped-for opportunity of being born an American citizen, she had elected to immigrate to the United States. Together with her brother, also born with American citizenship, Maria had gone to the American Consulate in Naples and they had both obtained the necessary visa to enter the country.

Hard work didn't scare her, she was used to it – she commented – and she certainly appreciated having the opportunity to live a more comfortable life than she had in Italy.

She was telling me all this in a very casual, matter-of-fact tone of voice, not maudlin at all. I got this image of a no-nonsense type of girl, one who had come over to improve her life, eager to carve a decent future for herself, an image of someone who had struggled and was still struggling, but didn't mind the struggle because the rewards were already showing.

Immediately after their arrival, she and her brother had stayed with a distant relative for a couple of weeks, but they now lived on their own. They were all settled and two of her brothers had even purchased a used car, she said beaming proudly.

I discreetly inquired where she lived. They were now renting a three-bedroom apartment on Howland Street, in the Little Italy section of Wilmington, about five blocks from the bank. Anticipating the arrival of the rest of the family, over the past several months they had it fully furnished, one room at a time. They were now looking to buy a home and had already looked at several properties in that neighborhood, setting their eyes on a row home on Union Street only six blocks from my branch.

Always looking for opportunities to get new business, I immediately invited her to stop in with her father for a mortgage, which they later did.

The actual sale of Traveler Checks had taken less than ten minutes, but I found her company so interesting and pleasant that I kept her in my office for about half an hour, just talking. I felt an immediate attraction for her, and I randomly kept selecting topics of conversation, wanting to prolong her stay in my office as much as possible.

I volunteered a few things about myself – how I had come to the United States, my schooling at West Nottingham, my Army career, and how I got the job at the bank. I purposely did not make any mention of my personal tragedy. It was an off-the-cuff decision on my part – I just felt a need for her to like me, but I did not want her feelings toward me to be influenced by sympathy or anything other than genuine fondness.

She told me more about herself. She was taking evening classes to learn English and had recently changed jobs. She had just quit her previous job because her boss was exploiting her by making her work overtime without paying her for it. She had found a new and better job immediately.

"It's so easy to find a job here." – She remarked, then quickly added – "As long as you don't mind working."

She also cheerfully appreciated how wonderful it was to be able to go to a shop and buy a new dress, cosmetics or whatever, or even go to a restaurant or a movie, something she could never have done on a routine basis in Italy.

"And I still can't believe you can actually return merchandise for a full refund if you are dissatisfied with it for whatever reason." – She marveled – "That's absolutely unheard of in Italy."

"And then," – she went on – "there is no way on earth we could have afforded to have telephone, TV, fridge and all this furniture in Italy. And my brother just got a car, a used car, but still it's something we couldn't even dream of having in Italy."

And all this after only about two years in this country.

Sensibly, her plans for the future were not grandiose daydreams. On her days off she would sometime go with her brothers to see the model homes sprouting up in new residential developments all around Wilmington.

"And if things go well," – she confided – "within five years we should be able to afford to buy one of those homes."

I would have liked to continue talking to her, but other customers were waiting in the lobby and I was forced to cut short our conversation. We shook hands and I wished her a good vacation and a safe return. Just before she left, I reminded her to come to see me with her father for a mortgage.

After she left, I felt curiously happy, elated. The conversation itself had been easy, spontaneous and pleasant. Banal as it was, I wished it could have continued even longer.

The days went by. To my surprise, her face and her voice kept popping up in my mind at the strangest moments – while waiting on a customer, while munching on a sandwich, as I opened my front door.

I tried to dismiss her from my thoughts, but I just couldn't get her out of my mind. And she stayed there, and stayed, and stayed, till I realized that her presence in my thoughts filled me with a feeling of joy and pleasure, a vague and suffused contentment to which I couldn't give a name or an explanation. I then began counting the days till she would come back – she had mentioned she would return from Italy at the end of June.

For the first time in nearly two years I began to feel the stirrings of an emotion that had lain dormant in my heart and soul. It was not animal heat, it wasn't even sexual desire. It was rather a longing to be close to somebody, a yearning to feel the warmth and softness of a woman's body, a need to have someone give me a welcome smile when I got home.

She walked in the bank on the evening of Friday, July 2nd. I was in my office waiting on a customer, and I just happened to raise my eyes and glance in the lobby. And there she was, waiting in line.

I literally felt my heart jump. I know, I know damn well it's a worn cliché, but it's true, it happens, I swear – my heart did jump, or it did something funny anyhow, and it shocked the hell out of me.

"Lillo, you are in love!" – I told myself, stunned.

"But how can that be?" – I answered myself, startled.

"Damned if I know, but you are in love!" – I told myself again, flabbergasted. But happy.

The customer in my office was telling me something, but I was grinning foolishly, not listening to one word he was saying.

In my head, Johnny Mathis was crooning.

"Chances are, though I wear a silly grin, the moment you come into view, chances are you'll think that I'm in love with you."

The customer repeated what he had said, jolting me out of my reverie. I excused myself telling him I had seen a friend in the lobby I hadn't seen in a long time and – would you mind if I go over to say hello before she left?

No, he wouldn't mind. I went in the lobby, approached her, and tapped her on the shoulder. She turned around surprised, and I smiled at her.

"Hi, welcome back… How was your Italian vacation?" – I asked her.
One year later, to the day, we were married.

CHAPTER 24

It wasn't all that easy though.

She turned around surprised. Then she smiled at me and ex-claimed: "Oh! Hi, Mr. Vadalà, how are you? Nice seeing you. Thanks, the vacation was great, but it's great to be back."

She paused for a while to advance a few steps in the line and I moved along to keep pace with her. She then turned toward me again, chuckled a bit covering her mouth as if to prevent a guffaw.

"And guess what? It turns out you were right." – She then told me. "I got engaged while I was in Italy."

I don't know how – or even if – I managed to hide my feelings, but if I did succeed it was an Academy Award performance.

I said earlier that my heart jumped when I saw her – a stale cliché, I know. This time my heart literally stopped – another stale and worn-out cliché, I know that also – but it did happen, or it felt like it happened. I felt a void in my chest, a paralysis like, I felt unable to move, unable to hear, to see, to utter one word, unable even to breathe.

That feeling only lasted a few seconds, fortunately, but in those few seconds I was totally unaware of my surroundings. I didn't know I was in the bank lobby, I didn't know there were a dozen people waiting in line, I didn't even know I was talking to Maria.

I just felt this brutal sensation of rejection – an unwarranted sen-sation, of course. Clearly, she could not have rejected me, as I had never made my feelings known to her. Still I felt rejected, I felt that some-how she should have known, my feelings for her were so strong that she had to know how much I had missed her, she had to know how I felt about her.

Yes! She knew, she had to know that's what I felt, and she had just turned me down with carefree nonchalance and cold indifference.

A tap on my shoulder brought me back to reality.

I turned around – it was Nick Tavani, a long-time customer as well as a personal friend of mine. He owned Tavani's Gas & Repair Service at 4th & Union where I always had my car serviced.

"Excuse me, Leo," – He said – "I don't mean to interrupt you. Have you heard anything about my mortgage application?"

God! Was I grateful for that interruption!

"Oh, hi, Nick! How are you?" – I asked with feigned enthusiasm, the first time ever that I feigned enthusiasm with one of my custom-ers – "No, I haven't heard anything yet. I would check on it right now but the Main Office is closed on Friday nights. Tell you what, Nick, I'll make a note and I'll check on it Monday morning. I'll call you and let you know."

He seemed a bit disappointed, so I quickly added: "But don't wor-ry, Nick, I am certain it will be approved."

He thanked me and went back to his place in line. I then turned again toward Maria.

"Well, heartfelt congratulations, Miss Flocco." – I managed to tell her, with some very feigned enthusiasm. – "I'm so happy for you, I hope you'll be very happy."

I excused myself blabbering something about having a customer waiting for me. Slowly, I managed to find my way back to my office.

Totally spent, dejected, a nullity. Those are just a few of the words that best describe how I felt, but it went way beyond that. I knew I had lost the battle before a single shot had been fired.

That night, after the bank closed, I got in my car and drove home slowly. Very slowly.

Almost halfway there, I realized I had no desire or even a reason to go home. Turning the car around, I suddenly began driving faster and faster without any specific destination in mind.

Wandering aimlessly around Wilmington, I wound up on Route 40 and soon found myself at the foot of the Delaware Memorial Bridge. On an impulse, I paid the toll, crossed the bridge, and entered the New Jersey Turnpike heading for New York.

The Ravello brothers had asked me several times to visit. Well and good – I thought – I would surprise them, and then, who knows?

I could tell immediately it wasn't like the old days, however. Back then, the minute I left the bank, the minute I turned on the ignition key I felt already keyed up, eager to get there, savoring, *tasting* the excitement I was sure would be waiting for me in the Big Apple. Now instead, there was no excitement, no urgency to reach New York, no sense of anticipation of the adventures waiting for me there.

And to confirm this atypical indifference, when I got near Elizabeth, New Jersey, I realized with bitterness that the refineries smelled like gasoline. But I moved forward.

It was just past 11 PM when I exited the Lincoln Tunnel and entered New York. To underscore my new state of mind, the jolting rush of adrenaline I always felt when I surfaced in Manhattan was also missing.

I headed in the direction of West 48th Street toward the *"Red Devil"* restaurant where the Ravello brothers worked.

Parking space was at a premium even at that late hour. I had to circle several blocks looking for one and I finally managed to find a spot five or six blocks away, on a quiet street with just a few random cars driving by.

It was still too early to go to see them. They usually didn't get off work till well past midnight, and on weekends even after 1 or 2 AM.

I couldn't even think of what to do while waiting. Walk around? Go to a movie? Just sit in the car?

Coming to New York had been an unplanned, spur of the moment decision fueled by the bitter, slap-in-the-face news I had just heard – I had lost Maria. As I sat brooding in my car I realized that, improvidently, I hadn't brought with me any toiletries or even a change of underwear. I looked in my wallet and saw I had less than thirty dollars. Well, that wasn't much of a problem – the Ravello brothers would gladly lend me some cash.

Fidgeting nervously, I tried not to think about Maria, but her face, her smile, her hair, her voice, everything about her was etched in my mind, everything was Maria, Maria, Maria...

Sitting in the car on that dark, quiet and lonely street, I tried to talk some sense into me.

"What are you, stupid?... Come on, Lillo, you're acting like a jerk. You don't even know her, goddamnit! And she doesn't even know you exist." – I kept mumbling to myself. "You only talked to her once, twice including this evening. How in hell can you even think of being in love with her? Or her with you?... Come on, grow up!"

I banged my hand against the steering wheel in frustration, the loud and sudden blast of the car horn startling me.

"Goddamned love! **GODDAMNED LOVE!!!!**" – I screamed out loud. – "What the fuck is it?!?... Come on, Lillo! Stop it! Stop it!... **STOP** thinking about her! Stop acting like an asshole!"

And on and on I kept going, berating myself out loud, until even I realized I was indeed acting like an asshole.

To get my mind off her, I forced myself to divert my attention to something else, anything, some inane distraction, something foolish. Incredibly foolish.

How inane? How foolish? Well, try this one on for size – I started looking at the license plates of cars parked around me and the ones of cars driving by, and I made up a game consisting of adding up the numbers on the plates to see which total was the highest and the lowest. And with each passing car, I would try to beat the previous record, high or low. Is that foolish enough?

No?... Well, then, let's try something else. When it was nearly impossible to beat the high or the low, I then switched to testing the law of averages – out of the next 50 cars, how many license plates numbers would be even or odd? Still not foolish enough?

Not yet?... Well then, how about staring fixedly at the traffic light at the corner and "ordering" it, "willing" it to change to red, yellow or green? Pathetic, I know, but I did that also.

But it didn't work, of course, nothing worked. In between license plates, in between my fixed stares, Maria's face kept popping up. I kept hearing her cheerful voice and I kept seeing her happy smile as she was telling me she had become engaged.

It was just a plain and simple happy smile of course, with no ulterior motive. I knew that! I was well aware of that! But that didn't stop me from seeing a touch of deliberate sadism in it. For some goddamned reason I felt she had smiled at me that way just to make me cringe, just to see me suffer.

More hand banging against the steering wheel! More cursing! More obsessed whimpering about love!

"Love, love, love, goddamned love! The most beautiful thing God ever invented. Yeah! Right!..." – I kept muttering.

"**BULLSHIT!** – I then exploded out loud – "If it's so beautiful, why the fuck does it have to make life so goddamned miserable."

And then, in my mind or just mumbling to myself, softly and yet forcefully I actually started talking to her as if she was with me in the car. I began explaining to her how I felt, clearing my position, proclaiming my sincerity, matching each word with pithy hand gestures.

"And no, no, Maria! **NO! NO! NO! NO!** You know damn well I'm not talking sex, Maria. I'm talking love, real love! I'm not looking for a one-night stand, you know that. It's not like I just want to fuck you!"

Even as I actually said that, or whispered it, or perhaps just thought it, I felt a wave of shame overwhelm me. I blushed furiously, as if I had farted loudly in a crowded church.

"Oh, God! No! No! I'm so sorry, Maria! I didn't mean that!" – I murmured dejectedly – "Please forgive me! I don't know what I'm saying, It just came out. It's just, it's just that..."

And that's when the tears started. Leaning on the steering wheel, sobbing softly, there I was, a pathetic, helpless soul wishing, wanting, needing the warmth of a woman who had turned a cold shoulder on me.

"It's just that I want you, baby, I want you to be mine. I need you, Maria, do you understand? Please, Maria, forgive me, I didn't mean to be so vulgar, I didn't mean to insult you."

And just like that, almost as a logical consequence of my abject apology, I straightened up, turned the car engine on, put the car in gear and headed back toward the Lincoln Tunnel.

A little over two hours later – at about 3 AM – I was home. But sleep was the last thing on my mind. Despite almost 5 hours of driving, and after a full day work at the bank, I felt wide-awake and alert. But mostly, a wretched mess.

Once inside my house, first thing I did was grab a half-full bottle of Chivas Regal, got ice cubes from the freezer and fixed myself a drink. In a large water tumbler.

I was well aware I was acting out the classic "feeling sorry for yourself" script, of course, and I did feel a bit foolish. More than a bit foolish in fact, incredibly foolish, even comically immature. But the last several hours had been a symphony of foolishness performed by a single player – me. So I kept on doing it until the damn bottle was nearly empty.

I finally fell asleep on the sofa.

That glum weekend lasted an eternity but somehow it went by. At work the following Monday, I was still in a foul mood and everyone could tell. For better or for worse, I have always worn my heart on my sleeve. Another goddamned cliché, I know – goddamned life is one goddamned cliché after another.

Fact is, I have always been unable to hide my emotions – when I'm happy, everyone knows it, and when I'm upset, everyone also knows it, and in spades. When I'm upset or unhappy, my face invariably looks like the Greek mask of sadness, with the corners of my mouth pointing due south.

On most Monday mornings, my entrance in the bank usually followed a certain script or variations of the same. I would enter radiating a clearly fictitious enthusiasm, rubbing my hands contentedly and shouting happily to my gloomy staff: "Hey, guys! Cheer up! It's Monday... Isn't it great?"

Or I would tap dance my way to my office whistling a happy tune – silly stuff, just to break the blues associated with the first day of the week. And it usually worked.

On that particular Monday, instead, the minute I walked in the bank all my employees knew immediately I had the male equivalent of PMS. And they were, of course, surprised and concerned because they always knew me as a jovial, friendly person with a happy disposition.

Kathy Clark, my assistant manager, kept glancing in my direction through the glass partition, checking my mood. Kathy was a stern-faced, no-nonsense lady, about 15 years my senior, and she was the one who provided much needed discipline in our group.

My managing style had always been somewhat permissive. Never a good disciplinarian, I was always reluctant or incapable of getting mad at my tellers when they screwed up. Kathy quickly realized it, and felt that my tellers could take advantage of my good nature – as they did occasionally – and she made sure they toed the line.

She waited about an hour to see if my mood changed. Then, seeing that the wind was still at hurricane force, she tapped on the glass partition between our offices and asked if she could come in. I motioned her in. She walked in, sat on the chair in front of my desk and came right out to the point.

"What's wrong with you, Leo?" – She asked bluntly.

"There's nothing wrong with me, Kathy." – I told her, pretending to be surprised – "Why do you ask?"

"You are in a bad mood." – She said – "Worse than bad. You look ready to kill, ready to explode, so don't tell me nothing is wrong."

I still went on acting surprised.

"Oh, it's just... it's just that it's Monday, you know how it is..." – I shrugged it off.

"Knock it off, Leo!" – She interrupted – "Last week there was a Monday also, if I recall, and the weeks before also, and you never looked the way you do today."

Then she became concerned.

"Is it some health problem?" – She inquired.

Abandoning all pretenses, I decided to open up some without going into details.

"No, Kathy, it is not a health problem, but thanks for being concerned." – I told her. Then, with a bitter smile I added: "Well, in a way I suppose it is. It does have something to do with my heart."

Startled, she seemed to jump on the chair, alarm all over her face. Her right hand quickly bolted to cover her mouth.

"Oh! No!" – She moaned.

"No, no, no, Kathy." – I hastened to reassure her – "I don't have heart problems, not that kind of heart problem, anyhow. It's just... Well, it's just that I'm in love."

Her face immediately changed, looking now like the Greek mask of happiness. She heaved a sigh of relief.

"Thank God! You had me scared." – She exclaimed – "I mean, I wouldn't mind having your job, but I sure don't want it that way."

I managed to laugh.

"Yes! I'm in love." – I muttered, then I ruefully added – "I'm very much in love. But she is not."

"Are you telling me she turned you down?" – She exclaimed genuinely astonished. "If she did, she's got to be the dumbest blonde who ever walked the earth." – This, by the way, coming from a real blonde.

"Listen to me, Leo!" – She then added – "Consider yourself lucky you found out before you got in too deep."

"No, no, Kathy, it's not quite like that, she didn't turn me down." – I tried to explain – "It's a bit complicated. I'm in love with her, head over heels in love with her, but she doesn't know it. She hardly knows me, she hardly knows I exist. And what's worst, I just found out last Friday she is engaged to be married to some lucky guy in Italy. But still, I cannot get her out of my mind."

She shook her head. "Jesus Christ, Leo!" – She sputtered – "If they gave a Nobel Prize for being unlucky in love, you would have no competition."

I managed to smile again, and my mood seemed to be a bit better.

"Anyone I know?" – Kathy inquired discreetly.

"Well, yes, I'm sure you've seen her, she is a customer here." – I told her – "but if you don't mind, Kathy, I won't tell you who she is. I don't want her to know how I feel."

Then I quickly added: "I mean, I'm sure you wouldn't do or say anything to her, but I just want to protect her privacy, and mine also. I'm sure you understand. And again, Kathy, thank you for being concerned."

"Don't mention it, Leo." – She said getting up from the chair. – "You know how we all feel about you." And she went back to her office.

Several weeks went by. Maria kept coming to the bank every Friday night, and whenever I saw her I would always try to find some pretext to engage her in conversation. Soon she started coming to the bank in the company of a beautiful young lady that she introduced to me as her sister Elisa.

Elisa had come over from Italy only a few months before and had already found work at the same factory where Maria worked. She was a couple of years younger than Maria and looked almost identical to her except for a darker shade of hair color.

Did I look at her as a possible match for me? Not for one second. Still and always, it was Maria, Maria, Maria, the most beautiful sound I ever heard, Maria. Much as I tried, though, our relationship never rose above the 'friendly acquaintance' level. And there it remained for a few months.

And then one day in early December Mrs. Parraciani walked in for her monthly visit to cash her Social Security check.

A benign, grandmotherly, Aunt Bee look-alike, Mrs. Parraciani was a sweet old lady who – I am sure – must have been a classmate of my mother at the marriage arranging school. She had taken a shine to me since I had started working at the bank. Over the past years she had tried to hook me up easily a dozen times with this or that girl, stopping only when I informed her I was going to marry Rosa.

Whenever she came in, she always stopped by my office to say hello, fussing excitedly, smiling amiably, and frequently bringing a batch of *pizzelle* she had just baked.

I was told that during my 16-months absence she inquired about my conditions every time she came in, and always asked when I would be back. The day I returned, she was practically the first in line and she cried just as much as I did, embracing me like a long-lost son.

She hadn't proposed any new candidate since my return to work, surely to give me time to get over my grief. It was now just before Christmas, a time for joy, a time for conviviality, and I guess she felt the time had come for me to stop grieving.

She walked in and knocked on my glass door. Glancing up from some loan applications I was reviewing, I saw dear old Mrs. Parraciani smiling at me and I rushed to open the door for the sweet old lady.

She came in, hugged me, sat down and gave me a package of delicious looking *pizzelle* she had just baked, plus a bottle of homemade wine her husband had made. I thanked her profusely but she just waved off my thanks.

She chatted about this and that, the way she always did when she visited. On this particular occasion, she prattled on about the new artificial Christmas tree she had just bought, mentioning she would be decorating it over the coming weekend. She then grumbled about the high cost of heating oil and finally she complained about the young hooligans who had scrawled something on the windows of a neighbor's car.

"I am telling you, Mr. Vadalà, – She huffed, – "this world is going crazy. No one has any respect for anyone anymore."

Suddenly, her behavior changed from voluble to purposeful. Pausing briefly – perhaps to build some drama – she then looked at me cheerfully as if she had a wonderful surprise for me. And indeed she had.

She first looked around to make sure no one could eavesdrop on what she had to say, and she then proceeded to tell me in strict confidence what she had obviously come to the bank for.

"Mr. Vadalà..." – She whispered – "I know you are still grieving, and I don't mean to be disrespectful to you or to the memory of your dear wife – God bless her soul – but there is a girl who I think you should meet. She's an Italian girl, beautiful and virtuous, and she lives right next door to me."

My ears perked up – I knew Mrs. Parraciani's address and I knew Maria lived right next door to her. I had found that out the hard way. Or the ridiculous way, if you will.

When I first met her, Maria used to live on Howland Street in an apartment right on top of DiFonzo's Bakery – Wilmington's best-known Italian bakery – about two blocks away from Mrs. Parraciani.

Well, for one full month, after the bank closed, this hopeless-ly-in-love idiot had spent countless hours in his car, parked about half a block away from her apartment, gazing at that apartment, just hoping to get a glimpse of her, all to no avail. Just about every evening, for one full month, you hear?

Eventually, even my love-obsessed mind realized something wasn't right. I mean – for Christ sake! – Maria lived there, she had to appear, even if it was for just a few seconds. But no, nothing. I repeat, one full month!

And so one day I went inside DiFonzo's bakery, ostensibly to buy some bread. I had to wait in line because everyone living within ten blocks of DiFonzo's bakery knew when his bread had just come out of the oven – they just had to follow their noses. DiFonzo's never advertised – the fragrance of his freshly baked bread was all the advertising he needed.

As I made my purchase, I casually inquired from Anthony DiFonzo – the owner and a personal friend of mine – about his tenants who lived upstairs. I hadn't seen them in a while – I lied – and I was wondering if they were OK.

He informed me they were no longer his tenants – they had moved about two blocks away to a house they had bought.

I could have shot myself! Maria had mentioned they were looking to buy a house, and I had told her to come in for the mortgage. I later found out she had come in with her father while I was on a training session, and they had moved to the new house – at 835 N. Union Street, right next door to Mrs. Parraciani. I didn't know about it and I had been waiting outside the wrong place every evening, like a damn puppet. For one full month!

Maria now looks at me with love when I recall those days and that experience in particular but – believe me! – it wasn't funny at all when it happened.

When Mrs. Parraciani mentioned that her latest candidate lived right next door to her, my ears did perk up, but for the briefest moment. Surely the old lady was trying to match me up with her sister Elisa.

Grasping at straws is an exercise in futility, but try telling that to a drowning man, or to someone who is madly in love. Anything, even the remotest mirage, can seem a feasible reality when you are hopelessly in love. And I was hopelessly in love.

"Mrs. Parraciani…" – I started telling her – "Thank you for your concern. I will always remember my poor wife, and she will always be in my heart, but I assure you I am no longer grieving for her."

I paused a while – what now? Do I continue or what?… What have I got to lose?…

I resolved to go on.

"As for the girl who lives next door to you, believe it or not, it just so happens that I am very much in love with one of them." – I told her – "But it is not Elisa, Mrs. Parraciani. I am in love with Maria but, unfortunately, she doesn't even know it. Furthermore, I know she is already engaged to someone in Italy."

Lowering my head, I hesitated for a few moments. Then, I looked up at her again.

"I suppose you are referring to Elisa," – I concluded – "and if you are… Thanks for thinking about me, Mrs. Parraciani, but I have no interest whatsoever in Elisa."

And here's where Mrs. Parraciani brought some hope into my miserable life.

"No, no, no, Mr. Vadalà." – She said excitedly, bouncing up and down on her chair – "I'm not talking about Elisa. I mean, don't get me wrong, she is a wonderful girl also and would be fine for you too, mind you, but I hear she already has a boyfriend. Her mother told me there's a boy from Philadelphia who is courting her. No, no, Mr. Vadalà, I'm talking about Maria."

Startled, I listened wide-eyed as Mrs. Parraciani, whispering now in a conspiratorial way, continued.

"I was talking to her mother, Mr. Vadalà," – she confided – "and she was telling me things are not working out with her fiancé. She is pretty sure they will break up because he wants her to remain in Italy after they marry, but Maria has no intention of returning there to stay."

Silently, I began imploring every heavenly guy I was acquainted with. "Oh, sweet, sweet Jesus, Joseph, and Mary! Oh, Madonna Mia Santissima! Oh, All Saints in Paradise! Please, please, dear God, let it be so. Please just give me this one little chance to win her heart, just this one little chance dear God, and if I fail I won't ever ask for anything else, I swear, and I'll even try to forget about her. Please, please, please, dear God!"

To some extent, the whole situation was ludicrous. Here I was, an up-and-coming young branch manager in an American bank secretly confabulating with a sweet, Italian old lady with a penchant for arranging marriages. Surely some movie director – say a Fellini, or a De Sica – could have made a brilliant comical script out of that. But my life, my happiness were at stake here, and I was even willing and ready to expose myself to ridicule just for a chance to have Maria.

With the practiced experience of a marriage arranger, Mrs. Parraciani hatched up a plan.

"Just let me handle it, Mr. Vadalà." – She said winking at me. – "Why don't you come to my house for a visit this coming Saturday, just for a cup of coffee. Better yet, why don't you come to help me decorate the Christmas tree? Yes, that's the best excuse, you come to help me with the tree. I know her family real well, and I'll ask both girls to come help me decorate the tree also, and then we'll see what happens."

That Saturday at the arranged hour I presented myself at Mrs. Parraciani's house dressed in my most elegant casual clothes, with a fresh haircut, an extra close shave and reeking with the fragrance of some very expensive cologne.

About fifteen minutes later Maria sauntered in through the adjoining covered front porch. She was wearing very simple clothes –

green corduroy jeans, a buttoned flowered blouse tied at the waist and a pair of white sneakers. No make-up, not even lipstick, and she still looked great. When she saw me, she seemed startled and she quickly excused herself for her appearance saying she had been doing some house cleaning. Her sister Elisa followed a few minutes later.

I greeted them cheerfully. We shook hands and we sat down to have coffee, biscuits and *pizzelle* Mrs. Parraciani had baked.

"I didn't know you lived next door to Mrs. Parraciani." – I lied, acting surprised – "When did you move here?"

Then, with mock seriousness I added: "Oh, and I want to hear you got the mortgage at my bank."

Lying again – I knew they had, I had checked.

"Of course we did." – Maria said earnestly – "I brought in my father, like you had asked me, but you were away. Mrs. Clark took our application. We moved here this past September."

I asked them to address me with the familiar "*tu*" instead of the formal "*voi*", and we then spent a pleasant hour hanging ornaments on Mrs. Parraciani's Christmas tree and just chitchatting.

We hit it off quite well talking mostly about things Italian, the latest hit songs, local Italian restaurants, a new band playing in a nearby Italian café, and so on.

At one point I casually asked about her marriage plans.

"Well, they are on hold right now." – Maria said noncommittally – "There are some problems we have to straighten out first."

"I am sorry to hear that." – I lied again, then added: "I certainly hope you'll be able to resolve your problems the best way for both of you."

And this time, in a way, I was sincere.

When we finished decorating the Christmas tree, the two girls invited me next door to meet their parents, the folks who would become my future in-laws.

When we entered, Mr. Flocco and three of his sons were playing "*scopa*", a popular Italian card game. A fourth son was watching a football game on a black and white TV set. When they saw us come in, they politely stopped playing cards and they all got up to greet the stranger the two sisters had just brought in.

Maria introduced me and I shook hands with all of them.

Mr. Flocco – a simple, rather gruff man named Angelo – shook my hand but looked at me rather diffidently. I got the feeling he suspected I was casting a dishonorable eye on either one or both of his daughters.

Mrs. Flocco instead – her name was Venera – was immediately love at first sight. The sweetest, gentlest, kindest, warmest human being I had ever encountered in my entire life, bar none – that's the only way I can describe her. A natural, luminous, innocent, heartfelt, beatific smile was a constant feature on her face, an angelic smile that simply illuminated any room she was in – plain and simple goodness personified, that's an even better way to describe her!

Within half an hour of meeting her I pledged to myself I would marry Maria one way or the other, by hook or crook, just to have the honor and pleasure of calling that marvelous lady *mamma*. And to my great pleasure, she seemed to like me also, treating me right off the bat with the utmost cordiality, as if I had been a friend of the family for years.

I realized later it wasn't so much a question of me making a good impression on her – she just had this instinctive pleasant disposition toward everybody she met. Still, I rejoiced to find out she liked me.

She inquired if I was married, but I could tell by the casual way she had asked that she wasn't prying to check on my marital status. When I somberly told her I was a widower, she was so visibly shocked and moved, and her concern was so palpably real that I almost felt guilty for having distressed her. She also had the instinctive good grace not to ask how I had become a widower. In her eyes, a widower meant a man unable to cope with domestic matters, especially cooking (a correct assumption in my case).

After expressing her sorrow, she immediately invited me for dinner the next day, Sunday, and I immediately and gratefully accepted.

The next day I showed up at the appointed hour bringing a bottle of fine wine. We sat down for dinner at a long table in a narrow kitchen.

As the honored guest, I sat at one end of the table, with Mr. Flocco at the other end. The four brothers were a tight fit on one side while Mrs. Flocco, Maria and Elisa – needing more space to maneuver – sat on the side of the table near the range as they, in typical Italian fashion, had to prepare and serve the dinner.

As the dinner started, there was at first embarrassed silence among the brothers – what little they said was spoken mostly in the Abruzzese dialect. They seemed to be self-conscious about and, understandably, reluctant to display their poor Italian grammar. Like many other bank customers, they looked at me with deference – I was a man of letters, a banker, an important man with arcane financial knowledge. On my part, I saw them exactly the same way I saw all my Italian customers – as good, hard workers far worthier of admiration than I was.

To break down this barrier, I purposely displayed my absolute ignorance of all agricultural matters and steered the conversation toward the what, the when and the how of just about every crop they used to grow.

They were all real experts in that field, and the ice was broken. They fell all over themselves explaining to me when and what they planted, when was harvest time for the various crops, how to guard against crop diseases, and how the weather could make or break an entire season.

After a great antipasto dish, Maria brought to the table a huge bowl of *"spaghetti alla chitarra"*, Abruzzo's most popular type of home-made pasta.

They served me the first dish and then handed me a small bowl of grated Parmesan cheese. After sprinkling lots of it on my steaming spaghetti, I started eating.

As soon as I placed the first forkful in my mouth, I realized the cheese had a funny taste, a spoiled taste. Still, I swallowed and kept my mouth shut. But then Antonio, Maria's oldest brother, took his first forkful. He immediately made a face and practically spat it out.

"Something is wrong with this cheese, *mamma.*" – He exclaimed – "It tastes awful."

Then, turning to me with a surprised look, he added: "How can you eat that? Can't you tell it's stale?"

A bit embarrassed, I just shrugged. Then I sheepishly mumbled the reason why I had kept quiet: "Well, yes, it did taste kind of stale to me also, but I thought maybe this cheese was some special cheese from your hometown, and I didn't feel right criticizing it."

I believe it was at that exact moment that Maria's mother began to love me as a son, even before she knew I had serious intentions of marrying her daughter.

She just voiced a long "Oooohhhh..." and rewarded me with a gentle, loving look that told me how much she appreciated my sensitivity.

They then threw away my pasta dish and served me a new one covered with freshly grated cheese. It was a fabulous meal, and I also found out Maria had prepared most of it – a detail of some relevance.

They invited me to dinner again for the following Sunday, and again I immediately and gratefully accepted. They also invited me for the upcoming Christmas and New Year dinners, but politely – and reluctantly – I had to refuse. My brother and Ange had asked me to spend the holiday dinners in Rising Sun, and I had promised I would be with them.

During dinner, I did not inquire about Maria's situation with her boyfriend, but I learned later it was still unsettled.

The opportunity to be near her was for me both a source of joy and a source of anguish. Having her near me, even for a couple of hours, made my day. On the other hand, having her near me and, at the same time, being forced to hide my feelings *un*made my day. But I had no choice – someone from her family was always present and I never had a chance to voice my feelings.

Not once did I succeed to be alone with her, just to talk of course. I did find out she worked in some factory on the Newport Pike making ladies stockings. With a few discreet inquiries I had also ferreted out she commuted to and from work by bus. Still chatting casually, I also learned at what time she usually got off from work.

There wasn't a set time when she finished work, she had told me. She did piece work, and once she reached her quota, she stayed there to earn extra money. She usually left the factory around 4:30 PM, however.

And, of course, two or three times a week I then 'just happened' to drive by the factory where she worked, always around 4:30 PM, when she hopefully left the workplace. I drew several blanks, getting there too early or too late, but a few times I did manage to spot her waiting at a nearby bus stop.

Pretending to be driving by there casually, I would stop and offer her a ride home. Unfortunately, Elisa was always with her also, as well as another Italian lady who lived near them. I couldn't very well offer a ride just to Maria – Elisa and the other lady gratefully accepted a ride also. But that was OK – I still had Maria in the car with me, and I could talk to her.

Things had to come to a head, though, but how? Once again I asked my brother for advice, but on this occasion he freely admitted he couldn't be of any help. He had never met any of the people involved, didn't know their customs or their temperament, and he was at a loss on how to deal with my particular situation.

My best bet – I decided – was to get some spiritual advice from Father Roberto, the parish priest at St. Anthony's, the church that has been the worshiping place of all Italians in Wilmington since it was built in 1924.

And on this one Sunday, right after Mass, I stopped to see Father Roberto whom I knew personally. He knew about my tragedy and had indeed officiated at Rosa's funeral service.

Baring my soul to him, I went straight to the point.

"Father, I am in love with this young lady." – I confided – "You may know her, her name is Maria Flocco, she is one of your parishioners. Her family lives on Union Street, just three blocks away from St. Anthony's. I have been in love with her for the past six or seven months, but she doesn't even know I love her, or at least I don't think she knows. But that's not the main problem. The main problem is that she is engaged to be married to someone in Italy. I know they are having some issues and their relationship is shaky, but mainly I don't know if she is really in love with this guy or not. I mean, if she is in love with him, I will resign myself and try to forget about her. I just want her to be happy, even if it is at my expense."

Rambling on and on, I poured out all my feelings. The good priest just let me get it off my chest without interrupting.

"Right now I would be satisfied if she just knew how much I love her. If she still prefers the other guy, like I said, so be it. That's all I want. But I just don't know how to do it. I do see her a lot, at the bank and at her house, I have even been picking her up at work several times, pretending I'm just passing by, but there's always her sister in the car, and some other Italian lady also and, anyhow, I'm never alone with her. I've become a friend of the family, they have invited me for dinner several times. But, like I said, I've never had the chance to be alone with her, and I can't very well talk about this when her family is around."

I said all I had to say. When I unburdened myself and couldn't think of anything else I could add, I just stopped and waited.

His advice was quick and to the point.

"*Giovanotto!* (Young man!)" – He told me – "If you can't, or if you don't know how to tell her in person, just write her a letter and tell her exactly what you have told me. By telling her you love her you are not committing a sin, even if she is engaged to somebody else. If she loves the other guy, then, as you said, so be it."

Why didn't I think of that?

CHAPTER 25

Jan. 17, 1966

Dearest Maria,

I left your house after a wonderful dinner only a few hours ago, and I am now home. It's 2:15 AM, but I cannot sleep. Unfortunately, I am used to it. I haven't been sleeping much at all for the past several months.

I have tried hard to talk to you privately, but I never had the opportunity; at the same time, I suspect that even if I had had the opportunity I would not have had the courage to open my heart to you.

I don't feel right in doing what I am doing now because I am well aware that I am trying to wreck somebody else's happiness to favor mine.

Please forgive me for doing this, and don't be mad at me – I am only doing it because I am sure that if you knew how much I am suffering now and how much I have suffered over the past six months, you would understand.

At this very moment you are probably asking yourself: "What does this fool want from me?" But you know the answer, you know it very well – I want you, and only you, Maria!

You see, now that I have written it and I know you will read it, I already feel better – I have taken an enormous weight off my heart. The consequences may be disastrous, but I want you to know it, I want the whole world to know it – I love you, Maria, I love you, there is no doubt in my heart that you are the only one for me.

And now, come to the bank, spit in my face, slap me if you want to, but the truth will remain the same – I love you, Maria!

How long have I been in love with you? That's easy enough to answer. In fact, I can tell you the exact date and time – I fell in love with you on April 30, 1965 at 7:15 PM. That's the day you came to the bank to buy Traveler Checks and we talked in my office for about half an hour. In that short period of time I got to know you well, and when you left I was already in love with you. I was attracted by your beauty, of course, but even more than that, I was attracted by what I think is your greatest virtue: an exquisite simplicity.

You may think: Is that it? Perhaps you expected a man madly in love with you to make a yard-long list of all your assets, your virtues, and your good qualities. No, that's not the case – I fell in love with you because you are what you are, and you do not pretend to be anything else. And nowadays, that's a very rare virtue.

After you left, nothing happened for a while. But then I began counting the days waiting for your return from Italy, and when I realized I was counting the days I knew I was in love with you. And that's when my life changed completely. During your absence, I daydreamed about asking you out on a date, talking to you, and telling you how much I loved you. I saw myself asking your father for your hand in marriage, I envisioned myself embraced like a son by your lovely mother, I already felt like a member of your family. There were no limits to my fantasy; I was a basket case, ready for the nut-house.

And then you returned, and the first thing you told me was that you had gotten engaged in Italy. I swear on the love that I have for you, my dear, if I had been told my parents had suddenly died I would not have suffered as much.

Under the circumstances, I should have just told my heart to resign itself. And I did try, I swear I did, but my heart would not hear of it. It still loves you and will continue loving you, even if you tell me to go to hell and leave you alone.

The past few weeks have been the worst – your family has extended me its friendship, and they have invited me several times for dinner; I have gratefully accepted because I need to be near you, but being near you and knowing you belong to someone else is unbearable – it is literally driving me insane.

Yesterday, right after Mass, I went to see Father Roberto and I opened up my heart to him, explaining my situation to him.

To be honest, I was afraid he would laugh in my face, but the good man was very understanding. He told me: "My son, just tell her you love her, and if *you cannot tell her privately, just write to her. If she is an intelligent girl, she will not resent it because it is not a sin to love someone."*

And I took his advice. And now, my dear, what next? I am not so ignorant or presumptuous to ask you point blank to leave your fiancé and to marry me. I know I cannot do that and, in fact, you should not do that; but all I want from you is just one favor – it's a favor that does not cost you anything, and can in a way repay me for loving you so much, maybe in vain.

I just want you to ask yourself sincerely just this one question: are you absolutely certain that the man you love is the one in Italy?

Do not think, I beg you, about the scandal or the gossip that would follow if you broke your engagement – your life and your happiness depend exclusively from you.

Just ask yourself that one question. If the answer is YES!, if you are absolutely certain your only love is in Italy, do not have any pity or mercy for me, and run to the man who will make you happy. To me your happiness is even more important than mine.

Therefore, if you honestly believe you will be happier with him, go to him. On the other hand, if you are not sure, or if the love for the other man has waned, I want you to know that there is a man here who has been dreaming of holding you in his arms and making you happy.

That is all I ask from you. It's a small favor that doesn't cost you anything – your answer may make me happy or break my heart, but I need to know it.

Just one more thing – regardless of your decision, please let us remain friends.

Yours, Lillo

P.S. I pray with all my heart that you will give me an answer quickly. Make me happy or make me miserable, but do it as quickly as possible.
If you are uncomfortable telling me in person, my phone number is WY 4-8883. Thank you

God! What a miserable night! How many times did I write that letter? Ten times? Twenty times? God only knows... God only knows how many times I snatched a finished piece from the table, crumpled it up and threw it in the nearby wastebasket, only to fish it out again to rescue some salvageable parts. God only knows how much editing, how much adding, subtracting, changing words and whole sentences I did before the definitive draft was approved. God only knows how much of myself went into that letter, how much of my emotions, how much of my soul poured through those words. God only knows that I worked on that letter practically all night long, all the while fueling myself with several cups of espresso coffee.

Finally I placed the conclusive draft in an envelope, wrote her name and address on it, affixed a stamp to it and sealed it. And then I tore everything up.

"Dear Christ in Heaven! This is way too long! What is this, a letter or an article for 'True Confessions'? This is crazy! It just won't work!"

Those were my vocal comments to no one in particular. I then picked up a new sheet of paper, three new sheets in fact.

"Screw it!" – I said firmly to myself – "After a night like this, I have to salvage something out of it."

I re-filled my *Bialetti* coffee machine with fresh ground coffee and water and placed it on the burner. Then I picked up the pieces of the letter I had just torn, copied it again word for word, placed it in a new envelope, wrote on it her name and address, affixed a stamp and finally sealed it.

It was now Monday morning, time to get ready for work. I had been up literally all night long without even taking a five-minute nap. Fatigue hadn't hit me yet – it would probably knock me out in late afternoon, at which point I would probably just hand the reins of the branch to Kathy and ask her to close the branch.

I barely had time to shower, shave and have some breakfast. I then eased into my car and left to go to work, bringing the letter with me.

There was a mailbox at the entrance to my development, but I passed it. Intentionally. I just didn't have the guts to drop the letter in.

One hundred yards past the mailbox I stomped on the brakes. Behind me, I heard the wheels of a car screeching sharply to avoid rear-ending mine. As the car passed me, the driver screamed a well-de-served curse and angrily raised his middle finger at me. Mouthing a si-lent apology, I then put the car in reverse, stopped right by the mailbox and brusquely dropped the letter in it. *Que serà, serà!*

I then went to work.

Requited love is beautiful and unrequited love is a bummer. Ei-ther way, it seems to affect time – when two people are in love, time ac-celerates to lightning speed, but when only one is in love it slows down to a crawl. For the one who is in love, at least.

For me, that particular week went by at a snail pace – and a crip-pled snail at that. Maria hadn't shown up at the branch, and I hadn't received any phone calls from her. The Postal Service was still efficient in those days, and I was sure she had received my letter by Tuesday, Wednesday at the latest.

Finally Friday arrived, the day when both Maria and Elisa always came in to cash their paychecks and to make a small deposit in their savings accounts.

Friday evening was also the busiest time of the week. Though constantly tied up in my office with customers, I kept glancing nervous-ly at the front entrance to check for their arrival.

Just before 7 PM Elisa walked in by herself. Was it just my im-pression or did she deliberately avoid looking in my direction?

Glancing up again and again, I covertly monitored all her move-ments. She first went to the customer counter, presumably to fill out a deposit ticket. She then went at the end of the line of customers waiting to be served and – yes, definitely! – she was purposely avoiding looking toward my office.

Whenever the two sisters came in, they always tried to catch my eye and wave a friendly hello, even if I was busy with a customer. This time, instead, nothing.

I waited a couple of minutes to see if Maria would follow, but she was a no-show. Of course, there could have been a perfectly legitimate reason for her being AWOL, but I was in no mood to believe in coinci-dences. She wanted to avoid me, that was the only reason.

A customer was in my office, but I was paying scant attention to him. My eyes kept darting to the front door, then to Elisa, back to the front door, briefly back to my customer, and then round about again.

Visibly fidgeting to the point that even my customer seemed to realize something was going on, I finally excused myself for one moment and went in the lobby approaching Elisa purposely.

As I approached her, she glimpsed me coming and turned slightly away pretending she hadn't seen me. I could tell she was flustered, though, as she had begun to blush noticeably, but I plunged straight ahead. And when I reached her, in front of a dozen customers waiting in line, I bluntly asked her point blank in Italian: "Elisa, *dov'è Maria?* (Where is Maria?)"

Visibly blushing now, Elisa kept staring at the floor, speechlessly. Realizing I had embarrassed her by addressing her with a brusque and demanding tone of voice in front of customers, I gently placed my hand on her shoulder.

Lowering my voice I asked again, pleadingly, almost whispering: "*Scusami, Elisa... ma per favore, dimmi dov'è Maria?* (I'm sorry, Elisa... but please, tell me where's Maria?)"

She didn't look up but just managed to mumble: "*Mi ha detto che andava al "Cinque e Dieci" qua di fronte.* (She told me she was going to the "5 and 10" store across the street.)"

"*Grazie, Elisa!* (Thank you!)" – I told her.

Turning around, I left her and made a brief stop in Kathy Clark's office. She was also waiting on a customer. I just knocked on the glass door and entered, excusing myself for the interruption.

"Kathy, listen, it's very important." – I told her hastily. – "I have to leave for a few minutes, it's a personal matter. Please take care of the customer in my office, tell him I had to leave for a few minutes. Just tell him I'll be back in a little while."

And I quickly left excusing myself again for the interruption. Kathy later told me she had understood immediately what it was all about.

Without even bothering to put on my overcoat I left the bank in freezing weather and rushed across the street to the "5 and 10" store.

I found Maria wandering in the cosmetics aisle. She was clearly startled when she saw me, and she quickly turned away. I approached her, placed my hand on her shoulder and forced her to turn around and face me.

"Maria, please, listen to me. I am sorry, I am sorry, I am sorry if I have embarrassed or offended you..." –I pleaded with her out loud, speaking in Italian. "But it's true, I love you, I love you, and I had to tell you. Please try to understand."

Other customers began glancing at us thinking surely it was a lover's quarrel. Clearly embarrassed, poor Maria was now looking around –dismayed –and seemed to pale seeing people looking at us.

"Leave me alone!" – She then whispered softly but firmly – "You have no right to interfere with my life."

Then, lowering her voice further, she almost hissed at me: "You are making a fool of yourself in front of all these people."

And again she turned away and began walking slowly down the aisle pretending to look at merchandise displayed on the shelves. I followed her, and again I reached for her shoulder, but she shrugged my hand away.

Unable to hide my feelings, I implored out loud: "Please, please, Maria... Just do me that one little favor, the one I asked you in the letter, call me and let me know, and I will never bother you again, I swear I won't. Please."

Near tears for being embarrassed in public, Maria turned around to face me.

"*Va bene, va bene, lo farò.* (OK, OK, I will.)" – She hissed at me impatiently – "Now, will you leave me alone?"

Turning away from me abruptly, she took a few steps then practically sprinted out of the store, leaving me with a sour taste in my mouth and an aching heart.

Shivering in the freezing weather, I slowly made my way back to the bank where my customer was still waiting for me. Excusing myself for leaving so abruptly, I made up a quick excuse. I had left my car down at Tavani's gas station for an oil change – I told him – and had to pick it up before the station closed.

When the bank closed, I briefly pondered going to New York but decided against it. Dejected, I went straight home.

Same old story, same old cure – scotch on the rocks in a large water glass and then passively staring at Johnny Carson's "Tonight Show" and whatever program came after that. When I finally went to bed, I was unable to sleep of course, and just kept tossing and turning restlessly in bed thinking about the previous evening's fiasco. It was nearly daybreak when I finally managed to fall asleep.

The phone jolted me awake at 8:00 AM. Cursing loudly, I ignored it and let it ring, hoping it would stop ringing. But the damn thing just wouldn't quit.

After about a dozen rings I picked up the damn receiver.

"Hello!" – I shouted at whoever was there.

There was silence for about five seconds, and I had to repeat my 'Hello' a couple of times. Then a voice – her voice! – hesitantly inquired: "Lillo?...", jolting me wide awake.

In subdued tones Maria told me she was calling to apologize for her rude manners the previous night. She had mistreated me unfairly – she acknowledged – but justified her behavior by the circumstances. She was too flustered to think straight, and didn't know how to act or what to say.

She confessed it really hadn't been her idea to call me. She was still too confused by last night's experience and said her mom had practically ordered her to call me and apologize.

Her mother knew about my letter, of course. Expecting her mother's approval, Maria had told her about her sharp and abrasive behavior during our encounter the previous evening. But *Mamma* Flocco, instead, had reproached her, telling her the least I deserved was to be treated like a *cristiano*, like a human being. Just like Father Roberto, she also believed that being in love was not a sin, regardless of the circumstances.

My love for *mamma* Flocco increased a hundred folds, a thousand folds, the moment I found out she had urged Maria to call me to apologize.

The second I heard Maria's voice on the phone was for me a defining moment, **THE** defining moment. In that precise moment, the instant I realized the voice on the phone was Maria's, even before she said she had called to apologize, even before she said all she had to say, I knew Maria was going to be mine.

I am not much of a telephone talker – in fact, by and large I detest telephones. But that one time I kept her on the phone for well over one hour.

What did I tell her? God knows. Other than her apology, I don't recall much of our conversation, and there's a good chance that my share of it didn't make much sense at all. But just to keep her talking to me I was ready to read the white and the yellow pages of the telephone directory, the Sears catalogue and the instruction manual for the assembly of a bicycle.

I do remember a few tidbits though. She did tell me she really never was in love with the guy in Italy. As a matter of fact, the engagement itself had been a hasty last-minute arrangement. The guy was quite good looking – she said – and she kind of liked him. She had agreed to the engagement only because she felt it was time for her to get married.

The biggest obstacles in their relationship were his insistence on her returning to Italy to stay when they got married and her absolute disinclination to do so. America was her home, she liked it here and here she intended to stay. Since they both were unwilling to yield, she said she would almost certainly break the engagement.

As for me, she could not and would not commit herself. She readily acknowledged she thought well of me and did like me, but she wasn't ready to say yes to me either.

She did not want to make the same mistake she had made with the first guy and she needed time to know me better before she could give me an answer. It wouldn't be fair to me either for her to decide quickly

– she asserted – and she told me up front that her final answer could go either way. And that was OK with me.

"Can I come to see you sometime?" – I pleaded – "Even if it's just for coffee, or just to chat. Please?"

"Of course you can, and I'm glad you reminded me." – She said – "My mother asked me to invite you for dinner tomorrow. Can you come? We'll have dinner around two o'clock, if you can make it."

Can you come?... If you can make it?... I would have cancelled an appointment with the Pope just so I could tell *mamma* Flocco I loved her!

The next day the atmosphere at the dinner table was a bit awkward. There was an air of uneasiness, of implicit embarrassment, as her entire family was well aware of our unusual situation. They all knew I was a 'pretender-in-waiting' for the hand of Maria – an unusual position to be in, but that's exactly what it was. None of us knew how to deal with it so, by tacit agreement, we simply ignored it.

That same week Maria wrote a curt letter to her fiancé breaking the engagement. She was now free, but she still just liked me, and I did not press her at all. She knew how I felt about her, and it was up to her to let me know if and when she was ready.

The Flocco's kept inviting me for dinner, and I kept accepting, and I also kept on occasionally picking up all three ladies after work, only now without pretending I was just passing by.

On Valentine Day, I gave Maria a dozen red roses and a huge heart-shaped box of chocolates.

Even under normal circumstances, a man madly in love is always a pathetic object of pity, and maybe I did look pitiful to her as I silently handed her my gifts. Or maybe it was the plaintive look in my eyes that made her fall in love with me, who knows?

Thanking me for the gifts, she first took the bouquet of roses, placed them in a flower vase and filled it with water. She then took the box of chocolates and deliberately placed it on the coffee table.

She finally turned toward me and there, in front of her parents, she told me: "I love you too, Lillo!"

And there, in front of her parents, she put her arms around me and kissed me, just a brief but intense kiss on the lips. And there, in front of her parents, I kneeled down in front of her and asked her to marry me. I then asked her father for Maria's hand in marriage, and he readily consented.

Next, I went to *mamma* Flocco who was already crying. As I hugged her, I called her *mamma* for the first time and thanked her for telling Maria to call me.

Through her tears, she confided to me that she knew I was in love with Maria, ten minutes after meeting me, just by the way I looked at her daughter. And just by the way I looked at her, she knew my love was deep and real, and she instinctively would have wanted to see her daughter married to me, but of course she had to leave that decision up to her daughter.

No, it wasn't easy, but four and one half months later we were married.

CHAPTER 26

Maria knew that my wife had died in a car crash – someone had mentioned it to her – but neither she nor any member of her family were aware of the details of my personal tragedy, and they had never pressed me for specifics.

Soon after our engagement I told her all about Rosa, disclosing every single detail, from my mom's first letter to my first trip to Italy, from our correspondence to my proposal of marriage, from our honeymoon to that fateful car trip from the airport.

I narrated everything in simple and neutral terms, as if I had been reading a newspaper account. I told her about my depression, my guilt feelings, I told her about the negligee, my return to Italy, my talks with Rosa's father, the discovery of her young love for me, my belief that she had died because of that love, my visits to the cemetery, even my suicidal thoughts, everything. I didn't hide anything because I had nothing to hide.

With much trepidation, I even found the strength to take her to the intersection where the tragedy had occurred. It was the first time I had been there since the day of the accident.

The intersection was only a couple of hundred yards away from my house. Before my marriage, I used to pass that intersection every weekday to go to and from work. Ever since returning to my job, however – and even before, during my convalescence – I was unable to drive through there.

I had developed a morbid phobia about it, a phobia so real, so palpable and so embarrassing that I never even mentioned it to anybody, not even to my brother. I never told anybody that I always drove an extra three miles both ways, every day, just to avoid that intersection.

The thought of seeing the scene of the tragedy terrified me. I was certain I would get a panic attack, I was certain I would be flooded by waves and waves of horrendous memories.

That phobia was at first so strong that even living so close to that location gave me cold sweats. At one point I had even seriously considered moving to a new home.

My anxiety turned out to be unwarranted. I had no visual memory of the accident – the only recollection I had, in fact, was the booming blast. And the only graphic bond to the accident was the fleeting glance at the photographs I had seen in the newspaper at the library.

Returning to the scene of the tragedy turned out to be a liberating, a cathartic move. When we arrived there, my anxiety seemed to disappear – the spot was simply the intersection of the Newport Gap Pike with Hercules-Millcreek Road.

Remarkably, I managed to relate to Maria even the most wrenching moments of my ordeal in a detached manner, without any emotional outbursts.

I had been reluctant to volunteer details of the tragedy to Maria and to her family before our official engagement because I needed to be sure that her love for me was not motivated, even remotely, by pity.

And I went over all the details somberly but calmly, almost dispassionately, so she could be sure that my first love was just a past episode in my life, not an insignificant one of course, but certainly of no major concern on the rest of my life; so she could be sure that my first tie was now undone; so she could be sure that I was ready to start a new life with her.

Maria listened to my story quietly, without once interrupting my narrative. When I finished, however, she was clearly touched – she burst into tears and embraced me.

"O God! Lillo, I am so sorry, for her and for you too, honey. What a horrible nightmare! Where did you… how did you find the strength to get through it?" – She kept asking as she sobbed uncontrollably.

I held her in my arms silently patting her back to calm her down. After a few minutes, through her tears she asked me: "Lillo, when we go to Italy, please take me to see her grave."

And at this point, tears of relief poured out of my eyes. Sharing my ordeal with someone who was now a part of me had unburdened me of all the angst, all the despair I had suffered, all the responsibilities I had assigned myself, all my doubts, all my guilt feelings, all my sorrows.

For the first time in years, I felt whole again.

I had informed my parents of my engagement and impending marriage, and I had also informed my in-laws – or was it my former in-laws? No, I knew they would always be my in-laws, and I knew I would always call them *mamma* and *papà*.

Talking to Maria about the Donatos was a bit awkward at first. They were my former in-laws but Maria, of course, had never even heard about them. And while I looked at them literally as a second set of parents whom I loved as deeply as my own parents, I certainly couldn't expect her to feel for them the same love I felt.

I made it clear to her that they considered me like their own son and emphasized that we had a special relationship, a relationship that I wanted to remain unchanged.

They were the ones who had encouraged me to go on with my life – I explained – and they had made me promise that, if and when I remarried, I would introduce my new wife to them, a promise that I definitely wanted to keep. They had also assured me they would consider my new wife as their own son's wife.

Deeply touched, Maria assured me she couldn't wait to meet them and said that she would ask their permission to call them *mamma* and *papà*.

What a strange situation! Having two sets of in-laws! Both Maria and me! An unusual situation at best but – to me at least – perfectly normal.

The Donatos were elated at the news of my impending marriage and they practically ordered me to honeymoon in Italy. They couldn't wait to meet Maria, their new daughter in law – no, their new daughter! We didn't have any problem obeying that 'order' because we intended to honeymoon there anyhow.

We were married on Saturday, July 2, 1966. The next day we boarded a plane to Rome and arrived in Torre Faro on the evening of the 4th of July – a day like any other in Italy.

We went to my parents' house first. My father – a shrewd judge of character – liked Maria immediately.

My mother, on the other hand, was cordial with her but I could tell she wasn't entirely pleased with my choice. And I knew why. Maria had not only taken Rosa's place but also – horror of horrors! – she wasn't from Torre Faro. In fact – horror of horrors of horrors! – she wasn't even Sicilian, a capital sin in my mother's eyes.

Maria sensed my mother's coolness and asked me about it. I explained the reason and told her not to worry about it. Mom would come around – I assured her – especially after we presented her with a grandchild or two.

The Donatos, on the other hand, were visibly overjoyed and pleased with my choice. *Mamma* Lucia took Maria aside and told her what a great boy I was, and how lucky she was to have me.

They were both embarrassed to ask her to call them *mamma* and *papà,* but they did tell her I was like a son to them, and she would be considered like a daughter.

Sensing their real affection for me and their sincere acceptance and delight in her taking their daughter's place in my life, Maria felt immediately at ease with them.

In our brief stay in Torre Faro, she got to know them well and felt warm and genuine fondness for them at once, just like I had three short years before. Within days, she won their everlasting affection when she shyly felt compelled to ask them: "Since Lillo calls you *mamma* and *papà,* may I have your permission to also call you *mamma* and *papà*?"

Both of them embraced her fondly, and thanked her. Before

leaving Torre Faro, Maria and I went to visit Rosa's grave.

At the cemetery entrance, Maria bought fresh flowers from the vendor outside the gates. When we reached Rosa's grave, Maria kneeled on the marble slab and silently said some prayers. She then stared closely at Rosa's picture.

"God! She was so beautiful! And she loved you so much..." – She exclaimed – "That smile says it all. It's the happy smile of a woman in love."

Then, as I stood quietly by her side, she removed the withered flowers from the receptacles and replaced them with the fresh ones she had bought.

Looking in silence at Rosa's picture – already a bit faded – memories of my visits there two short years before flooded my mind.

The immense love I felt for my first wife, the intense pain her death had caused me, the unbearable guilt feelings that had oppressed me, the indelible belief that my life was not worth living... Where had they gone? What had happened to them?

With genuine surprise I realized that all of them seemed to have dissipated. Different emotions spun serenely in my head now.

How did I feel? It's hard to put into words. Nothing had happened, really – my love for Rosa had been just as true and just as strong as the love I now felt for Maria, but had it died? Could I have been so fickle that the deep love I felt for my first wife until less than two years before had now been forgotten and tossed in the dustbin?

No, that love had not died and I had certainly not forgotten it – a new one, equally true and equally strong, had simply replaced it. In my mind and in my heart, I knew that this new love was a natural continuum, a logical progression of the first one, like a caterpillar morphing into a butterfly.

And what about the devastating pain, the bottomless depression, the guilty feelings, the tears. What about them? Were they real?

Of course they were real! I can never and will never deny or ever forget how deeply Rosa's death had affected me or how much I had suffered because of it.

While acknowledging that reality, however, I now felt that all my grief, all my depression and all my sufferings were the spiritual equivalent of my physical wounds. They were feelings and emotions that had caused me an enormous amount of pain and distress but had now healed.

Yes! The emotions I was now feeling were different, vastly different from the ones I felt when I first saw that picture. But even her picture seemed to radiate a different emotion. She had first smiled that radiant smile to reveal to me, and to the entire world, how happy she was. But that smile seemed now to be a happy smile of approval. Absolutely.

Just before leaving Rosa's grave, Maria bent down to kiss Rosa's picture, and I heard her murmur: "Thank you, Rosa!"

We stayed in Torre Faro for one week, and we then went to Abruzzo where I met Maria's sisters. Our visit there further increased my love and admiration for Maria. I saw firsthand how hard her two sisters and their husbands worked their lands, and how little they had to show for all that hard work.

Maria's sisters were only in their late 20s, yet they both looked like they were in their 40s. Unkempt hair, no make-up, and faces deeply lined and scorched by the sun were testimony to their harsh, no-frills life.

Old, sparsely furnished homes with no indoor plumbing, chickens running outside and inside their houses, the water supply coming up in buckets from a well outside, those were all further proof of their bleak existence. And this had been Maria's life until about three short years before.

They did eat exceptionally well, though. Every day they had an unbelievable spread!

Garden fresh vegetables daily, farm-raised chickens and rabbits, homemade pasta and bread, homemade wine. Man! What a feast! And they knew how to cook, of course! Best of all, Maria was just as good as her sisters in the kitchen! I gained five pounds in one week, and I was almost at my normal weight.

Pietro, our first son, was born eleven months after our wedding. We call him Pete, though, to distinguish him from my brother's Pietro.

Eighteen months later Maria gave birth to a baby girl. Following Sicilian tradition, I wanted to call her Domenica, like my mother, maybe anglicizing the name into Dominique, but Maria pleaded with me to name her Rosa.

I nixed it, for two reasons. First of all – I explained – if I say yes, you may think Rosa is still in my mind and heart. Second and most important, if I say yes, who the hell is going to explain it to my mother?

"Honey," – Maria told me – "as for reason number one, if I thought you still had Rosa in your mind or in your heart I would not have married you in the first place, OK?"

"Point well taken and conceded." – I said. "What about reason number two? How do we handle that?"

"Let me handle it." – She said. And she did.

She wrote my mom a letter but never showed it me. I got to read it the following year when we went to Italy. My mom had kept it – she figured I had not read it, and she wanted to show it to me. It said:

Dear Mamma,

As you know, our family has been blessed with a new baby, a new baby girl that Lillo wants to name after you.

I agree that tradition demands that the baby be named after you; we have a similar tradition in Abruzzo. But, with all my respect and love for you, I would like to ask your permission to name the baby Rosa, and I want to explain why.

Rosa was Lillo's first wife. You knew her and I never got to know her, and I am sure that, in addition to being a very beautiful girl, she was a marvelous human being, a perfect match for your son.

Lillo told me everything about her, about how much she loved him, how she chose him above everybody else, and how she literally died as a result of her choice.

While I know that Rosa is not in Lillo's mind and heart anymore, I am also fully aware that Lillo is now my husband, the husband I love very much, only because Rosa is dead. Naming our baby after her is my way of honoring Rosa and thanking her for the supreme sacrifice she made. I feel it is the least I could do in her memory.

I told Lillo that I would leave the decision up to you. While I hope you will agree with me, if you insist on the baby being named after you, we will do so; maybe we will name another girl after Rosa, if we will have another one that is. I also promise I will not think any less of you, I will still love you and respect you as much as I do now.

Please let me know your decision as soon as possible.

All my love,
Maria

My mom's letter – addressed to Maria – arrived eight days later and Maria made me read it. In broken Italian (mom had only had a fourth grade education) it said:

Dear Maria,

I insist that the baby be named Rosa. Not only I agree with you, but also I am glad you will not saddle the baby with a stupid name like Domenica. Why anybody would want to name a baby after a day of the week is beyond me ('Domenica' means Sunday in Italian). I have always hated my first name, and in fact I am not at all in agreement with this stupid tradition of naming babies after the grandparents. It's not too bad if a grandparent has a sensible name, but life is hard enough for a boy or a girl to face with a stupid first name. Just ask Lillo about it – he knows what it's all about.

Additionally, I must apologize to you. Yes, I have to apologize because I must confess that when I first met you I had foolishly believed you were not good enough for my Lillo, and for the stupidest of reasons – because you were not Sicilian.

I can see now by your letter that you are a caring, sensitive woman, and I am proud that Lillo has chosen you as a wife. I am certain you will make him very happy, just as happy as Rosa would have made him, had she lived, bless her soul.

By all means, you have my blessings in naming the new baby Rosa, and if you have another baby girl, do not even consider naming her Domenica. It's a stupid name, and I really mean it.

Please give a thousand kisses to baby Rosa for me, and baby Pietro too, and your husband of course (judging by how fast you guys are producing babies, I'm sure you are already doing that with him, and something more).

All my love,
Mamma Domenica

And so it was baby Rosa.

Our Donato in-law's cried tears of joy and gratitude when mom showed them the letter Maria had written.

"Didn't I tell you Maria was a great girl, just like Rosa?" – *Mamma* Lucia had told her through her tears. – "Didn't I tell you she was perfect for Lillo? And you kept saying maybe so, but she is not Sicilian. So what do you say now?"

When we made our second trip to Italy, my parents and the Donatos spoiled both Pete and Rosa beyond belief. We alternated eating at my parents' and at the Donatos', but we stayed at my in-laws' house because they had more room.

And one evening, *Mamma* Lucia took Maria aside in her bedroom. She first embraced her and thanked her for the honor of naming our baby Rosa. She then opened a jewelry box, took out a gold necklace – a family heirloom that must have weighed a pound – and handed it to her.

"I want you to have this." – She told her.

Shocked and reluctant to accept such an extravagant gift, Maria protested: "*Mamma*, no! Please don't be offended but I cannot accept this, it must be worth a fortune. Naming our baby Rosa was something I felt I had to do. I am in her place only because she is gone."

But *mamma* Lucia brushed aside her objections.

"Maria, this was going to be Rosa's, anyhow," – She explained – "but you are our daughter now, so now it's yours, and after you it will belong to my granddaughter Rosa, *capisci?*"

Three years later the twins were born.

We were ecstatic when we learned Maria was expecting twins. Anticipating the various possibilities – boy and girl, both boys, or both girls – we also debated what to name them.

When the twins were born – a boy and a girl – I suggested we name them after Maria's parents, although I wasn't too crazy about either name. But I adored my mother-in-law and had the greatest respect for my father-in-law, and I was willing to honor them by naming the twins with their names.

But this time also Maria nixed the idea. She assured me that in Abruzzo, tradition dictates that as long as one of the sons or daughters names a kid after the parents, the other siblings are under no obligation to select the same name.

As it happened, one of Maria's brothers had already named his first-born son after her father, and another brother had named his first-born daughter after her mother. That meant we were free to name the twins whatever we wanted. She suggested – in fact, insisted – we name them Philip and Lucia, like our Donato in-laws.

I hugged Maria and, as Ralph Kramden used to say to Alice at the end of just about every episode of "The Honeymooners", I told her: "You are the greatest!"

And Philip and Lucia it was.

EPILOGUE

Our children are now adults and have their own families. They are fully Americanized, of course, but they still retain strong ties to Italy. Maria and I are very proud of them – and of ourselves as well – because we insisted and made sure they learned how to speak Italian and to be proud of their heritage. And to this day they not only understand and speak that language quite well but they have made sure our grandchildren understand and speak it also.

When they were still little tykes, they would sometime ask us why they had three sets of grandparents when all the other kids had only two.

"Well!" – We would answer – "I guess it's because you are luckier than most other kids."

Until they went off to college, we took them to Italy on vacation just about every other year. We mostly stayed at *Nonno* Filippo's house because his villa had four bedrooms, plus a large garden, and could easily accommodate the six of us.

My parents' house couldn't comfortably host all of us because it was just a two-room summer cottage, but once in a while the kids would sleep over at *Nonno* Pietro and *Nonna* Nella's house, only two at a time.

Nonno Pietro took immense pride and joy just parading around the streets of Torre Faro with his four grandchildren in tow. Every *passeggiata* (walk) always included a stop for their favorite treat, a *granita al limone* (lemon ice water) or *granita al caffè con panna* (coffee water ice topped with whipped cream) with a brioche. And it was always at *Babbuzza's*, of course, who reputedly had the best *granita* in town.

Nonno Filippo took Pete and little Philip fishing on his rowboat and taught his two grandsons how to fish. The salt in their DNA – that same salt that has somehow bypassed me – turned that early training into a lifelong passion for both of them. Like uncle Mimmo, both Pete and Philip own their own boats now and they go fishing whenever they can. And like their uncle Mimmo, every time they go they will laughingly ask me if I want to join them, and my answer still is and always will be: "No way, Josè, just bring me some fish. If you catch any, that is."

Nonna Lucia took both Rosa and Lucia under her wings and gave them cooking lessons. That early training turned them both into exceptional cooks, and both my sons-in-law will testify to that.

Nonna Domenica taught Rosa and Lucia how to sew and embroider. Mom believed that being an accomplished seamstress and embroiderer was a virtue comparable to virginity. Probably even more important.

She taught Pete and Philip several Sicilian cuss words. She always stated she couldn't live in a world without cuss words, and if there were no cuss words she would have had to invent them. And I'm inclined to agree with her.

All four kids have also inherited from her a wild and somewhat raunchy sense of humor. When we reunite for a birthday, a holiday or whatever, they all seem to want to top each other with one-liners and zingers, and each get-together is a comedy show.

My father passed away in Genoa in 1982. He died happy, knowing his two sons were doing well in a foreign land. They had both produced male offspring bearing his name and, more important, they were both happily married. His death came suddenly and neither my brother nor I were able to be at his bedside or even attend his funeral. Of course, he was buried in his beloved Torre Faro.

Nick Ravello died a couple of years before my father. He had been retired for several years and lived a quiet life in Torre Faro with his wife.

Nick had lived a fascinating life, a picaresque life, even a tumultuous one at times, a life that had run the gamut from abject poverty to considerable wealth. A life that would best be described as full.

And he too died happy, happy for its unbridled recklessness, the glowing memories, the proud conquests, the incredible accomplishments, even the stupendous errors. And happy also for a seemingly insignificant matter to a man of his stature – happy to know that my brother, maintaining the Sicilian tradition, had honored him by naming his second son after him.

His only regret – I am certain – was that such a full life had to come to an end.

I liked Nick a hell of a lot and I always loved being in his company. I was very fond of him – indeed I felt real affection for the old man. And tremendous admiration.

Like many other Italian-Americans, he had achieved a comfortable upper middle class economic status against great odds, all on the strength of his hard work. I always believed he was the kind of guy who could have become a tycoon had he just had the opportunity to go to school and learn the ropes of running a business. Considering he had only had a third grade education, he had done fantastically well.

Yes! I liked the old man, and I am sure he liked me too. I will always cherish the memory of the great times we had whenever we were together, in Rising Sun or in Italy. There would always be a joyous songfest, with the two of us trying to outdo each other.

But he was the better singer, no questions about it.

My mother died in Genoa eight years after my father and she is now resting next to him. Dad waited a long time for her, and I know he is happier now that she is next to him forever. And I like to imagine that a smile, or even a loud laugh, cracks now and then through his always-serious demeanor – mom will make sure of that. And I also like to imagine all their neighbors eavesdropping, listening to what my mom is saying, and laughing their carcasses off.

When our sisters informed us she was in bad shape, Mimmo and I immediately rushed to her bedside, leaving our wives in America. Upon our arrival we went straight from the airport to the hospital, accompanied by our three sisters. When she saw us, mom couldn't help making a little salacious remark.

"You left your wives home just to come and see me?" – She said in a weak voice – "How do you know somebody won't do the job on them?"

My brother tried to banter with her.

"Don't worry mom, there's no way that can happen." – He told her playfully – "We had them fitted with a chastity belt."

Mom had the last word, of course. Her laconic reply, in Sicilian, was: "*Nu puttusu sulu cummogghia.*" – (That only covers one hole.)

And there we were, the five of us – my brother, my sisters and I – laughing hysterically with our dying mother in front of us, with doctors and nurses all around us thinking, without a doubt, that grief had made us lose our collective minds.

She died two days later. At her request, we had her body transported to Torre Faro for burial next to our dad.

After the funeral, we gathered for a family dinner at my sister Flora's house. It was the first time in God knows how many years that all five siblings were together.

The dinner started out as a sad, melancholy affair, but in no time at all it turned into a wildly funny one. The turning point came when one of my sisters made us smile as she somberly recalled one of my mother's zingers. That zinger set the wheels in motion as it reminded us of the countless comical expressions and episodes our mom had been responsible for – and each one of us, in turn, began recalling them. In no time at all we were literally crying tears of unrestrained laughter, an unending series of absolute, pure, sidesplitting, uproarious belly laughs that had us all gasping for breath.

But that was our mom, a laugh factory to the very end!

Four years ago *mamma* Lucia had a serious stroke that left her partially paralyzed and at death's door. Maria and I, both already retired, rushed to her bedside and barely managed to see her alive.

When we arrived in Torre Faro, *mamma* Lucia had already been taken home to die. We found her quietly laying in her bed, a nurse tending to her most immediate needs.

Papà Filippo – a shell of a man now – just sat stone faced next to her waiting for the inevitable end.

The left side of *mamma* Lucia's face was distorted by paralysis, and her right eye seemed to float lazily in its orbit, looking aimlessly around the room, fleetingly settling its dwindling visual powers on the familiar objects and the few people around her – her husband, the nurse, and now the two newcomers.

When her eye settled on us, she seemed to have a slight jolt – she had recognized us. Only the right side of her face moved in a contorted grimace as she tried to smile weakly.

She seemed to look at Maria and with one finger she motioned for her to come near. Maria rushed to her side, bent down to kiss her and then reached to hold her right hand.

With her last ounce of strength, *mamma* Lucia grabbed Maria's hand and tried to raise herself to a sitting position, but was unable to. Sensing she was trying to tell her something, Maria lowered her head placing her ear next to the dying woman's mouth.

Still holding on to Maria's hand, *mamma* Lucia managed to whisper with slurred speech: "Maria, *dirò a Rosa che Lillo è in buone mani* (Maria, I'll tell Rosa that Lillo is in good hands)."

Those were her last words. A few minutes later a tearful Maria felt *mamma* Lucia's grip on her hand suddenly fading. She was gone.

Her funeral was held the next day. Immediately after the funeral we returned to our father-in-law's house.

Maria prepared a simple lunch, but none of us felt like eating, least of all *papà* Filippo. He just sat at the table staring in space, nodding his head repeatedly, as if in agreement with some private thought. We kept encouraging him to eat, but he hardly touched his food and just nibbled at a few morsels.

Maria cleared the dishes and prepared to wash them in the kitchen sink while my father-in-law and I sat silently at the kitchen table, the only sound the tinkling of the eating utensils being washed. Our common grief made any semblance of conversation unwanted, unneeded.

I sat motionless staring at the tabletop, occasionally looking up to quickly glance at my father-in-law. He kept staring vacantly in space, still nodding his head.

We were scheduled to leave in three days. Both Maria and I were worried sick about his welfare, wondering who would be taking care of him. He had always been a self-reliant, vigorous man but what remained now was a broken old man, all alone, and in the immediate aftermath of the loss of his beloved life companion.

On the plane trip over we had discussed the various scenarios. We knew *mamma* Lucia's conditions were very serious. If she had a chance to survive, we would stay next to her until she recovered or until she got suitable help. If she died – a more likely possibility –we had decided to encourage *papà* Filippo to come with us to America for a couple of months at least, or even longer if necessary.

Again, I looked at my father-in-law. Reaching over, I softly tapped his hand. He stirred and turned his head to look at me, seeming almost surprised to see me there.

"*Papà*... please listen to me. I need to talk to you about something." – I told him quietly.

He sighed audibly. Making an effort to focus on what I had to say, he then cupped his right ear to compensate for his worsening hearing problems.

When I had his complete attention, I said: "*Papà*, perhaps it's too soon for you to make a decision, but Maria and I would like to ask you to consider..."

He must have read my mind. Shaking his head and hand to indicate his refusal, he interrupted me.

"No, Lillo, *grazie*." – He murmured softly. – "And you too Maria, *grazie, grazie tanto*... but my place is here."

He lowered his head and just stared at the tabletop for a few seconds. He then looked up again. With a tremulous, almost pleading voice he then asked me: "But if at all possible, Lillo...If at all possible, do you think you could stay here just a few days longer? If at all possible, please..."

He then timidly lowered his head again as if embarrassed to ask us to make this sacrifice.

Barely looking up, he then whispered: "I would really appreciate it."

I looked at Maria to see if she had any objections. She just shrugged her shoulders and nodded – we were both retired, and there was no immediate need for us to be back in the States.

"Sure, *papà,* there's no problem." – I assured him – "we can keep you company for a few days or for as long as you want, really. I'll call "Alitalia" today to cancel our reservations. There is no need for us to go back to the States. We can stay here as long as we want."

There is no doubt in my mind that he had asked us to stay because he knew his broken heart wouldn't mend a second time. Exactly four days later we found him dead in his bed, a serene smile on his face. His eyes were open and turned toward an old framed picture laying on the pillow next to him, a picture of *mamma* Lucia in her wedding gown.

We buried him in the grave they had prepared for themselves right next to Rosa's grave.

We had changed our reservations to return to the States two days after his funeral but we were forced to cancel them again and remain in Torre Faro for an additional two months. We got a call from his attorney informing us that he had left all his property to Maria and me in trust for our four kids, his grandchildren.

Mamma and *papà* Flocco returned to Italy soon after he retired.

Against the advice of all his children, he had decided to return to his homeland, settling in a small house he had built with his savings in his hometown in Abruzzo. *Mamma* Venera followed him because she believed her place was next to her husband, but her heart remained in America, a land she deeply loved and never wanted to leave.

Like me, *mamma* Venera always said she had two birthdays to celebrate – the day she was born and the day she arrived in America. In this wonderful land she had found exactly the same thing millions of other immigrants from all over the world had found.

And no, I am not going to blather patriotic gibberish – the flag, motherhood, apple pie, freedom of this and freedom of that. America is not unique because of that - to a large extent, one can get those same freedoms in many other countries.

Mamma Venera loved this country for what it had provided for her, her entire family and everyone who has come and still comes here ready and willing to work – the opportunity to work coupled with the just reward for all the hard work one had done.

Mamma Venera's last years were not happy – she missed America, her six children there, and her several grandchildren. Her unhappiness affected her health and she died in 1991, her angelic smile on her face to the very end.

Within a year of repatriation, *Papà* Angelo realized that returning to Italy had been a foolish mistake, a monumental blunder. He later privately admitted to me that only pride had stopped him from packing his suitcases to return to America – he just couldn't face the many 'I told you so' of all the friends and relatives who had advised him not to return to Italy.

Just before *mamma* Venera exhaled her last breath, *papà* Angelo begged for and readily received her forgiveness for the unhappiness he had caused her by taking her back to Italy.

Papà Angelo lived an additional fourteen years, his loneliness and regret briefly tempered by a few visits he made to the United States to see his children and grandchildren.

Mimmo died in May 2006 – he seemed to be in pretty good health when, all of a sudden, he took ill and was diagnosed with terminal cancer.

Sustained by his strong Catholic faith, he accepted his fate stoically without uttering one single word of complaint or self-commiseration. One month later he was gone, leaving a void that will never be filled in my heart and in the heart of all who knew him.

When he died, Ange – his loving wife and my loving sister-in-law – had already been mercifully afflicted with senile dementia for about four years.

Yes! Mercifully – that's what I said. The advent of the disease had mercifully destroyed her short-term memory.

Mercifully, she did not suffer when her beloved Mimmo died. Mercifully, she didn't even realize he was gone.

For quite a while, though, her long-term memory had remained quite sharp. During my weekly visits, trying to stimulate her memory with subjects she was familiar with, I would ask her if she knew the lyrics of old Italian songs, the standards we both loved. Amazingly, she could still recite them accurately.

Like her dad, she loved to sing and was quite a good singer herself. But now, when I prodded her to sing-along with me, she did it with a tinny, quavering, childish voice, and way off-key. But she did not miss one single word of the lyrics.

And whenever I just talked to her, it was always about things long past – that was all she remembered.

And I would ask her: "Ange, do you remember what you prepared for me when I came over from Italy?"

And she would unhesitatingly answer in baby talk: "A strawberry shortcake!"

And then I would jokingly shake my head and ask her: "And then... tell me, and then what happened?"

And she would smile an impish smile of amusement and feign childish reproach as she answered: "You threw up!"

But then, inexorably, her dementia deteriorated to the point where her brain simply ceased to function.

She just occupied a wheelchair, unable to talk, unable to feed herself, unable to do anything. She would just stare at visitors with a hapless look, a look half dazed and half dismayed, a look that always made me wonder if whatever filtered through her eyes triggered some hazy, muffled memory in the now-murky labyrinth of her brain.

To the immense grief and sad relief of all who knew and loved her, she mercifully passed away in November of 2009, and she is now resting beside her beloved Mimmo.

My friends, Jack and Tony Ravello, are both alive and well.

Our Saturday night poker games ended several years ago. We stopped playing by tacit agreement after Vince's tragic death – it just seemed improper and disrespectful to his memory. Joe Rossi, who had barely managed to survive the accident and had been paralyzed from the waist down, sadly passed away a few months later.

A year or so later we tried to resume our poker nights in a desultory fashion, but it just wasn't the same – gone were the gaiety, the raunchy wit, the bullshitting, the laughter, the teasing, the alibis, the cursing.

From weekly affairs our poker games changed first into bi-weekly, then monthly, and then once-in-a-rare-while affairs.

They came to a quiet halt when Danny – sweet old Danny – also passed away. Nicky, the best player in our group, had moved out of state and it's now just the three of us left of the old crowd.

It would have been easy enough to find replacements, but we didn't even try – perhaps we didn't even want to. We do keep in touch weekly, though, just to reminisce or to give our 'expert' opinion on Italian soccer.

Maria and I have been retired for quite a while and every year we spend nine months in Delaware and three months in Italy in the Donatos' home, our home now.

Our kids come to Italy every few years or so, not as frequently as we would like, but we understand – they have jobs and families. When they do come, they bring our grandchildren, of course – there are nine of them so far.

Three of them are named Leo – Leo, not Letterio, I insisted on that! – three are named Maria, there is one Philip, one Lucy, and there is also one named Rosa, Rosa Jr. actually. My daughter Rosa was always touched by the story of how she got her name and decided to give the same name to her first baby girl.

When we are in Italy, we go at least once to the cemetery to pay our respects to our folks – all of them, my mom, my dad, my other mom, my other dad, Nick Ravello and his wife… and Rosa, of course.

Her pink marble grave is now weathered and her picture is quite faded. Her hairstyle, the wedding veil, the brooch at her neck, they are all outdated now and the picture itself has an antique-ish patina that makes it look almost like a sepia-tinted daguerreotype.

But her smile is still that same radiant smile. It was at first the deliriously happy smile of a woman in love who has seen her dream become reality. It had then changed to a smile of approval – it was not an easy task, but the man she left behind had made a good choice in choosing a companion who would worthily take her place. And it is now a serene smile, a contented smile – she is now smiling simply because she is happy for all of us.

She knows we haven't forgotten her, she knows her memory will remain in our family – her family! – until the last one of us will have joined her, wherever she is.

I do not believe in an afterlife. And yet, I do have my will-o'-the-wisp moments, moments when fantasies run free from reality, and in those moments I try to imagine what it would be like to meet up with her.

That flame has now been extinguished for nearly fifty years. The fire that blazed in my life almost half a century ago is now just a memory, a fading memory of just one of the many significant events that pile up in the trunk of everyone's life.

It is now relegated to the kind of event one recalls when looking at a photograph casually found in a drawer ("This one was taken at Philip's wedding, wasn't it?") or when trying to establish the exact or approximate date of some other meaningful event ("No, that happened when Pete broke his arm...")

Most of my memories of that very significant event are now faded but a few still remain quite sharp. Yes, it was a brief, very brief chapter of my life, barely longer than a flash in the pan, but I clearly recall that it most certainly was not a flash in the pan. I also recall that the feelings associated with it were intense, very intense, but that fiery intensity or the agonizing grief I felt when I lost her are now indistinct, muted, unfocused emotions – melancholy, of course, but no longer painful; somber, yes, and yet pleasantly mellow to remember.

In those crazy, will-o'-the-wisp moments I also try to imagine what it would be like to meet up with Mimmo, with Ange, with my mom and dad, with *papà* Filippo, *mamma* Lucia, *mamma* Venera, *papà* Angelo, Nick Ravello, even with that sweet busybody Mrs. Parraciani. Yes, with all the folks who left a meaningful mark on my life.

And when I do – being the emotional fool that I am and will always be – my mind inevitably wallows in a mawkish reverie replete with warm embraces, tender sharing of fond moments, an unending series of "Do you remember when...?"

And then the tears would start, tears, tears, rivers of tears, an endless stream of tender, melancholy and yet joyful tears. This gooey bit of pleasant nonsense invariably concludes with a self-congratulatory assessment of what we have accomplished and what we will leave on Earth.

We will determine that our lives – like millions of other lives – may be anonymous and colorless, but they are not entirely useless.

We will acknowledge that while our lives have bravely borne a good share of grief, painful grief, at times unbearable grief, we have somehow managed to overcome all the rough spots. In fact, in our final judgment, we will all agree that grief made us stronger and made us enjoy and appreciate the many, many joys that followed.

And as the fantasy fades, we will all be pleased with ourselves, we will know we will leave meaningful memories, we will be satisfied that we did well, very well indeed.

APPENDIX

This novel – my first serious literary effort – has an unusual structure. It is written in the first person and, as the narrator, I even use my real name. Several other characters in the novel are real as well, but while the story does contain several autobiographical details and indeed reads like a memoir, it is not an entirely true chronicle of my life. What is it then? I really don't know what to call it – for lack of a better word I'll call it a fictional autobiography. Some wit may observe that all 'real' autobiographies frequently contain elements of fiction, along with sundry untruths and fabrications ranging from simple embellishments to outright falsehoods. So what's so different about this one?

There is just one very significant difference – the 'fictional' part of most other autobiographies is palmed off as unvarnished truth, real stuff. Mine, on the other hand, makes no such attempt – I have just told you, it is not an accurate chronicle of my life, and a substantial chunk of this novel is fiction.

So what's the point? Damned if I know – I can't give a clear-cut answer. The only rationale for writing it is a flimsy one, I suppose – but it's quite real. And here it is.

My entire life has been an ordinary life with few, indeed very few highs or lows. So far, at least. As I review its salient moments, I can best assess it as a generally pleasant life, a typical, anonymous life, a life with its average share of happiness and sorrow, a life much the same as millions of other lives.

Like millions of other folks, I have rejoiced for happy events (weddings, births, promotions), and I have shed tears of sadness for unhappy ones (loss of parents, close relatives, dear friends, even the death of a cherished pet). These latter events, however –distressing as they were – were for the most part expected events, inevitable events.

What has been totally lacking in my life is the unexpected event, the shocking event, the tragedy. Not that I'm complaining, mind you. Even as I knock on wood or – in the typical Italian fashion – even as I duly touch the family jewels, I can gratefully say that my life hasn't experienced yet the searing shock of a sudden, unexpected, catastrophic, heartbreaking event. Again, so far, at least.

What's it like when an unexpected tragedy strikes? What kind of emotions does one feel, how does one react to it? How does one face the immediate or the long-range future? Say, you are home quietly watching TV or reading a newspaper, and someone knocks at your front door. You open it, and you see two cops who have come to your house to somberly inform you that a car careening out of control jumped a sidewalk and killed three people including your wife. Or that your son has been an innocent victim in a drive-by shooting. What's it like? How does one react?

Very morbid thoughts, to be sure, but these things do happen on a daily basis. On page three of the "Local" section of that same newspaper you were reading or on the TV newscast you were watching almost certainly there will be one or two stories detailing those very events, events that unquestionably devastated someone's life.

Someone else's life.

And as I mused about that, another thought came into mind. What would it be like, how would one react if such a tragedy happened concurrently with its very opposite, a most joyous occasion? And I decided to imagine and explore that type of event and its related emotions also.

I wrote this novel – or rather, this fictional autobiography – with those thoughts in mind. I injected a fictitious calamity and a fictitious joyous event in my real 'generally pleasant' life just to imagine what it must be like to feel your whole world, your entire existence crash around you. I have simply added some grief to some joy, if you will.

Fictitious as it was, writing about personal tragedy was a disturbing experience, a traumatizing experience. It's hard to describe – and it may even sound ridiculous, I know – but as I was writing about it I felt at times real pain, real anguish. I must also add that writing it was a marvelous experience – and an instructive one also.

Yes, especially instructive! Because when I thought I had finished writing the novel, I discovered that the real work had barely started. I had then an incredibly difficult but still marvelous time making umpteen thousands modifications, plot revisions, additions, subtractions and sundry other changes. And I learned a very important lesson – I learned that the real part of writing, the most challenging aspect of writing is in the revisions.

Marvelous as it was, I got to the point where I threw in the towel and said, "That's it! I've had it! No more changes."

Surely more changes are needed but like I said: "That's it! I've had it! No more changes!"

And here it is.

ABOUT THE AUTHOR

Born in Genoa (Italy) in 1935, Leo Vadalà came to the United States as a student in 1951. In 1954 he enlisted in the U.S. Army to become an American citizen and served 18 months in Korea. Upon his discharge, he was employed by WSFS (Wilmington Savings Fund Society) where he worked in several executive positions. He retired in 1999 after 40 years of service. He lives in Elkton MD.

He has been married to Maria Flocco, a native of Torino di Sangro (Chieti) since 1964.

He has been active in the Italian community of Wilmington, Delaware and has been a member of the Giuseppe Verdi Lodge, OSIA (Order Sons of Italy in America) since 1975 serving as Treasurer, Vice President and President. In 1995 he also founded the Lodge's monthly newsletter, "Va Pensiero", editing it and providing all articles for the first 7 years. He relished the editorial functions in 2002 but still provides monthly articles.

In 2015 the Lodge honored him as "Man of the Year" with the "Dr. Vincenzo Sellaro Distinguished Service Award" for his contributions to the Lodge.

He started writing "Some Grief, Some Joy" in 2006.

"It took me all of three months to write it, and when I finished it I thought it was great, I was very proud of myself." – he says – "One month later I reread it and realized it was terrible, absolute junk. I was ready to throw it away".

But he decided to persevere and started rewriting it in its entirety making changes practically on a daily basis. Twelve years later, here it is.